FUNDAMENTALS OF CONTINUUM MECHANICS

Quality Graduate Teaching Materials for
the 14th Five-Year Plan of Xi'An Jiaotong University

FUNDAMENTALS OF CONTINUUM MECHANICS

Zishun Liu
Xi'an Jiaotong University, China

World Scientific

NEW JERSEY • LONDON • SINGAPORE • BEIJING • SHANGHAI • HONG KONG • TAIPEI • CHENNAI • TOKYO

Published by

World Scientific Publishing Co. Pte. Ltd.

5 Toh Tuck Link, Singapore 596224

USA office: 27 Warren Street, Suite 401-402, Hackensack, NJ 07601

UK office: 57 Shelton Street, Covent Garden, London WC2H 9HE

Library of Congress Cataloging-in-Publication Data

Names: Liu, Zishun, author.

Title: Fundamentals of continuum mechanics / Zishun Liu, Xi'an Jiaotong University, China.

Description: New Jersey : World Scientific, [2024] | "Quality Graduate Teaching Materials for the 14th Five-Year Plan of Xi'An Jiaotong University." | Includes bibliographical references and index.

Identifiers: LCCN 2023040944 | ISBN 9789811283789 (hardcover) | ISBN 9789811283796 (ebook for institution) | ISBN 9789811283802 (ebook for individuals)

Subjects: LCSH: Continuum mechanics--Textbooks. | Finite element method--Textbooks.

Classification: LCC QA808.2 .L583 2024 | DDC 531/.7--dc23/eng/20231221

LC record available at https://lccn.loc.gov/2023040944

British Library Cataloguing-in-Publication Data

A catalogue record for this book is available from the British Library.

For any available supplementary material, please visit
https://www.worldscientific.com/worldscibooks/10.1142/13608#t=suppl

Desk Editors: Balasubramanian Shanmugam/Amanda Yun

Typeset by Stallion Press
Email: enquiries@stallionpress.com

Preface

Mechanics serves as the foundation of engineering disciplines, making it an indispensable component of any engineering field. When engineers face an engineering problem, their initial task is to establish a mathematical model and determine the appropriate methods for solving it. However, none of this can be accomplished without the fundamental laws of mechanics. As part of their studies, engineering students are introduced to various mechanics courses, including theoretical mechanics, mechanics of materials, and engineering mechanics, all falling under the category of continuum mechanics.

Throughout its history, Xi'an Jiaotong University (XJTU) has consistently prioritized the development of mechanics knowledge among its engineering and science students. As a result, the university has produced numerous renowned experts in the field of mechanics. Some notable figures include Professor Hsue-shen Tsien, an alumnus of Jiaotong University, who introduced the renowned Kármán–Tsien method in 1936. This method is an approximation technique for estimating the effects of compressibility in subsonic flow, which finds wide application in engineering practices. Additionally, in 1942, Professor Tsien developed a theory for predicting the buckling behavior of thin shell and column structures. During the 1950s, Professor Zhenbang Kuang, formerly a professor at XJTU, independently formulated the generalized variational principle of elasticity, known as the Hu–Washizu three-field generalized variational principle. This principle has been influential in the field of elasticity. In recent years, Professors Huajian Gao and Zhigang Suo, both alumni of XJTU, have made significant contributions to the field of solid mechanics as well as emerging disciplines such as nanomechanics, biomechanics, and the mechanics of soft materials. Their groundbreaking works have expanded the boundaries of knowledge in the area of mechanics.

Continuum mechanics serves as a fundamental pillar for engineering students, providing them with a strong foundation to pursue specialized courses and delve deeper into their respective fields of study. However, despite its importance, many students perceive continuum mechanics as a challenging subject due to the rigorous mathematical treatments found in classical textbooks. The author of this text shares the same viewpoint as these students.

However, in 2006, the author had the privilege of teaching the Principles of Continua course to junior students in the Engineering Science program at the National University of Singapore (NUS) under the guidance of Prof. J. N. Reddy. It was through Prof. Reddy's teaching style that the author's perspective on the difficulty of the continuum mechanics course underwent a transformation. Prof. Reddy demonstrated that continuum mechanics could be presented in a simple and easily understandable manner, making it more accessible to students. Some classical books on continuum mechanics may lack detailed explanations and provide only a few examples and problem sets, making them less suitable as textbooks. However, Prof. J. N. Reddy's textbook and lecture notes offer comprehensive problem sets and illustrative examples that allow students and readers to assess their understanding of the subject matter and apply the developed tools to solve engineering problems effectively.

Between 2006 and 2012, the author taught the Principles of Continua course to junior undergraduate students at NUS. Since 2013, the author has been teaching the Fundamentals of Continuum Mechanics to graduate students at XJTU. Drawing from the teaching experience gained over the past 15 years, the author has decided to author a textbook on continuum mechanics that is accessible and less challenging for students and readers to learn from.

In 2021, the author's idea to publish a textbook on the fundamentals of continuum mechanics for XJTU students received support from the Graduate School of XJTU, and was further chosen as one of the "Quality Graduate Teaching Materials" for the university's 14th Five-Year Plan. As a result, the author embarked on the task of writing this book, *Fundamentals of Continuum Mechanics*.

This textbook takes a unique approach compared to traditional continuum mechanics textbooks used at XJTU, which typically teach tensor analysis as part of an engineering mathematics course. In this book, tensor analysis is instead integrated with mechanical analysis, and the fundamentals of tensor analysis are covered in a dedicated chapter. The book is designed to be accessible even for readers who have not previously studied tensor analysis in engineering mathematics, making it suitable for undergraduate students outside the field of mechanics.

Moreover, the textbook introduces deformation and kinematics using the concept of stretch rather than the traditional strain-based approach. This allows for easier extension to large deformation problems, particularly in the study of mechanics related to soft materials. Additionally, the book incorporates the current research focus on the large deformation problems of new smart soft materials.

While the textbook covers the fundamental objectives of continuum mechanics and elasticity, its main purpose is to facilitate a comprehensive and straightforward understanding of these concepts. Furthermore, it also assists students and engineers who utilize finite element method (FEM) software by helping them interpret the results produced by such software. Throughout the book, concise yet rigorous explanations are provided, and each chapter includes problem examples.

Overall, this book is suitable as a textbook for introductory courses on continuum mechanics for junior, senior, and postgraduate students, as well as for engineers.

The author would like to express heartfelt gratitude to the students who participated in the course on the Fundamentals of Continuum Mechanics at XJTU in the semesters spanning 2014–2023. Their attendance and valuable feedback have played a pivotal role in improving the course material.

Special thanks are extended to my collaborators: Associate Professor Jincheng Lei, Dr. Shuai Xu, Dr. Linchun He, and Dr. Danyang Wang from XJTU, China. Their contributions, insights, and collaborative efforts have greatly enriched the development of this book. Additionally, the author would like to express sincere appreciation to the dedicated Ph.D. and master's students Chong Wang, Jingang Zhu, Zidi Zhou, Yiheng Xue, Yetong Jia, Wenjing Lu, Han Li, and Jiapeng You from XJTU, China. Their constructive comments and invaluable assistance have significantly contributed to the refinement and completion of this book. The collective contributions and support from all these individuals have been instrumental in shaping the content and ensuring the quality of this book.

The author would also like to extend sincere appreciation to Ms. Amanda Yun from World Scientific Publishing Company for her continuous support and invaluable assistance throughout the production process of this book. Her dedication and guidance have been instrumental in bringing this project to fruition.

Furthermore, special thanks are extended to the Graduate School of XJTU for their generous financial support, which greatly facilitated the publication of this book. Their contribution has been instrumental in making this work possible.

Additionally, the author is grateful to the Graduate School of XJTU for selecting this book as one of the "Quality Graduate Teaching Materials" for the 14th Five-Year Plan of the university. This recognition further emphasizes the significance and value of the book as a resource for graduate education.

The author acknowledges the collective support and assistance provided by these individuals and institutions, which have greatly contributed to the successful completion and publication of this book.

As the author acknowledges the limitations of his knowledge, he understands that errors in the book may be inevitable. Therefore, the author kindly requests readers to help identify and correct any errors they come across. The author highly appreciates any comments, feedback, and corrections that readers may have regarding the book. Readers are encouraged to send their comments and corrections to Prof. Zishun Liu at zishunliu@gmail.com.

About the Instructor and Author of Text Book

Zishun Liu is a Professor at Xi'an Jiaotong University (XJTU) and serves as the executive director of the International Center for Applied Mechanics. He also holds the position of general secretary at the International Association of Applied Mechanics (IAAM) and is the honorary president of the Singapore Association of Computational Mechanics. Dr. Liu is a fellow of the International Association of Applied Mechanics, the International Association of Advanced Materials, and the Singapore Association of Computational Mechanics.

He obtained his B.Eng. and M.Eng. degrees from XJTU and his M.Eng. and Ph.D. degrees from the National University of Singapore (NUS). From 1986 to 1994, he was a faculty member at XJTU. He has also held various positions, including senior scientist and capability group manager at the Institute of High Performance Computing (IHPC), Singapore, as well as associate professor at the NUS between 1999 and 2012. As a visiting scientist, he conducted research at the Max Planck Institute for Metals Research in Stuttgart, Germany, and the University of Glasgow, UK, in 2005 and 2006, respectively.

Dr. Liu's research interests lie in the areas of mechanics of soft materials, computational solid mechanics and biomechanics, nanomechanics, and vibro-acoustics. He has authored over 220 SCI-referenced research papers, many of which have received the Most Cited Author Award. Additionally, he currently holds adjunct professorships at NUS.

Dr. Liu holds various leadership roles in editorial boards and professional communities. He serves as the editor-in-chief of the *International Journal of Applied Mechanics* and the *International Journal of Computational Materials Science and Engineering*. Additionally, he is an editor of the *Journal of Mechanics of Materials and Structures* and an associate editor of the *Journal of Applied and Computational Mechanics*. Furthermore, Dr. Liu contributes to several editorial boards, including the *International Journal of Computational Methods*, the *International Journal of Structural Stability and Dynamics*, *Acta Mechanica Sinica*, and *Acta Mechanica Solida Sinica*. He has also served as a guest editor for *Computational Materials Science* and *Structural Engineering and Mechanics* for special issues.

Dr. Liu is a general committee member of the Association of Asia-Pacific Computational Mechanics (APACM) and a general member of the International Association for Computational Mechanics (IACM). In addition, he has taken on the role of chairman, organizing more than 20 international conferences in the fields of computational mechanics and applied mechanics.

Web: https://www.zsliu-group.com and http://gr.xjtu.edu.cn/web/zishun/home.

Contents

Chapter 1

Introduction

Table of Contents

1.1 New Research Areas and Directions of Mechanics

As science and engineering students and researchers, we are familiar with the concept of mechanics, which can have different definitions depending on the perspective. Here are a few examples of this concept: Mechanics is the science concerned with the motion of bodies under the action of forces, including the case where a body remains at rest. In this definition, the focus is on the forces that bodies exert on each other, characterized by their direction, magnitude, and point of application. From a mathematician's point of view, mechanics is a branch of applied mathematics that deals with motion and the forces that produce it. From this viewpoint, mechanics is seen as a mathematical framework for analyzing motion and the underlying forces. Furthermore, mechanics is a branch of physics that analyzes the actions of forces on matter or material systems. Here, the emphasis is on understanding how forces interact with physical objects and their effects.

Mechanics can be further categorized based on the objects of study or physical properties being investigated. Some branches of mechanics include:

- classical mechanics, or Newtonian mechanics, which is based on Newton's laws of motion;
- fluid mechanics and hydraulics, which study the mechanics of fluids;
- pneumatics, which deals with the mechanical properties of gases;
- statics, which focuses on forces in equilibrium;
- dynamics, or kinetics, which examines the forces that cause motion in bodies;
- kinematics, which studies motion without reference to force or mass;
- aerodynamics, or aeromechanics, which analyzes the motion of gases (particularly air) and their effects on bodies in motion.

Mechanics can also be divided into three major areas based on the study method: theoretical mechanics, applied mechanics, and computational mechanics. Furthermore, it can be distinguished based on the physical focus of attention, such as nanomechanics and micromechanics, continuum mechanics, and physical mechanics.

Indeed, the study of mechanics encompasses various levels of matter in nature, ranging from cosmic systems and macroscopic celestial bodies to conventional objects, microscopic particles, fibers, crystals, and even down to the molecular, atomic, and elementary particle levels. While mechanics traditionally focuses on the study of macroscopic objects, the development of interdisciplinary fields and the interconnectedness of disciplines have led to the inclusion of objects and laws at various levels of cosmography, mesoscopics, and even microscopics within the realm of mechanics. Mechanical movement, or the mechanics of movement, involves changes in material position in time and space, encompassing concepts such as translation, rotation, flow, deformation, vibration, waves, and diffusion. These phenomena have given rise to new branches of mechanics that address specific aspects. For example, the National Natural Science

Foundation of China (NSFC) classifies mechanics into different subdisciplines, including dynamics and control, solid mechanics, fluid mechanics, biomechanics, physical mechanics, explosion and shock dynamics, and environmental mechanics. This classification highlights the diverse areas of study within mechanics, reflecting the wide range of phenomena and systems that can be analyzed using mechanical principles.

To comprehend the advancements and new research directions in mechanics, it is helpful to further explore the research topics within each subdiscipline. Here are some of the research directions within each subdiscipline:

1. **Dynamics and control**: The research topics include
   (1) analytical mechanics;
   (2) nonlinear vibration and its control;
   (3) stochastic dynamics and its control;
   (4) nonlinear dynamics of multibody and higher-dimensional systems;
   (5) vehicle and transport system dynamics and rotor dynamics;
   (6) dynamics of nervous and intelligent systems;
   (7) dynamic design and inverse problems.
2. **Solid mechanics**:
   (1) solid deformation and constitutive theory;
   (2) solid strength, damage, fracture, and fatigue;
   (3) wave, vibration, and noise;
   (4) contact, friction, and surface interface mechanics;
   (5) micro-nano mechanics and multi-scale mechanics;
   (6) optimal design, manufacturing, and reliability of materials and structures;
   (7) composite materials and structural mechanics;
   (8) multi-field coupling and intelligent structural mechanics;
   (9) mechanics of soft matter and flexible structures;
   (10) fluid–solid interaction mechanics;
   (11) mechanochemical coupling;
   (12) experimental solid mechanics;
   (13) computational solid mechanics;
   (14) materials and structural mechanics under extreme conditions.

3. **Fluid mechanics**:
   (1) turbulence and flow stability;
   (2) vortices and separation flows;
   (3) aerodynamics and hydrodynamics;
   (4) multiphase flow, percolation, and non-Newtonian fluid dynamics;
   (5) flow noise and aeroacoustics;
   (6) micro-nano scale flow and interfacial flow;
   (7) multi-field and multi-medium coupling and flow control;
   (8) experimental fluid mechanics;
   (9) computational fluid mechanics;
   (10) special topic: critical fluid dynamics problems in aircraft and engines.

4. **Biomechanics**:
   (1) biosolid mechanics and biofluid mechanics;
   (2) multi-scale mechanobiology;
   (3) new emerging topics: natural biomaterials, biomimetics, and sports biomechanics;
   (4) mechanical principles and design of medical materials and instruments.

5. **Physical mechanics**:
   (1) solid physical mechanics;
   (2) fluid physical mechanics;
   (3) physical mechanics of complex and intelligent media.

6. **Explosion and shock dynamics**:
   (1) mechanics of explosion;
   (2) impact dynamics;

7. **Environmental mechanics**:
   (1) rock mass mechanics and soil mechanics;
   (2) environmental fluid dynamics and particle flow;
   (3) extreme environments and disaster mechanics.

For engineering students and researchers, understanding these new emerging subdisciplines can be particularly valuable in keeping up with the latest developments in the field.

1.2 Concepts of Continuum Mechanics

In continuum mechanics, the focus is on the analysis of deformations and forces within different types of matter, including solids, liquids, and gases. To facilitate mathematical analysis, a simplifying assumption is made that the matter is distributed continuously without any gaps or empty spaces. This means that the molecular structure of matter is disregarded for analytical purposes. The continuous matter, in this hypothetical scenario, is referred to as a continuum. Within a continuum, various quantities such as mass density, displacements, velocities, and stresses are assumed to vary continuously. This implies that their spatial derivatives exist and remain continuous throughout the continuum. This assumption allows for the application of mathematical techniques and equations to describe the behavior of matter under deformation and the forces acting upon it. By treating matter as a continuum, continuum mechanics provides a framework for analyzing the behavior and response of materials to external forces and deformations, enabling the study of a wide range of physical phenomena in different types of matter.

Continuum mechanics is concerned with describing the mechanical behavior of materials under the assumption that they can be treated as uniform continua. The name itself reflects the fundamental assumption that materials are homogeneous (having uniform properties throughout), isotropic (exhibiting the same mechanical response in all directions), continuous (without any gaps or discontinuities), and independent of any specific coordinate system. Although nanoscale studies have revealed the atomic and molecular nature of matter, continuum mechanics operates at a macroscopic level where the appearance of solid objects is continuous and their properties appear to vary smoothly without any sudden discontinuities. This assumption allows for the development of mathematical models and equations that describe the behavior of materials under various mechanical loads and conditions. The "black box" approach mentioned refers to the use of continuum mechanics as a predictive tool for mechanical behavior, even in cases where the underlying mechanisms and details are not fully understood. It is an engineering and scientific approach aimed at predicting the response of materials and structures without necessarily delving into the microscale details. This approach is useful in practical applications where a detailed understanding of the microstructure or molecular interactions may not be necessary. In summary, continuum mechanics provides a framework for describing and predicting the mechanical behavior of materials based on the assumption of uniform and continuous properties, even though the underlying nature of matter may be discrete at the atomic or molecular level.

The continuum assumption is fundamental to continuum mechanics. However, in actual cases, continua do not exist. For instance, when studying the cell (plasma) membrane in the human body, it is necessary to define cell boundaries. Internal membranes further delineate various cell organelles, as depicted in Figure 1.2.1. Despite the intricate nature of cell structure, we can ultimately consider the cell membrane as an isotropic material with equivalent material properties, which can be derived from molecular dynamic simulations.

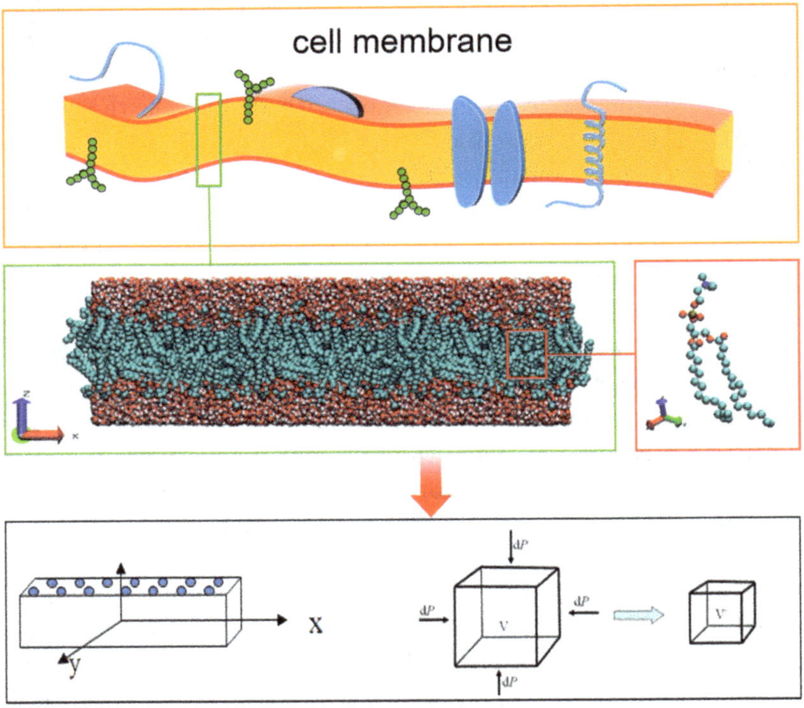

Figure 1.2.1 A schematic model of a biological membrane which can be assumed as an isotropic material or even a shell in continuum mechanics.

The continuum assumption is a simplifying approximation in continuum mechanics, and it may not accurately capture the detailed structure of certain materials or systems at smaller scales. In the case of a cell membrane, it is indeed a complex structure composed of various components such as lipids, proteins, and carbohydrates. At the nanoscale, the discrete nature of molecules and the specific arrangement of these components play a significant role in the behavior of the membrane. To model and analyze the mechanical behavior of a cell membrane, one approach is to employ molecular dynamics simulations that consider the interactions and movements of individual molecules. These simulations can provide insights into the material properties and behavior of the membrane at a more detailed level.

However, when studying larger-scale phenomena or when the focus is on macroscopic mechanical properties, the continuum mechanics framework can still be applied effectively. In such cases, the complex structure of the cell membrane can be simplified by treating it as an isotropic material with equivalent material properties. These properties can be derived from experimental measurements, molecular simulations, or other relevant sources. The continuum assumption allows for the formulation of mathematical models and equations that describe the overall mechanical response of the membrane, such as its elasticity. Although it may not capture the fine-scale details, it provides a practical and efficient way to analyze and predict the behavior of the membrane in a larger context.

It is important to note that the continuum assumption is an approximation, and its validity depends on the specific context and scale of the problem being studied. In some cases, more detailed or refined models, such as those incorporating nanoscale effects or molecular interactions, may be necessary for a more accurate description of the system.

Therefore, the continuum assumption enables us to condense any arbitrary volume of cell material into a single point, similar to how we define limits when defining derivatives. This allows us to define relevant quantities at a specific point. For instance, the mass density (mass per unit volume) of a material at a point is determined by the ratio of the material's mass to the volume surrounding that point. The mathematical investigation of the mechanics of this idealized continuum is known as continuum mechanics.

The continuum assumption allows us to treat a material as if it were continuous, even though in reality it is composed of discrete particles or molecules. By shrinking the volume of the material to a point, we can define various quantities of interest at that point, such as mass density, stress, strain, and velocity.

In continuum mechanics, the behavior of the material is described mathematically using field quantities that vary continuously in space and time. These quantities, such as displacement, velocity, stress, and strain, are defined at every point within the material. By considering the relationships between these quantities, continuum mechanics provides a framework for studying the mechanical response and deformation of materials.

The mathematical study of continuum mechanics Involves formulating equations and principles that govern the behavior of the material. These equations are typically partial differential equations that describe the relationships between the field quantities, such as the balance of forces or the conservation of mass and momentum. By using the continuum assumption and treating the material as a continuous medium, continuum mechanics allows us to analyze and predict the macroscopic mechanical behavior of materials in various applications, such as solid mechanics, fluid mechanics, and biomechanics. It provides a powerful tool for understanding and engineering the mechanical response of materials, structures, and systems.

In Chinese history, the philosopher Zhuangzi (also spelled Zhongzi) mentioned a concept that can be interpreted as an early understanding of continuity. He said, "一尺之捶,日取其半，万世不竭" (pronounced as "*yī chǐ zhī chuí, rì qŭ qí bàn, wàn shì bù jié*"), which translates to "half of a one-foot stick was cut off every day, and this process could go on indefinitely." This concept implies an infinite division of space and time (as shown in Figure 1.2.2). By applying this concept to continuum mechanics, we can consider a "unit cell" as a representation of a point. This means that we can view the material as an infinitely divisible continuum, in which the behavior and properties can be analyzed at a smaller and smaller scale. This idea helps us study the mechanics of materials and phenomena in a simplified and mathematically tractable manner. It's interesting to see how ancient philosophical ideas can relate to modern scientific concepts, and this quote provides a philosophical insight that aligns with the basic principles of continuum mechanics.

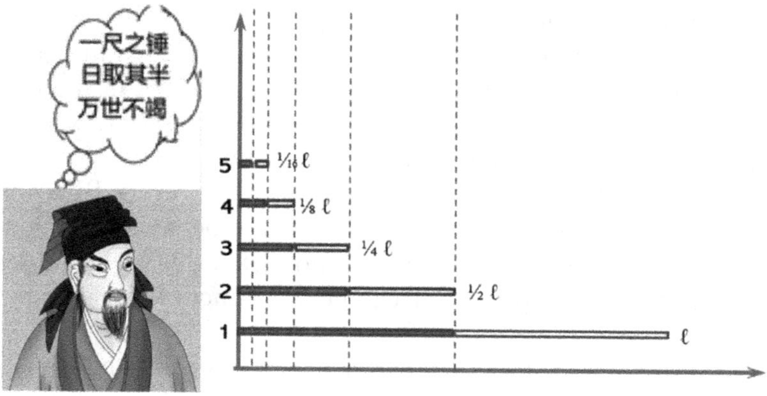

Figure 1.2.2 A schematic diagram of the philosophy by Zhuangzi (BCE 369–286).

The idea expressed in the quote suggests a process of continuously dividing a one-foot stick by half, with the belief that this division can continue indefinitely without exhausting the stick. This concept reflects the notion of infinitesimal subdivision and the potential for infinite divisibility. In the context of continuum mechanics, this can be related to the concept of a "unit cell," or an infinitesimally small volume element that represents a point within the material. By considering the behavior and properties of such unit cells, continuum mechanics allows us to analyze and describe the mechanical response of the material as a whole, even though it is composed of countless individual unit cells. The analogy of continuously dividing the stick can be seen as a metaphor for the subdivision of a material into smaller and smaller elements, eventually approaching the continuum limit. In this sense, the concept of a continuum can be considered an idealized representation of the material, whose behavior is described by continuous fields rather than discrete particles.

1.3 Objectives of the Book

The primary objective of this book is to investigate the conservation principles in the mechanics of continua and formulate equations that describe the motion and mechanical behavior of materials. Additionally, the book aims to demonstrate the practical applications of these derived equations in solving simple problems related to fluid flows, heat conduction, and solid body deformations. Furthermore, the book explores the applications of these equations in more complex systems, such as soft materials, including hydrogels and shape memory polymers. The first objective, i.e., understanding the conservation principles and formulating equations, is crucial because it allows for a quantitative comprehension of the behavior of engineering systems. This quantitative understanding is valuable in the design and manufacture of improved mechanical products for scientists and engineers in the field.

Even for materials scientists and engineers, continuum mechanics provides a language and framework for understanding the physical and morphological foundations of mechanical behavior. For instance, through the utilization of the tensorial nature of modulus, materials engineers can describe and comprehend the modulus and fracture strength of a single crystal silicon wafer, taking into account its crystallographic orientation. Furthermore, materials engineers employ the terminology of continuum mechanics to explain phenomena such as die swell during the extrusion of a polymer filament. Similarly, the piezoelectric behavior of ceramic crystals can also be described using tensorial continuum mechanical descriptions. Therefore, continuum mechanics not only offers quantitative tools for analyzing and predicting mechanical behavior but also provides a language and framework for understanding the underlying physical and morphological aspects of materials.

1.4 Looking Forward

The primary objective of this book has the following two main aspects: (1) deriving the equations that govern the motion and thermomechanical response of materials using physical principles, and (2) applying these equations to solve specific problems related to linearized elasticity, heat transfer, fluid mechanics, and the mechanics of soft materials. These governing equations provide an analytical representation of the overall laws of conservation of mass, balance of momenta and energy, and the constitutive response of the continuum. It's important to note that these equations are applicable to all materials considered as a continuum. For instance, hydrogels, which consist of a polymer network and water, are treated as isotropic materials. Therefore, the derived equations from continuum mechanics can be applied to study the deformation, stress, and other mechanical properties of hydrogels.

In this introductory chapter, we present fundamental concepts that form the basis of the continuum theory of materials. These concepts are crucial for continuum modeling, although they are often used implicitly without extensive discussion. However, in this chapter, we delve into these notions to ensure a clearer understanding in the subsequent chapters.

These concepts encompass various fundamental notions, such as:

- **Body**: refers to the physical object or material under consideration.
- **Configuration of the body**: describes the spatial arrangement of the body in a particular state.
- **Reference configuration of the body**: represents the initial or undeformed state of the body.
- **Region occupied by the body in some configuration**: specifies the spatial extent or volume that the body occupies in a given configuration.
- **Particle (or material point)**: denotes an infinitesimally small element within the body used to describe its behavior.
- **Location of a particle in some configuration**: specifies the position or coordinates of a particle within a particular configuration.
- **Deformation**: describes the change in shape, size, or arrangement of the body from its reference configuration to a subsequent configuration.
- **Motion**: refers to the movement or displacement of particles within the body as it undergoes deformation.
- **Eulerian and Lagrangian descriptions of a physical quantity**: provide different perspectives for describing and analyzing the behavior of a quantity within the body. The Eulerian description focuses on fixed points in space, while the Lagrangian description focuses on the motion of particles.
- **Eulerian and Lagrangian spatial derivatives**: represent the derivatives of a physical quantity with respect to space in the Eulerian and Lagrangian frameworks, respectively.

- **Eulerian and Lagrangian time derivatives (including the material time derivative)**: signify the derivatives of a physical quantity with respect to time in the Eulerian and Lagrangian frameworks, respectively. The material time derivative accounts for changes experienced by a particle as it moves with the material.

The study of the motion and deformation of a continuum body, which is composed of continuously distributed material, can be broadly categorized into four main areas:

(1) **Kinematics**: This field focuses on the geometric changes and deformations in a continuum, without considering the forces causing the deformation. It involves equations related to strain–displacement and strain rate–velocity relations. Variables such as displacements, velocities, strains, and strain rates are utilized in this study.

(2) **Kinetics**: This involves the study of the equilibrium of forces and moments acting on a continuum. It utilizes the principles of balance between linear and angular momentum. This study leads to the derivation of equations of motion and establishes the symmetry of the stress tensor in the absence of body couples. Variables such as stresses and velocities are used and discussed in this context.

(3) **Thermodynamics**: Thermodynamic principles pertain to the balance of energy and the relationships between heat, mechanical work, and the thermodynamic properties of a continuum. This field encompasses the discussion of variables such as temperature, heat flux, stresses, and velocities.

(4) **Constitutive equations**: These equations describe the thermomechanical behavior of the material within the continuum. They establish relationships between the dependent variables introduced in the kinetic description and those introduced in the kinematic and thermodynamic descriptions. Variables involved in constitutive equations include stresses, strains, flux, temperature, pressure, velocities, and density.

In addition to the traditional applications, this book will also cover new emerging applications for continuum mechanics, including the mechanics of soft materials, such as hydrogels and shape memory polymers. These materials possess unique mechanical properties and behaviors that require specialized constitutive models for their characterization and analysis. The book will delve into these topics, providing students with insights into the application of continuum mechanics in these novel areas.

1.5 Summary

In this chapter, the concepts of mechanics and a continuous medium were discussed. The primary objectives of the study were outlined, which include deriving the equations governing a continuous medium using physical principles and applying these equations to solve specific problems in linearized elasticity, heat transfer, and fluid mechanics. The study of physical principles is divided into four main topics, which are covered in subsequent chapters.

While this textbook provides a basic and self-contained introduction to the fundamentals of continuum mechanics, it also lays the foundation for further advanced study in mechanics. We hope that the book will be valuable, particularly in exploring new applications of continuum mechanics. By studying this subject and engaging with the material presented in this book, students will gain a solid understanding of continuum mechanics and hopefully overcome any perception of it as a difficult subject.

For students who are interested in exploring more examples and exercise problems, they can refer to the reference list provided in the book. One recommended source is the book series on continuum mechanics authored by Prof. J.N. Reddy, who is a renowned educator and scientist in the field of mechanics, and his books on continuum mechanics are widely recognized and respected. By referring to Prof. J.N. Reddy's books, students can delve deeper into the subject matter and find additional examples and exercises to enhance their understanding of continuum mechanics.

General References

Liu, Z.S. (2014). *Frontiers of Applied Mechanics* (Imperial College Press, London, UK).

Liu, Z.S. *et al.* (2022). *Mechanics of Soft Materials: Large Deformation Behavior of Hydrogels* (Xi'an Jiaotong University Press, Xi'an China).

Oden, J.T. (2011). *An Introduction to Mathematical Modeling: A Course in Mechanics* (John Wiley & Sons Inc., New Jersey, USA).

Reddy, J.N. (2013). *An Introduction to Continuum Mechanics* (Cambridge University Press, New York, USA).

Reddy, J.N. (2017). *Principles of Continuum Mechanics: Conservation and Balance Laws with Applications* (Cambridge University Press, New York, USA).

Chapter 2

Mathematical Fundamentals: Vectors and Tensors

Table of Contents

2.1 Background and Overview

In mechanics and other fields of physics, many quantities are represented by vectors and tensors. In the mathematical description of equations governing a continuous medium, we need to establish relationships between various quantities that characterize the stress, strain, and deformation of the continuum using the laws of physics (such as Newton's laws and the balance of energy). Therefore, vectors and tensors are often employed. In mathematics, vectors and tensors are sometimes considered subfields of engineering mathematics.

As a way of expressing natural laws, a coordinate system is often introduced in a chosen frame of reference. The mathematical representation of the law depends on the selected coordinate system and may appear differently in another type of coordinate system. However, the laws of nature should be independent of the choice of the coordinate system, and we aim to represent them in a manner that is not tied to a specific coordinate system. Vector and tensor analysis provides a highly convenient method for achieving this. By using vector notation, there is no need to introduce a specific coordinate system. Consequently, formulating natural laws using vector notation ensures their invariance to coordinate transformations. Studying physical phenomena through vector equations often leads to a deeper understanding of the problem and brings simplicity and versatility to the analysis. Therefore, vectors and tensors are highly useful for describing the laws of mechanics or continuum mechanics.

In basic engineering courses and some subjects, the term "vector" is often used to refer to a physical vector that possesses both magnitude and direction, following the parallelogram law of addition. However, in mathematics, vectors are more abstract entities than physical vectors. Therefore, from a physical standpoint, it is easier for engineering students to grasp the concepts of vectors and tensors. Like physical vectors, tensors are more general objects that have magnitude and multiple directions, and they adhere to the rules of tensor addition and scalar multiplication. In fact, physical vectors are often referred to as first-order tensors, such as force vectors and velocity vectors. On the other hand, specifying stress (i.e., force per unit area) requires a magnitude and two directions: one normal to the plane on which the stress component is measured, and the other to uniquely define its direction. These entities are known as tensors.

This chapter of the book focuses on the study of the fundamental principles of algebra and calculus related to vectors and tensors. It covers essential elements of matrix theory and explores eigenvalue problems associated with second-order tensors. Additionally, the chapter introduces index and summation notations, which are widely utilized in mechanics textbooks and research papers. For students who have previously encountered these concepts in their prior studies, this section can serve as a valuable refresher or review, as we approach them from different perspectives, such as index notation.

This book is the culmination of our efforts to present the fundamental concepts of vector and tensor analysis in a manner that is particularly suited for our mechanics postgraduate students. Traditionally, courses on vectors and tensors have been taught in engineering mathematics, following a more conventional approach. However, in this book, we adopt an application-based perspective to teach students about vectors and tensors.

In this book, you will learn to identify vectors and tensors through formal transformation rules rather than solely relying on their mathematical structures. This approach is better suited for engineering students. Before applying vector and tensor analysis to our research area of modern continuum mechanics, we found ourselves needing to relearn the subject. Hence, one of our main objectives when writing this book or note is to provide a modern introductory textbook that serves as the first comprehensive exposure to vectors and tensors. Due to our focus on applications, we hope that this book will assist students in effectively utilizing vectors and tensors in the field of applied mechanics.

We have made an effort to present the basic mathematical concepts as clearly and concisely as possible without becoming overly abstract. As this is an introductory text, we have not attempted to cover every aspect of this topic, which is why we have dedicated only one chapter to vector and tensor analysis.

As discussed in Prof. J.N. Reddy's book, we would like to adopt the profound words of the renowned mathematician David Hilbert to encapsulate the objectives of this chapter: "A mathematical theory is not to be considered complete until you have made it so clear that you can explain it to the first person you meet on the street." With this in mind, our textbook is designed to strive toward this goal as we present this chapter.

2.2 Concept of Vectors

In this section, our first objective is to provide a formal definition of a geometric vector. We then discuss the different products of vectors and delve into the physical significance of vectors.

Vectors are employed to describe physical quantities that possess both magnitude and direction. Examples include force, velocity, displacement, and acceleration. To facilitate a physical interpretation of these vectors, we introduce index notation. This notation simplifies the representation of vectors in terms of their components as well as the operations performed on them. Additionally, we cover the transformation equations that relate the components of a vector expressed in two different coordinate systems.

In contrast, a physical quantity that can be fully described by a single real number is known as a scalar. Scalars possess magnitude, and their complete description relies solely on this magnitude. Examples of scalars include temperature, density, and mass. In this section, we also address the concept of scalars in order to highlight the distinction between vectors and scalars. Students and readers may consider scalars as a special case of vectors or tensors.

2.2.1 *Definition of a Vector*

In engineering and everyday life, when describing physical phenomena, we commonly utilize "quantities" that can be classified into two groups based on the information required to fully specify them: "scalars" and "non-scalars." Scalars are quantities that can be expressed by a single number alone. On the other hand, non-scalars possess additional information beyond magnitude, such as direction. Non-scalars that adhere to specific rules are referred to as vectors. It's worth noting that not all non-scalar quantities are vectors. For instance, a finite rotation is not considered a vector. We will explore this concept further in subsequent chapters.

To represent a vector, a common approach is to use a directed line segment with an arrowhead at one end, which is often referred to as a physical vector. In this representation, the length of the line segment represents the magnitude of the vector, while the arrow indicates its direction. Thus, a physical vector, possessing both magnitude and direction, can be regarded as a normed vector.

Figure 2.2.1 Geometrical representation of a vector **A**: (a) free vector and (b) fixed or bound vector.

For instance, a vector **A** can be denoted by using a boldface letter, such as **A**. The magnitude of a vector is a scalar quantity, typically denoted by $|\mathbf{A}|$. Therefore, a vector represents a physical quantity characterized by both its direction and magnitude. The length of the vector represents its magnitude, while its direction is indicated by a unit vector along its axis. Geometrically, a vector is often depicted as an arrow, where the arrowhead signifies the direction of the vector. The magnitude of the vector is represented by the length of the arrow, as illustrated in Figure 2.2.1. A vector is referred to as a free vector if its specific location or starting point (i.e., the base of the arrow) is not specified (see Figure 2.2.1(a)). On the other hand, a fixed or bound vector is associated with a specific location in space, denoted by the base point O from which the vector originates (Figure 2.2.1(b)).

A vector with unit magnitude is a unit vector. The unit vector along vector **A** is defined as

$$\mathbf{e_A} = \frac{\mathbf{A}}{|\mathbf{A}|}. \tag{2.2.1}$$

Note that the zero vector is a special vector with zero magnitude.

Two vectors, **A** and **B**, are considered equal if their magnitudes are equal ($|\mathbf{A}| = |\mathbf{B}|$) and their directions are equal. Importantly, a vector remains unchanged if it is moved parallelly. Hence, the position of a vector in space, or the specific starting point from which the line segment is drawn, can be chosen arbitrarily.

However, in certain applications, the actual point of location of a vector may be significant. For example, when representing moments or forces acting on a body, the vector needs to be associated with a specific starting point. Such vectors are known as localized or bound vectors. It is important to note that the graphical representation of

Figure 2.2.2 The schematic diagram of velocity fields in segments A and B in a river.

vectors is not a fundamental aspect of the vector concept but rather an incidental feature.

Bound vectors are particularly useful in applications such as representing the velocity of fluid at different points in a river. In this case, a bound vector can be drawn at each point of interest, depicting the speed and direction of the fluid at that location. A collection of such vectors is referred to as a vector field, as depicted in Figure 2.2.2.

If you think about the ways in which you might represent a bound vector, you may realize that the vector can be defined simply by specifying the start and end points of the arrow.

The direction of vector **A** can be quantified by its direction cosines, which are given by the cosines of the angles between **A** and a set of "**n**" arbitrary but linearly independent base vectors comprising a basis. A standard Euclidean basis is a set of right-hand mutually orthogonal unit vectors located at the base O and denoted $(\mathbf{e}_1, \mathbf{e}_2, \mathbf{e}_3, \ldots, \mathbf{e}_n$, where $n = 1, 2, \ldots)$. The index n represents the specific base vector in the set.

Now, we consider the special case in which the vector is anchored to the origin of a three-dimensional (3D) Cartesian coordinate system. Thus, in a 3D Cartesian coordinate system with base vectors $(\mathbf{e}_1, \mathbf{e}_2, \mathbf{e}_3)$, you only need to know the values of (A_1, A_2, A_3), or the magnitudes of $(\mathbf{a}_1, \mathbf{a}_2, \mathbf{a}_3)$, as shown in Figure 2.2.3.

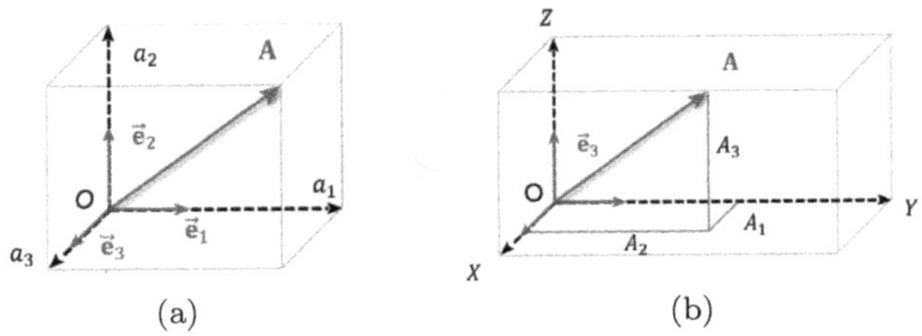

Figure 2.2.3 A vector represented in a 3D Cartesian coordinate system: (a) a fixed vector, (b) components of a vector **A**.

When representing a bound vector, one can define it simply by specifying the start and end points of the arrow that represents the vector.

2.2.2 *Vector Algebra*

2.2.2.1 *Vector addition*

Let **A** and **B** be any vectors. Then, there exists a vector $\mathbf{C} = \mathbf{A}+\mathbf{B}$, called the sum of **A** and **B**, with the following properties.

(1) $\mathbf{A}+\mathbf{B} = \mathbf{B}+\mathbf{A}$ (commutative).
(2) $(\mathbf{A}+\mathbf{B})+\mathbf{C} = \mathbf{A}+(\mathbf{B}+\mathbf{C})$ (associative).
(3) $\mathbf{C} = \mathbf{A}+\mathbf{B}$, where **C** is also a vector.
(4) There exists a unique vector, **0**, independent of **A**, such that $\mathbf{A}+\mathbf{0} = \mathbf{A}$ (existence of the zero vector).
(5) For every vector **A**, there exists a unique vector $-\mathbf{A}$ (that depends on **A**) such that $\mathbf{A}+(-\mathbf{A}) = \mathbf{0}$ (existence of the opposite vector).

The opposite $-\mathbf{A}$ has the same magnitude as **A**, but its direction is opposite that of **A**. Subtraction of vectors is carried out along the same lines. To form the difference between **A** and **B** (i.e., $\mathbf{A}-\mathbf{B}$), we can write $\mathbf{A}+(-\mathbf{B})$, and the subtraction is converted into the operation of addition, as shown in the schematic diagram in Figure 2.2.4.

2.2.2.2 *Multiplication of a vector by a scalar*

Let **A** and **B** be vectors and α and β be real numbers (scalars). For every vector **A** and every real number α, there corresponds a

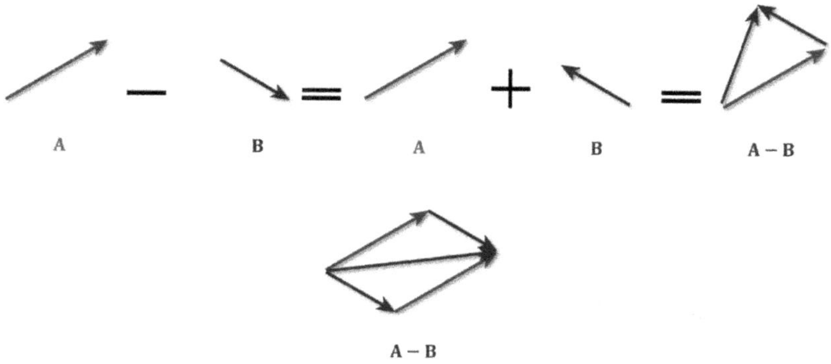

Figure 2.2.4 Vector addition.

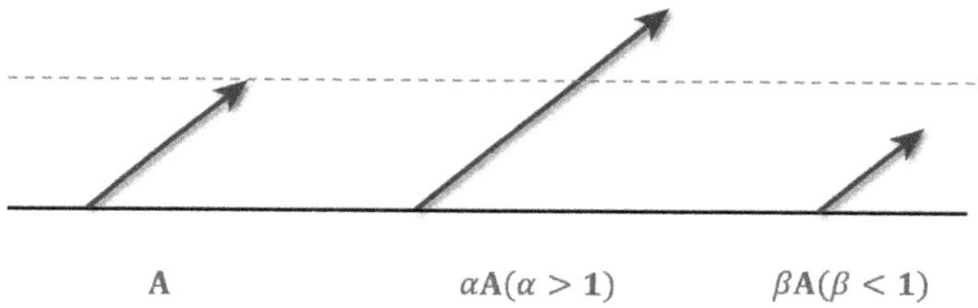

Figure 2.2.5 The vector **A** is multiplied by a scalar α. $\alpha < 1$ may lead to negative values, for which the direction can be opposite, $0 < \alpha < 1$.

unique vector $\alpha\mathbf{A}$ which exhibits the following properties, as shown in Figure 2.2.5:

(1) $\alpha(\beta\mathbf{A}) = (\alpha\beta)\mathbf{A}$ (scalar multiplication is associative).
(2) $(\alpha + \beta)\mathbf{A} = \alpha\mathbf{A} + \beta\mathbf{A}$ (scalar addition is distributive).
(3) $\alpha(\mathbf{A} + \mathbf{B}) = \alpha\mathbf{A} + \alpha\mathbf{B}$ (vector addition is distributive).
(4) $1 \cdot \mathbf{A} = \mathbf{A}, \quad 0 \cdot \mathbf{A} = \mathbf{0}$.

Indeed, the properties mentioned above highlight the similarities between the operations of vector algebra and scalar algebra. Unlike scalars, two vectors **A** and **B** are considered equal if their magnitudes are equal $|\mathbf{A}| = |\mathbf{B}|$ and their directions are equal. This means that for vectors, equality is determined by both magnitude and direction, which is different from how it is determined for scalars.

Moreover, the laws governing addition, subtraction, and scalar multiplication of vectors are similar to those of scalar algebra. To add or subtract vectors, we combine or subtract their corresponding components. Scalar multiplication, on the other hand, involves multiplying each component of the vector by the scalar. These operations follow the same rules as scalar algebra. By acknowledging these similarities, we can apply familiar concepts and operations from scalar algebra to manipulate and analyze vectors. This allows for a unified framework in which vectors and scalars can be treated consistently.

2.2.3 *Scalar and Vector Products*

Indeed, in addition to the operations of vector addition, subtraction, and scalar multiplication, we also encounter the product of two vectors. There are several ways to define the product of two vectors, with the two most commonly used ones being the scalar product (also known as the dot product) and the vector product (also known as the cross product).

2.2.3.1 *Scalar product*

In the general case, the scalar product (also known as dot product or inner product) of two vectors **A** and **B**, denoted as $\mathbf{A}\cdot\mathbf{B}$, is a scalar defined as

$$\mathbf{A}\cdot\mathbf{B} = |\mathbf{A}||\mathbf{B}|\cos\theta, \tag{2.2.2}$$

where θ is the angle between the vectors when their initial points coincide and is restricted to the range $0 \leq \theta \leq \pi$, as shown in Figure 2.2.6. Such an operation may be defined for any two vectors. Since the result of the product is a scalar, it is called the scalar product. Therefore, the scalar product of two vectors yields a scalar quantity.

Figure 2.2.6 The scalar product (or dot product) of two vectors.

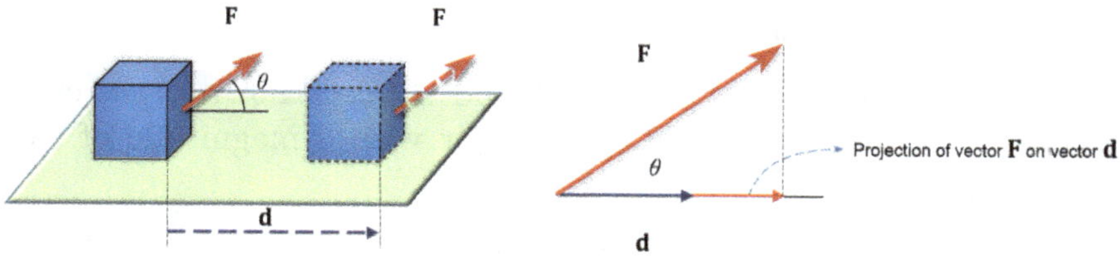

Figure 2.2.7 Schematic diagram of vector representation of work done.

What is the physical meaning of the dot product of vectors? We can consider a scenario where a force vector $\mathbf{F}$ acts on a mass point and causes it to move with a displacement vector $\mathbf{d}$. The work done by the force vector is defined by taking the projection of the force in the direction of the displacement, as illustrated in Figure 2.2.7, and multiplying it by the magnitude of the displacement. We denote this product as $\mathbf{F} \cdot \mathbf{d} = (\mathbf{F}, \mathbf{d})$, and it is defined as follows:

$$\mathbf{F} \cdot \mathbf{d} = (\mathbf{F}, \mathbf{d}) = |\mathbf{F}||\mathbf{d}| \cos\theta \quad 0 \leq \theta \leq \pi. \tag{2.2.3}$$

Therefore, the work done by the force vector is a scalar, which can be expressed by the doc product of the force vector and the displacement vector.

The definition of the dot product of vectors leads to several simple results or properties, including the following:

(1) The scalar product is commutative: $\mathbf{A} \cdot \mathbf{B} = \mathbf{B} \cdot \mathbf{A}$.
(2) If the vectors $\mathbf{A}$ and $\mathbf{B}$ are perpendicular to each other, then $\mathbf{A} \cdot \mathbf{B} = |\mathbf{A}||\mathbf{B}| \cos\frac{\pi}{2} = 0$. Conversely, if $\mathbf{A} \cdot \mathbf{B} = 0$, then either $\mathbf{A}$ or $\mathbf{B}$ is a zero vector or $\mathbf{A}$ is perpendicular, or orthogonal, to $\mathbf{B}$.
(3) If two vectors $\mathbf{A}$ and $\mathbf{B}$ are parallel, then $\mathbf{A} \cdot \mathbf{B} = |\mathbf{A}||\mathbf{B}| \cos\theta = |\mathbf{A}||\mathbf{B}|$ since $\cos\theta = 1$. Moreover, the scalar product of a vector multiplied by itself equals the square of its magnitude (we denote the magnitude of $\mathbf{A}$ as $A = |\boldsymbol{A}|$); hence,

$$\mathbf{A} \cdot \mathbf{A} = AA = A^2. \tag{2.2.4}$$

(4) The orthogonal projection of a vector $\mathbf{A}$ in the direction $\mathbf{e}$ is given by $\mathbf{A} \cdot \mathbf{e}$.
(5) The scalar product also follows the distributive law:

$$\mathbf{A} \cdot (\mathbf{B} + \mathbf{C}) = (\mathbf{A} \cdot \mathbf{B}) + (\mathbf{A} \cdot \mathbf{C}). \tag{2.2.5}$$

2.2.3.2 *Vector product*

The vector product of two vectors **A** and **B** (also known as the cross product), denoted by $\mathbf{A} \times \mathbf{B}$, is a vector with a magnitude of (see Figure 2.2.8)

$$|\mathbf{A} \times \mathbf{B}| = |\mathbf{A}||\mathbf{B}| \sin\theta, \tag{2.2.6}$$

where θ is the angle between the two vectors **A** and **B**. The magnitude of the cross product $|\mathbf{A} \times \mathbf{B}|$ is equivalent to the area of the parallelogram formed by these two vectors, as shown in Figure 2.2.8. The direction of the resulting cross product vector is perpendicular to both **A** and **B**. Whether the vector $\mathbf{A} \times \mathbf{B}$ points "up" or "down" is determined by the right-hand rule: Point four fingers (except for the thumb) of the right hand in the direction of vector **A** and curl the fingers toward the direction of vector **B**, then the right-hand thumb points in the direction of the cross product vector. Examples illustrating this concept are shown in Figure 2.2.8(b), where vector **D** is a vector whose direction is opposite to that of vector **C**.

To illustrate the physical meaning and usefulness of the vector product, let's consider the concept of the moment caused by a force around a point. We want to describe the moment about a point O that is generated by a force vector **F** acting at a point P, as depicted in Figure 2.2.9. By definition, the magnitude of the moment is given by $|\mathbf{F} \times \mathbf{r}| = |\mathbf{F}||\mathbf{r}| \sin\theta$, where $|\mathbf{F}|$ represents the magnitude of the force and $|\mathbf{r}|$ represents the magnitude of the position vector **r**.

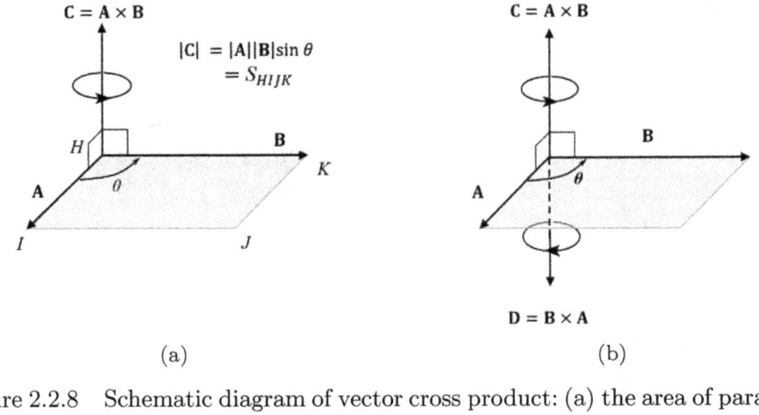

Figure 2.2.8 Schematic diagram of vector cross product: (a) the area of parallelogram represents the magnitude of cross product of vectors, (b) different directions of the vector cross product.

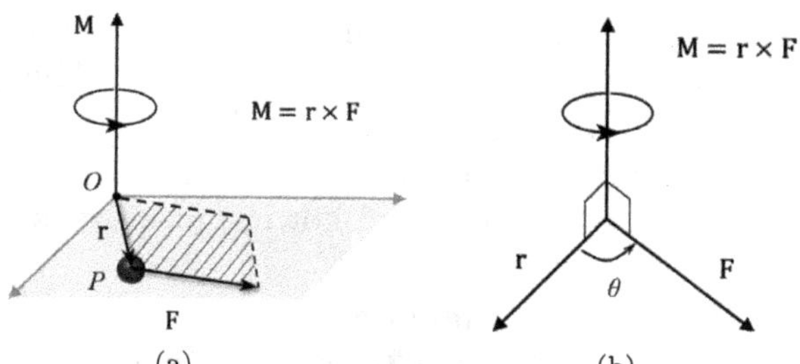

Figure 2.2.9 (a) Representation of a moment about a point and (b) direction of moment rotation.

A direction can now be assigned to the moment. By drawing the vectors **F** and **r** from the common origin O, we observe that the rotation caused by **F** tends to bring **r** into **F**. This can be seen in Figure 2.2.9. To define the direction of the moment, we establish an axis of rotation that is perpendicular to the plane formed by **F** and **r**. Along this axis, we establish a preferred direction based on the concept that a right-handed screw would advance when turned in the direction of the moment's rotation, as depicted in Figure 2.2.9(b). We then draw a unit vector $\hat{\mathbf{e}}$ along this axis of rotation and agree that it represents the direction of the moment. Therefore, the moment **M** can be defined as follows:

$$\mathbf{M} = \mathbf{r} \times \mathbf{F} = |\mathbf{r}||\mathbf{F}| \sin\theta\, \hat{\mathbf{e}}, \tag{2.2.7}$$

where **M** is the result of the cross product of vectors **F** and **r**.

The cross product of two vectors **A** and **B** is a vector **C** whose magnitude equals the product of the magnitudes of **A** and **B** times the sine of the angle θ between **A** and **B**, such that $0 \leq \theta \leq \pi$. The direction of **C** is perpendicular to the plane determined by vectors **A** and **B**, and follows the right-handed screw, as shown in Figure 2.2.8(b). The vector product is usually denoted by

$$\mathbf{C} = \mathbf{A} \times \mathbf{B} = |\mathbf{A}||\mathbf{B}| \sin\theta\, \hat{\mathbf{e}} = AB \sin(\mathbf{A},\, \mathbf{B})\hat{\mathbf{e}} = AB \sin\theta\, \hat{\mathbf{e}}, \tag{2.2.8}$$

where $\sin(\mathbf{A}, \mathbf{B})$ denotes the sine of the angle θ between vectors **A** and **B**. This product is called the cross product, skew product, outer product, or vector product. When $\mathbf{A} = A \cdot \hat{\mathbf{e}}_{\mathbf{A}}$ and $\mathbf{B} = B \cdot \hat{\mathbf{e}}_{\mathbf{B}}$ are the vectors representing the sides of a parallelogram, with A and B

denoting the lengths of the sides, then the vector product $\mathbf{A} \times \mathbf{B}$ represents the area of the parallelogram, $AB \sin\theta$. The unit vector $\hat{\mathbf{e}} = \hat{\mathbf{e}}_{\mathbf{A}} \times \hat{\mathbf{e}}_{\mathbf{B}}$ denotes the normal to the plane area. Therefore, an area can be represented as a vector. We will discuss this later.

The cross product possesses the following properties:

(1) $\mathbf{A} \times \mathbf{B} = -\mathbf{B} \times \mathbf{A}$ (not commutative).
(2) $\mathbf{A} \times (\mathbf{B} + \mathbf{C}) = \mathbf{A} \times \mathbf{B} + \mathbf{A} \times \mathbf{C}$ (distributive).
(3) $\alpha(\mathbf{A} \times \mathbf{B}) = \mathbf{A} \times (\alpha\mathbf{B})$.
(4) $\mathbf{A} \times \mathbf{B} = \mathbf{0}$ if and only if $\mathbf{A}$ and $\mathbf{B}$ ($\neq \mathbf{0}$) are parallel.

2.2.3.3 *Scalar triple product of vectors*

Once you have grasped the concepts of dot product and cross product explained in the previous sections, you might wonder if it is possible to combine these two vector operations. Fortunately, not only is it possible, but it is also highly useful to do so. After all, creating mathematical operations is interesting; however, unless they have practical applications for problem-solving, they remain purely theoretical. We have seen how the dot product is employed for finding projections of vectors onto specific directions and for calculating work done by force, and how the cross product is used for dealing with torques and magnetic forces. But does it make sense to combine the dot and cross product operations, such as $\mathbf{A} \cdot (\mathbf{B} \times \mathbf{C})$? The answer is yes. This combination is known as the "triple scalar product," "scalar triple product," or "box product," and it finds various practical applications.

The triple scalar product of three vectors $\mathbf{A}, \mathbf{B}$, and $\mathbf{C}$ is defined by

$$\mathbf{A} \cdot (\mathbf{B} \times \mathbf{C}) = \mathbf{B} \cdot (\mathbf{C} \times \mathbf{A}) = \mathbf{C} \cdot (\mathbf{A} \times \mathbf{B}). \tag{2.2.9}$$

One geometrical interpretation of the triple scalar product can be understood with the help of Figure 2.2.10. In this figure, vectors $\mathbf{A}$, $\mathbf{B}$, and $\mathbf{C}$ represent the sides of a parallelepiped. The area of the base of this parallelepiped is $|\mathbf{B} \times \mathbf{C}|$, as in Figure 2.2.8, and its height is equal to $|\mathbf{A}| \cos\varphi$, where φ is the angle between $\mathbf{A}$ and the direction of $|\mathbf{B} \times \mathbf{C}|$. This means that the volume of the parallelepiped (the height times the area of the base) must be $|\mathbf{A}| \cos\varphi \cdot (|\mathbf{B} \times \mathbf{C}|)$.

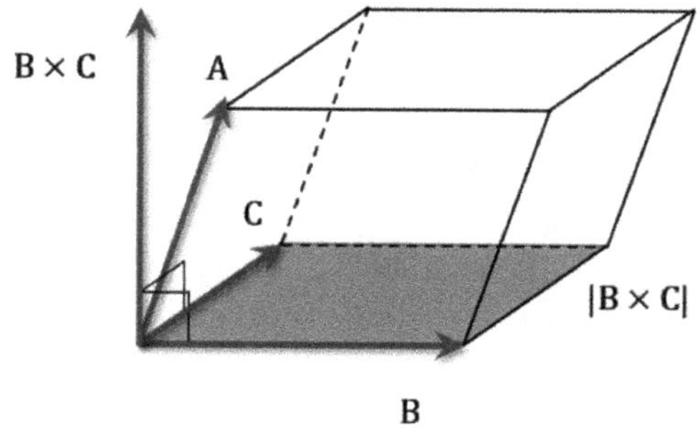

Figure 2.2.10 Scalar triple product represents the volume of a parallelepiped.

We note the following properties of a scalar triple product:

(1) The dot and cross can be interchanged without changing the value. A cyclical permutation of the order of the vectors leaves the result unchanged:

$$\mathbf{A} \cdot (\mathbf{B} \times \mathbf{C}) = \mathbf{B} \cdot (\mathbf{C} \times \mathbf{A}) = \mathbf{C} \cdot (\mathbf{A} \times \mathbf{B}).$$

(2) If the cyclic order is changed, the sign changes:

$$\mathbf{A} \cdot (\mathbf{B} \times \mathbf{C}) = -\mathbf{B} \cdot (\mathbf{A} \times \mathbf{C}) = -\mathbf{C} \cdot (\mathbf{B} \times \mathbf{A}).$$

(3) A necessary and sufficient condition for any three vectors, **A**, **B**, and **C**, to be coplanar is that $\mathbf{A} \cdot (\mathbf{B} \times \mathbf{C}) = 0$. Note also that the scalar triple product is zero when any two vectors are the same.

2.2.3.4 *Vector triple product*

The vector triple product $\mathbf{A} \times (\mathbf{B} \times \mathbf{C})$ is a vector normal to the plane formed by **A** and $(\mathbf{B} \times \mathbf{C})$. The vector $(\mathbf{B} \times \mathbf{C})$, however, is perpendicular to the plane formed by **B** and **C**. This means that $\mathbf{A} \times (\mathbf{B} \times \mathbf{C})$ lies in the plane formed by **B** and **C** and is perpendicular to **A**, as shown in Figure 2.2.11. Thus, $\mathbf{A} \times (\mathbf{B} \times \mathbf{C})$ can be expressed as a linear combination of **B** and **C**:

$$\mathbf{A} \times (\mathbf{B} \times \mathbf{C}) = m_1\mathbf{B} + n_1\mathbf{C}, \tag{2.2.10}$$

where $m_1 = \mathbf{A} \cdot \mathbf{C}$ and $n_1 = -\mathbf{A} \cdot \mathbf{B}$. Likewise, we would find that

$$(\mathbf{A} \times \mathbf{B}) \times \mathbf{C} = k\mathbf{A} + l\mathbf{B}, \tag{2.2.11}$$

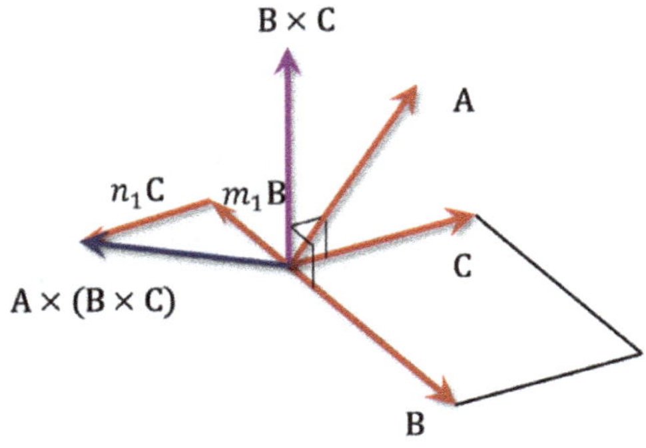

Figure 2.2.11 The vector triple product.

where $k = -\mathbf{B} \cdot \mathbf{C}$ and $l = \mathbf{A} \cdot \mathbf{C}$. Note that the parentheses cannot be interchanged or removed. Hence, it can be shown that

$$\mathbf{A} \times (\mathbf{B} \times \mathbf{C}) = (\mathbf{A} \cdot \mathbf{C})\mathbf{B} - (\mathbf{A} \cdot \mathbf{B})\mathbf{C},$$
$$(\mathbf{A} \times \mathbf{B}) \times \mathbf{C} = (\mathbf{A} \cdot \mathbf{C})\mathbf{B} - (\mathbf{B} \cdot \mathbf{C})\mathbf{A}, \tag{2.2.12}$$

and one can show that $\mathbf{A} \times (\mathbf{B} \times \mathbf{C}) = (\mathbf{A} \times \mathbf{B}) \times \mathbf{C}$ if and only if $\mathbf{B} \times (\mathbf{C} \times \mathbf{A}) = 0$.

2.2.3.5 *The normal and plane area as a vector*

From the cross product of two vectors, we can determine that the magnitude of the vector $\mathbf{C} = \mathbf{A} \times \mathbf{B}$ equals the area of the parallelogram formed by the vectors $\mathbf{A}$ and $\mathbf{B}$, as illustrated in Figure 2.2.12(a). Additionally, the vector can be seen as representing both the magnitude and direction of the product of $\mathbf{A}$ and $\mathbf{B}$. Consequently, a plane area can be viewed as having not only a magnitude but also a direction, with the directional aspect arising from the necessity of specifying the orientation of the plane in space. For instance, it is sometimes useful to associate a specific vector $\mathrm{d}\mathbf{S}$ with a differential element of surface area $\mathrm{d}s$, where

$$\mathrm{d}\mathbf{S} = \mathbf{n}\mathrm{d}s \tag{2.2.13}$$

so that $\mathrm{d}\mathbf{S}$ is the vector with a magnitude of $\mathrm{d}s$ and the direction of the unit normal vector $\mathbf{n}$ to the surface. In continuum mechanics, we use the representation of an area as a vector.

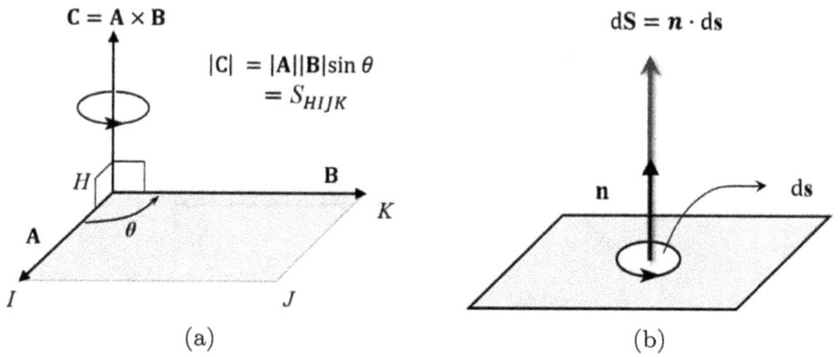

Figure 2.2.12 (a) An area as a vector and (b) a differential element of surface area.

2.2.4 *Cartesian Vectors*

Up until now, we have primarily focused on a geometric interpretation of vectors. We have mainly discussed vectors using symbolic notation without referencing "axes," "components," or "coordinates." As mentioned earlier, vectors exist independently of any coordinate system. It turns out that most vector calculations can be expressed more concisely and easily using this notation rather than relying on component notations. However, there are many situations in mechanics where using component forms of vectors is more helpful and necessary. In this section, we explore vectors in terms of their component forms.

We now begin an analytical description of vectors based on the concept of their components. In the following discussion, we consider a 3D space or Euclidean space, with the understanding that the principles can be extended to n dimensions.

2.2.4.1 *The Cartesian basis*

In 3D space, it is possible to find a set of three linearly independent vectors. Let's consider a 3D Cartesian coordinate system and denote these three linearly independent vectors as $(\mathbf{e}_1, \mathbf{e}_2, \mathbf{e}_3)$. This set of vectors, $(\mathbf{e}_1, \mathbf{e}_2, \mathbf{e}_3)$, is commonly referred to as a basis, base vectors, or a Cartesian basis. It is important to note that the magnitude of each base vector is 1, indicating that they are unit vectors. These base vectors provide a framework for representing any vector in this 3D space by expressing it as a linear combination of the base vectors.

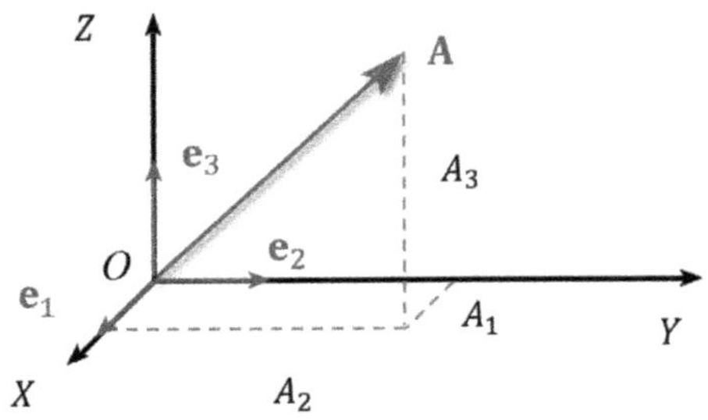

Figure 2.2.13 A vector represented in 3D Cartesian coordinate system.

We consider a 3D (Euclidean) space. In this space, the three unit vectors $(\mathbf{e}_1, \mathbf{e}_2, \mathbf{e}_3)$ have the following properties (see Figure 2.2.13):

$$\mathbf{e}_1 \cdot \mathbf{e}_2 = \mathbf{e}_2 \cdot \mathbf{e}_3 = \mathbf{e}_1 \cdot \mathbf{e}_3 = 0, \tag{2.2.14}$$

i.e., these unit vectors are mutually perpendicular (mutually orthogonal) according to the definition of vector dot product, and

$$\mathbf{e}_1 \cdot \mathbf{e}_1 = \mathbf{e}_2 \cdot \mathbf{e}_2 = \mathbf{e}_3 \cdot \mathbf{e}_3 = 1, \tag{2.2.15}$$

as they are unit vectors. Such a set of orthogonal unit vectors is called an orthonormal set, as shown in Figure 2.2.13. Note that this orthonormal system $(\mathbf{e}_1, \mathbf{e}_2, \mathbf{e}_3)$ is right-handed, meaning that $\mathbf{e}_1 \times \mathbf{e}_2 = \mathbf{e}_3$ (or $(\mathbf{e}_2 \times \mathbf{e}_3 = \mathbf{e}_1)$ and/or $(\mathbf{e}_3 \times \mathbf{e}_1 = \mathbf{e}_2)$).

2.2.4.2 *The components of a vector*

We can represent any vector in this 3D space as a linear combination of the basis vectors (shown in Figure 2.2.13):

$$\mathbf{A} = A_1\mathbf{e}_1 + A_2\mathbf{e}_2 + A_3\mathbf{e}_3. \tag{2.2.16}$$

The three vectors $A_1\mathbf{e}_1, A_2\mathbf{e}_2, A_3\mathbf{e}_3$ are the vector components of $\mathbf{A}$, and A_1, A_2, A_3 are the scalar components of $\mathbf{A}$ associated with the basis $(\mathbf{e}_1, \mathbf{e}_2, \mathbf{e}_3)$.

From Figure 2.2.13, we can easily obtain $|\mathbf{A}|$, the magnitude of a vector $\mathbf{A}$, as

$$\mathbf{A} = |\mathbf{A}| = \sqrt{A_1^2 + A_2^2 + A_3^2}. \tag{2.2.17}$$

Applying Equation (2.2.16) and using unit vector properties, the scalars in Equation (2.2.16) can be expressed as

$$A_1 = \mathbf{A} \cdot \mathbf{e}_1, A_2 = \mathbf{A} \cdot \mathbf{e}_2, A_3 = \mathbf{A} \cdot \mathbf{e}_3. \tag{2.2.18}$$

The scalars A_1, A_2, and A_3 are also called the Cartesian components of $\mathbf{A}$ in the given basis of $(\mathbf{e}_1, \mathbf{e}_2, \mathbf{e}_3)$. The unit vectors are called base vectors. In some cases, we use a cap base vector to represent unit vectors, i.e., $(\hat{\mathbf{e}}_1, \hat{\mathbf{e}}_2, \hat{\mathbf{e}}_3)$ is the same as $(\mathbf{e}_1, \mathbf{e}_2, \mathbf{e}_3)$.

It is worth noting that while a right-handed orthonormal set of three vectors is commonly used as a basis in engineering practice due to its simplicity, it is not a strict requirement for forming a basis. The essential criterion is that the three vectors are not coplanar, meaning they do not lie in the same plane. As mentioned above, there are cases where a curved coordinate system may be more suitable for describing objects with curved boundaries. However, the discussion of such coordinate systems is beyond the scope of this book, and it is recommended for students to refer to relevant reference books for more detailed information on these topics.

2.2.5 *Index Notation*

The equations governing continuous mechanics, particularly in three dimensions, often consist of lengthy expressions with numerous additive terms. When students encounter these equations, they tend to perceive them as troublesome or tedious. However, it is worth noting that these terms frequently possess a similar structure, allowing for the identification of a typical term within the expression. For example, consider the component form of vector $\mathbf{A}$, such as $\mathbf{A} = A_1\mathbf{e}_1 + A_2\mathbf{e}_2 + A_3\mathbf{e}_3$.

In mathematics, index notation is a concise way to represent vectors, matrices, and tensors. Instead of writing the components separately as $A_1\mathbf{e}_1 + A_2\mathbf{e}_2 + A_3\mathbf{e}_3$, the indexed variable A_i $(i = 1, 2, 3)$ represents all components collectively as follows:

$$A_i \quad \Leftrightarrow \quad (A_1, A_2, A_3). \tag{2.2.19}$$

By convention, the index takes the value $i = 1, 2, \ldots, n$. Using index notation, the complete vector $\mathbf{A}$ can be written as

$$\mathbf{A} = \sum_{1}^{3} A_i \mathbf{e}_\mathrm{i} = A_1\mathbf{e}_1 + A_2\mathbf{e}_2 + A_3\mathbf{e}_3 \quad \text{or} \quad \mathbf{A} = \sum_{1}^{3} A_j \mathbf{e}_\mathrm{j}. \quad (2.2.20)$$

The summation index i or j is arbitrary as long as the same index is used for both $\mathbf{A}$ and $\mathbf{e}$. Thus, the three-term expression for $\mathbf{A}$ can be written more simply, as discussed in the following sections.

2.2.5.1 *Einstein summation convention*

The above expression can be shortened further by omitting the summation sign and understanding that a repeated index means summation over all values of that index. The important summation convention states that if an index appears twice in a single term, then it is understood that the repeated index is summed over its range. The summation symbol is then redundant, and the vector $\mathbf{A}$ can be written concisely as

$$\mathbf{A} = A_i \mathbf{e}_\mathrm{i} = A_j \mathbf{e}_\mathrm{j}. \quad (2.2.21)$$

This notation is called the summation convention, or Einstein summation convention. Here, the index i represents the components of the vector $\mathbf{A}$, and the repeated index implies summation over its range of values. This notation allows for a more compact representation of vector equations and simplifies the expression of mathematical operations. Note that the range of the index i should be specified, typically from 1 to n, where n represents the dimensionality of the vector space.

Moreover, note that in some cases, if the base vectors $\mathbf{e}_\mathrm{i}$ have been clearly defined in the context, all vectors and tensors can be unambiguously represented by their components alone. The actual display of the base vectors is unnecessary and purely a matter of notational preference.

In such cases, instead of explicitly showing the base vectors, the components of the vectors or tensors are used to represent them. This notation simplifies the expressions and calculations, as the focus is primarily on the values of the components rather than the base vectors themselves.

It is important to ensure that the base vectors have been properly defined and understood in the given context to avoid any confusion or ambiguity when using the component representation.

Note that this approach may depend on the specific mathematical framework or notation being used, and it is important to follow the conventions and guidelines established in the particular field or discipline.

For example, an arbitrary vector **A** can be expressed in terms of its components as

$$\mathbf{A} = (\mathrm{A} \cdot \mathbf{e}_{\mathrm{i}})\mathbf{e}_{\mathrm{i}} = (\mathrm{A} \cdot \mathbf{e}_{\mathrm{j}})\mathbf{e}_{\mathrm{j}}. \tag{2.2.22}$$

An index letter that occurs twice in a single term is called a summation index. The repeated index invokes a summation over its range (1 to n).

2.2.5.2 *Index rules and terminology*

The index notation can be used with any number of subscripts. For example, E_{ij} denotes the components of the matrix. In general, the indices i and j can be assigned different ranges, for example to represent a 3×5 matrix.

For range convention, variables, terms, and expressions may be assigned one or more Latin index letters, such as i, j, k. Each of these indices can independently take on integer values in their range $1, 2, \ldots, n$. For example, $A_i B_j$ and $A_i E_{jk}$ are terms combining vectors **A** and **B** and the matrix $\mathbf{E} = [E_{jk}]$.

According to the index rule, each index letter can occur either once or twice in a single term, but no index can occur more than twice. For example, $A_j E_{jk}$ is a valid term, but $A_j E_{jj}$ is invalid.

2.2.5.3 *Free index*

An index letter that occurs exactly once within a single term is referred to as a free index (or range index). A free index is one that appears in every expression of an equation, except for expressions that contain only real numbers (scalars). For example, $A_i = B_i C_j D_j$ and $G_k = H_k(2 - 3B_i C_i) + D_k P_j Q_j$ are valid, where i and k in the equations are free indices.

The expressions $A_i = B_jC_k$, $A_i = C_j$, and $A_i = B_iC_jD_k$ do not make sense and should not arise because the indices on both sides of the equal sign do not match. A valid equation must have the same free indices in each term. For example, $E_{ij} = U_{ij} + V_{ij}$ is valid, but $E_{ij} = U_{ik} + V_{jk}$ is invalid.

One must be careful when substituting a quantity with an index into an expression with indices, and when solving for one quantity with an index in terms of the others with indices in an equation. For example, consider the equations $p_i = a_ib_kc_k$. It is correct to write $a_i = p_i/(b_kc_k)$, but it is incorrect to write $b_kc_k = p_i/a_i$, which has a totally different meaning.

Before substituting one expression into the other, one should examine the indices and determine which ones are free and which ones are dummy indices (which is discussed in the following section) and then make suitable changes to the indices before substitution. Next, we introduce the concept of dummy indices.

2.2.5.4 *Dummy index*

The repeated index is referred to as a dummy index because it can be substituted with any other symbol that has not been previously used in the expression. Consequently, a summation index is also termed a dummy index since it can be exchanged with a different index letter without altering the meaning. For instance,

$$\mathbf{A} = A_i\mathbf{e}_{\mathrm{i}} = A_j\mathbf{e}_{\mathrm{j}} = A_k\mathbf{e}_{\mathrm{k}}. \tag{2.2.23}$$

As a rule, no index can appear more than twice in an expression. For example, $A_iB_iC_i$ is not a valid expression because the index i appears more than twice. Other examples of dummy indices are

$$A_i = B_iC_jD_j. \tag{2.2.24}$$

Equation (2.2.24) indicates three equations where the range of i and j is 1–3, as shown in the following equations:

$$\begin{aligned} A_1 &= B_1(C_1D_1 + C_2D_2 + C_3D_3), \\ A_2 &= B_2(C_1D_1 + C_2D_2 + C_3D_3), \\ A_3 &= B_3(C_1D_1 + C_2D_2 + C_3D_3). \end{aligned} \tag{2.2.25}$$

2.2.6 *Special Symbols*

The following are two symbols that are specially defined to simplify index notations and operations: the Kronecker delta and the permutation symbol.

2.2.6.1 *The Kronecker delta*

For a set of basis vectors $(\mathbf{e}_1, \mathbf{e}_2, \mathbf{e}_3)$ in the rectangular coordinate system, as shown in Figure 2.2.14, we have the following relation:

$$\begin{array}{lll} \mathbf{e}_1 \cdot \mathbf{e}_1 = 1 & \mathbf{e}_1 \cdot \mathbf{e}_2 = 0 & \mathbf{e}_1 \cdot \mathbf{e}_3 = 0 \\ \mathbf{e}_2 \cdot \mathbf{e}_1 = 0 & \mathbf{e}_2 \cdot \mathbf{e}_2 = 1 & \mathbf{e}_2 \cdot \mathbf{e}_3 = 0 \\ \mathbf{e}_3 \cdot \mathbf{e}_1 = 0 & \mathbf{e}_3 \cdot \mathbf{e}_2 = 0 & \mathbf{e}_3 \cdot \mathbf{e}_3 = 1. \end{array} \tag{2.2.26}$$

Therefore, it is convenient to introduce the Kronecker delta δ_{ij} because it allows for the simple representation of the scalar product of orthonormal vectors in a right-handed basis system. We define the scalar (or dot) product $\mathbf{e}_\mathrm{i} \cdot \mathbf{e}_\mathrm{j}$ as

$$\delta_{ij} = \mathbf{e}_\mathrm{i} \cdot \mathbf{e}_\mathrm{j} = \delta_{ji}, \tag{2.2.27}$$

where

$$\delta_{ij} = \begin{cases} 1 & \text{if } i \text{ has the same value as } j, \\ 0 & \text{if } i \text{ has a different value than } j. \end{cases} \tag{2.2.28}$$

For example, we have $\delta_{ii} = \delta_{11} + \delta_{22} + \delta_{33} = 3$. The Kronecker delta δ_{ij} modifies (or contracts) the subscripts in the coefficients of an expression in which it appears:

$$A_i\delta_{ij} = A_j, A_iB_j\delta_{ij} = A_iB_i = A_jB_j. \tag{2.2.29}$$

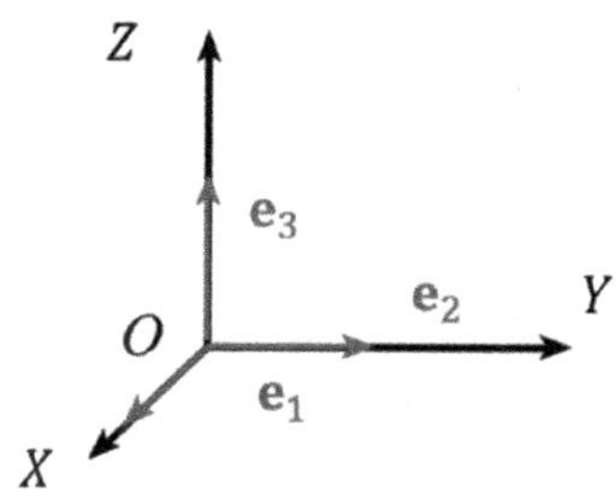

Figure 2.2.14 3D Cartesian coordinate system.

As we will see shortly, δ_{ij} denotes the components of a second-order unit tensor, so we also have

$$\delta_{ij}\delta_{ik} = \delta_{jk}. \tag{2.2.30}$$

2.2.6.2 *The permutation symbol*

We define the vector (or cross) product as

$$\mathbf{e}_\mathrm{i} \times \mathbf{e}_\mathrm{j} = e_{ijk}\mathbf{e}_\mathrm{k}, \tag{2.2.31}$$

where e_{ijk} is called the alternating symbol or permutation symbol. We know that

$$\begin{array}{lll} \mathbf{e}_1 \times \mathbf{e}_1 = \mathbf{0} & \mathbf{e}_1 \times \mathbf{e}_2 = \mathbf{e}_3 & \mathbf{e}_1 \times \mathbf{e}_3 = -\mathbf{e}_2 \\ \mathbf{e}_2 \times \mathbf{e}_1 = -\mathbf{e}_3 & \mathbf{e}_2 \times \mathbf{e}_2 = \mathbf{0} & \mathbf{e}_2 \times \mathbf{e}_3 = \mathbf{e}_1 \\ \mathbf{e}_3 \times \mathbf{e}_1 = \mathbf{e}_2 & \mathbf{e}_3 \times \mathbf{e}_2 = -\mathbf{e}_1 & \mathbf{e}_3 \times \mathbf{e}_3 = \mathbf{0}. \end{array} \tag{2.2.32}$$

Thus,

$$e_{ijk} = \mathbf{e}_\mathrm{i} \times \mathbf{e}_\mathrm{j} \cdot \mathbf{e}_\mathrm{k} = \begin{cases} 1 & \text{if } i,\ j,\ k \text{ are in natural cyclic order} \\ \square & \quad \text{and not repeated } (i \neq j \neq k), \\ -1 & \text{if } i,\ j,\ k \text{ are opposite to the natural} \\ \square & \quad \text{cyclic order and not repeated,} \\ 0 & \quad \text{if any of } i,\ j,\ k \text{ are repeated.} \end{cases} \tag{2.2.33}$$

The natural order of i, j, and k is the order in which they appear alphabetically. A natural cyclic order means going from i to j and k, from j to k and i, or from k to i and j. By definition, the subscripts of the permutation symbol can be permuted in a natural cyclic order without changing its value. An interchange of any two subscripts will change the sign (hence, an interchange of two subscripts twice keeps the value unchanged). Therefore, $e_{ijk} = e_{kij} = e_{jki}, e_{ijk} = -e_{jik} = -e_{kji}$. One can also show that $e_{ijk}\ e_{ijk} = 6$ and $e_{imn}e_{jmn} = 2\delta_{ij}$. From Equation (2.2.33), we can obtain

$$e_{ijk} = \frac{1}{2}(i-j)(j-k)(k-i) \quad \text{for any } i,j,k = 1,2,3. \tag{2.2.34}$$

On an orthonormal basis, the scalar and vector products can be expressed in index form using the Kronecker delta and the permutation symbols:

$$\mathbf{A} \cdot \mathbf{B} = (A_i \mathbf{e}_i) \cdot (B_j \mathbf{e}_j) = A_i B_j \delta_{ij} = A_i B_i, \qquad (2.2.35)$$

$$\mathbf{A} \times \mathbf{B} = (A_i \mathbf{e}_i) \times (B_j \mathbf{e}_j) = A_i B_j e_{ijk} \mathbf{e}_k. \qquad (2.2.36)$$

Furthermore, the Kronecker delta and the permutation symbol are related by the following identity, known as the $e - \delta$ identity:

$$e_{ijk} e_{imn} = \delta_{jm}\delta_{kn} - \delta_{jn}\delta_{km}. \qquad (2.2.37)$$

The permutation symbol and the Kronecker delta prove to be very useful in establishing vector identities and in continuum mechanics.

2.2.7 *Transformation Law for Different Bases*

The components of a vector are often known in one coordinate system, but it may be necessary to determine them in another. For instance, consider a vector **A** acting in the $(\mathbf{e}_1, \mathbf{e}_2, \mathbf{e}_3)$ coordinate system along the x-direction, as illustrated in Figure 2.2.15. In this case, we have the x-component of the force in the $(\mathbf{e}_1, \mathbf{e}_2, \mathbf{e}_3)$ coordinate system. However, we might be interested in determining the force acting in a different direction, such as in the $(\hat{\mathbf{e}}_1, \hat{\mathbf{e}}_2, \hat{\mathbf{e}}_3)$ coordinate system along the x-direction, as depicted in Figure 2.2.15. This would involve finding the component of the force in the new $(\hat{\mathbf{e}}_1, \hat{\mathbf{e}}_2, \hat{\mathbf{e}}_3)$ coordinate system.

Any change in the Cartesian coordinate system can be decomposed into a translation and a rotation of the base vectors. It is important to note that a translation of the base vectors does not

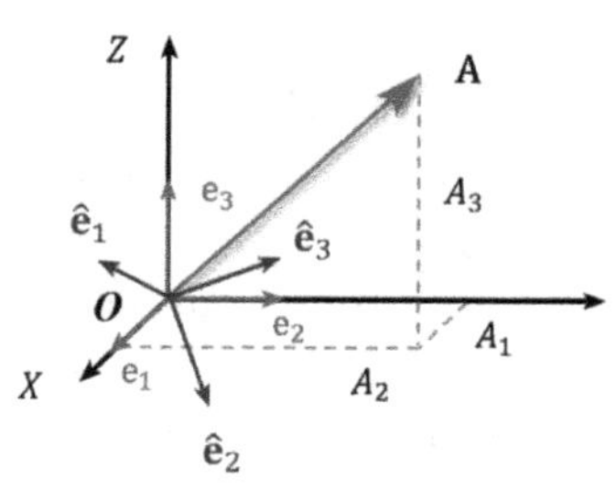

Figure 2.2.15 A vector represented in different Cartesian coordinate systems.

alter the components of a vector. Mathematically, this can be stated as that the components of a vector $\mathbf{A}$ are $A_i = \mathbf{A} \cdot \mathbf{e}_{\rm I}$, being in the unbarred coordinate system, and these three quantities remain unchanged under a translation of the base vectors.

The focus here is on the rotation of the base vectors. Let us consider two orthonormal Cartesian bases denoted by $(\mathbf{e}_1, \mathbf{e}_2, \mathbf{e}_3)$ and $(\hat{\mathbf{e}}_1, \hat{\mathbf{e}}_2, \hat{\mathbf{e}}_3)$. We aim to establish the relationship between the components of a vector in two different orthonormal coordinate systems, referred to as unbarred and barred, as depicted in Figure 2.2.15.

In the unbarred coordinate basis, a vector can be expressed as $\mathbf{A} = A_i\mathbf{e}_{\rm i} = (\mathbf{A} \cdot \mathbf{e}_{\rm i})\mathbf{e}_{\rm i}$. In the barred coordinate basis, we assume that the components of vector $\mathbf{A}$ can be expressed as $\hat{A}_j$, and they are related by the following equations:

$$\hat{A}_j = \mathbf{A} \cdot \hat{\mathbf{e}}_{\rm j} = (A_i\mathbf{e}_{\rm i}) \cdot \hat{\mathbf{e}}_{\rm j} = A_i\mathbf{e}_{\rm i} \cdot \hat{\mathbf{e}}_{\rm j} = A_i\hat{\mathbf{e}}_{\rm j} \cdot \mathbf{e}_{\rm i} = l_{ji}A_i, \quad (2.2.38)$$

$$l_{ji} = \mathbf{e}_{\rm i} \cdot \hat{\mathbf{e}}_{\rm j} = \hat{\mathbf{e}}_{\rm j} \cdot \mathbf{e}_{\rm i} \quad \text{or} \quad l_{ij} = \mathbf{e}_{\rm j} \cdot \hat{\mathbf{e}}_{\rm i} = \hat{\mathbf{e}}_{\rm i} \cdot \mathbf{e}_{\rm j}. \quad (2.2.39)$$

It can further yield, as a special case, the following relations:

$$\hat{\mathbf{e}}_{\rm i} = l_{ij}\mathbf{e}_{\rm j}, \quad \hat{A}_i = l_{ij}A_j. \quad (2.2.40)$$

Equation (2.2.40) provides the relationship between the base vectors as between $\hat{\mathbf{e}}_{\rm i}$ and $\mathbf{e}_{\rm j}$, as well as the components of the barred and unbarred coordinate systems. Specifically, the relationship between the components $(\hat{A}_1, \hat{A}_2, \hat{A}_3)$ and (A_1, A_2, A_3) is known as the transformation rule between the barred and unbarred components in the two orthogonal coordinate systems. The coefficients l_{ij} represent the direction cosines of the barred coordinate system with respect to the unbarred coordinate system, denoting the cosine of the angle between $\hat{\mathbf{e}}_{\rm i}$ and $\mathbf{e}_{\rm j}$.

Note that the first subscript of l_{ij} corresponds to the barred coordinate system, while the second subscript corresponds to the unbarred system. It is important to note that l_{ij} is not symmetric (i.e., $l_{ij} \neq l_{ji}$). The direction cosines enable us to establish a relationship between the components of a vector (or a tensor) in the unbarred coordinate system and the components of the same vector (or tensor) in the barred coordinate system. This relationship proves to be valuable in the field of continuum mechanics.

Example 2.2.1

Consider the points $A(1,3,1)$, $B(2,-1,1)$, $C(0,1,3)$ and $D(1,2,4)$ defined in the Cartesian coordinate system.

(1) Find the parallelogram area defined by vectors AB and AC
(2) Find the volume of the parallelepiped defined by the vectors AB, AC, and AD.

Solution:

(1) First, we calculate the vectors AB and AC; assume the origin of the Cartesian coordinate system is O, $\mathbf{a} = AB$, and $\mathbf{b} = AC$; thus,

$$\begin{aligned}\mathbf{a} = AB = OB - OA &= (2\mathbf{e}_1 - \mathbf{e}_2 + \mathbf{e}_3) \\ &- (\mathbf{e}_1 + 3\mathbf{e}_2 + \mathbf{e}_3) = \mathbf{e}_1 - 4\mathbf{e}_2, \\ \mathbf{b} = AC = OC - OA &= (\mathbf{e}_2 + 3\mathbf{e}_3) \\ &- (\mathbf{e}_1 + 3\mathbf{e}_2 + \mathbf{e}_3) = -\mathbf{e}_1 - 2\mathbf{e}_2 + 2\mathbf{e}_3.\end{aligned}$$

With reference to the equation, we can evaluate the vector product as follows (in the following expression, we use the matrix form; it will be discussed in detail in the following section):

$$\mathbf{a} \times \mathbf{b} = \begin{vmatrix} \mathbf{e}_1 & \mathbf{e}_2 & \mathbf{e}_3 \\ 1 & -4 & 0 \\ -1 & -2 & 2 \end{vmatrix} = -8\mathbf{e}_1 - 2\mathbf{e}_2 - 6\mathbf{e}_3.$$

Then, the parallelogram area can be obtained using its definition. Thus,

$$A = |\mathbf{a} \times \mathbf{b}| = \sqrt{(-8)^2 + (-2)^2 + (-6)^2} = \sqrt{104}.$$

(2) Next, we can evaluate the vector AD as $\mathbf{c}$:

$$\begin{aligned}\mathbf{c} = AD = OD - OA &= (\mathbf{e}_1 + 2\mathbf{e}_2 + 4\mathbf{e}_3) - (\mathbf{e}_1 + 3\mathbf{e}_2 + \mathbf{e}_3) \\ &= -\mathbf{e}_2 + 3\mathbf{e}_3,\end{aligned}$$

and using Equation (2.2.9), we can obtain the volume of the parallelepiped:

$$\mathbf{V} = |\mathbf{c} \cdot (\mathbf{a} \times \mathbf{b})| = |(0\mathbf{e}_1 - \mathbf{e}_2 + 3\mathbf{e}_3) \cdot (-8\mathbf{e}_1 - 2\mathbf{e}_2 - 6\mathbf{e}_3)| = 16.$$

Example 2.2.2

Find the equation of a plane connecting the terminal points of vectors **A**, **B**, and **C**. Assume that all three vectors have a common origin.

Solution:

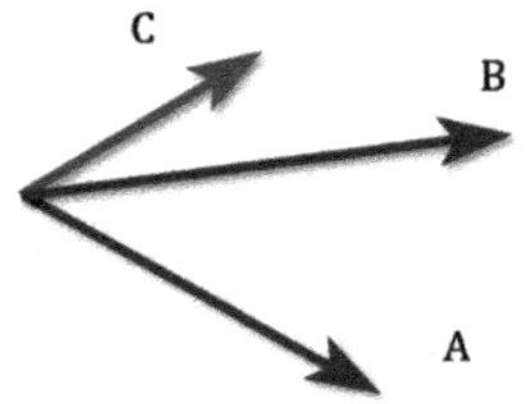

The vector connecting the terminal points of vectors **A** and **B** is $\mathbf{A}-\mathbf{B}$. Similarly, the vector connecting the terminal points of vectors **B** and **C** is $\mathbf{B}-\mathbf{C}$. Finally, the vector connecting the terminal points of vectors **A** and **C** is $\mathbf{A}-\mathbf{C}$. The three vectors $\mathbf{A}-\mathbf{B}$, $\mathbf{B}-\mathbf{C}$ and $\mathbf{A}-\mathbf{C}$ all lie in the plane connecting the terminal points of the three vectors **A**, **B**, and **C**. Then, a necessary and sufficient condition for the three vectors to be coplanar is that

$$(\mathbf{A}-\mathbf{B}) \times (\mathbf{B}-\mathbf{C}) \cdot (\mathbf{A}-\mathbf{C}) = 0,$$

which provides an equation for the required plane. The volume of three coplanar vectors is zero.

Example 2.2.3

Assume **A** and **B** are any two vectors in space. Express vector **A** in terms of its components along (i.e., paralleled) and perpendicular to vector **B**.

Solution:
According to the properties of vector dot product and vector cross product, the component of **A** along **B** can be expressed as is given by $A_1 = A_i\mathbf{e}_{\mathrm{i}} = (\mathbf{A}\cdot\mathbf{e}_{\mathbf{B}})\mathbf{e}_{\mathbf{B}}$, where $\mathbf{e}_{\mathbf{B}} = \frac{\mathbf{B}}{|\mathbf{B}|}$ is the unit vector in the direction of **B**.

For the component of **A** perpendicular to **B**, we can consider the cross product **A** and the unit vector of **B**. This new cross product of vectors will be perpendicular to vector **B**. Further, consider the cross product of the new vector, and the unit vector of **B** will be perpendicular to vector **B** also. Thus, the component of **A** perpendicular to **B** can be expressed as $\mathbf{A}_2 = \mathbf{e_B} \times (\mathbf{A} \times \mathbf{e_B})$.

Thus,

$$\mathbf{A} = \mathbf{A}_1 + \mathbf{A}_2 = (\mathbf{A} \cdot \mathbf{e_B})\mathbf{e_B} + \mathbf{e_B} \times (\mathbf{A} \times \mathbf{e_B}).$$

The component of **A** perpendicular to **B** and in the plan of vector **A** and vector **B** is also given by the vector triple product $\mathbf{e_B} \times (\mathbf{A} \times \mathbf{e_B})$, which is also in the plan spanned by vectors **A** and **B**.

Alternatively, using Equation (2.2.12) gives the same result with $\mathbf{A} = \mathbf{C} = \mathbf{e_B}$ and $\mathbf{B} = \mathbf{A}$:

$\mathbf{e_B} \times (\mathbf{A} \times \mathbf{e_B}) = \mathbf{A} - (\mathbf{A} \cdot \mathbf{e_B})\mathbf{e_B}$ and $\mathbf{A} = \mathbf{A}_1 + \mathbf{A}_2 = (\mathbf{A} \cdot \mathbf{e_B})\mathbf{e_B} + \mathbf{e_B} \times (\mathbf{A} \times \mathbf{e_B})$.

Example 2.2.4

Simplify the following expressions:

(1) $\delta_{ij}\delta_{jk}\delta_{kp}\delta_{pi}$, (2) $e_{mjk}e_{njk}$.

Solution:

(1) Successive contraction of subscripts yields the results

$$\delta_{ij}\delta_{jk}\delta_{kp}\delta_{pi} = \delta_{ik}\delta_{kp}\delta_{pi} = \delta_{ip}\delta_{pi} = \delta_{ii} = 3.$$

(2) Expending using the $e - \delta$ identity, $e_{ijk}e_{imn} = \delta_{jm}\delta_{kn} - \delta_{jn}\delta_{km}$,

$$e_{mjk}e_{njk} = \delta_{mn}\delta_{jj} - \delta_{mj}\delta_{nj} = 3\delta_{mn} - \delta_{mn} = 2\delta_{mn}.$$

Example 2.2.5

Rewrite the following equations using indicial notation:

(1) $a_1x_1x_3 + a_2x_2x_3 + a_3x_3x_3$, (2) $x_1x_1 + x_2x_2$,

(3) $\begin{cases} a_{11}x + a_{12}y + a_{13}z = b_x \\ a_{21}x + a_{22}y + a_{23}z = b_y \\ a_{31}x + a_{32}y + a_{33}z = b_z \end{cases}.$

Solution:

(1) $a_ix_ix_3$, (2) $x_ix_i(i = 1, 2)$, (3) $a_{ij}x_j = b_i$.

2.3 Basic Theory of Matrices

2.3.1 *Definition of Matrix and Matrix Notation for Vectors*

The symbolic notation $\mathbf{A}$ and index notation $A_i\mathbf{e}_i$ can be used to denote a vector. Another notation is the matrix notation; for example, the vector $\mathbf{A}$ can be represented by a 3×1 matrix (a column matrix):

$$[\mathbf{A}] = \begin{bmatrix} A_1 \\ A_2 \\ A_3 \end{bmatrix}. \tag{2.3.1}$$

Matrices are commonly denoted by square brackets. Therefore, a shorthand notation for the matrix–vector relationship discussed earlier would be $\mathbf{A}$. In this notation, the elements of the matrix are represented as A_i. The element form of a matrix is essentially equivalent to the index notation used for representing vectors.

It is important to note the distinction between a vector and a matrix. A vector is a mathematical object that exists independently of any basis, while a matrix represents a vector with respect to a particular basis. Changing the set of basis vectors will lead to different matrix elements, but the matrix still describes the same vector. The vector maintains its inherent properties of magnitude and direction, regardless of the chosen basis. Therefore, while a matrix is used to represent a vector in a specific coordinate system, the vector itself remains independent of any particular basis.

As an example, the dot product of two vectors can be written in matrix notation as

$$\mathbf{A} \cdot \mathbf{B} = [\mathbf{A}^T]\,[\mathbf{B}] = \begin{bmatrix} A_1 & A_2 & A_3 \end{bmatrix} \begin{bmatrix} B_1 \\ B_2 \\ B_3 \end{bmatrix} \tag{2.3.2}$$

In the preceding sections, we have explored the algebraic properties of ordinary vectors and examined the transformation of vector components between different coordinate systems. For instance, the transformation equation (2.2.40) establishes the relationship between the components of a vector in the barred coordinate system and the unbarred coordinate system. By substituting $\hat{A}_j = l_{ji}A_i$ into Equation (2.2.40), we can expand it in the following form:

$$\begin{aligned}\hat{A}_1 &= l_{11}A_1 + l_{12}A_2 + l_{13}A_3,\\ \hat{A}_2 &= l_{21}A_1 + l_{22}A_2 + l_{23}A_3,\\ \hat{A}_3 &= l_{31}A_1 + l_{32}A_2 + l_{33}A_3.\end{aligned} \tag{2.3.3}$$

We see that there are nine coefficients relating the components $(\hat{A}_1, \hat{A}_2, \hat{A}_3)$ and (A_1, A_2, A_3). The form of these linear equations suggests writing down the scalars of l_{ij} (jth components in the ith equation) in the rectangular array

$$[\mathrm{L}] = \begin{bmatrix} l_{11} & l_{12} & l_{13} \\ l_{21} & l_{22} & l_{23} \\ l_{31} & l_{32} & l_{33} \end{bmatrix}. \tag{2.3.4}$$

This rectangular array [L] of scalars l_{ij} is called a matrix, and the quantities l_{ij} are called the elements of [L].

If a matrix has m rows and n columns, we denote it as m by n (or $m \times n$), with the number of rows always being listed first. The element in the ith row and jth column of a matrix [L] is generally denoted by l_{ij}, and we will sometimes designate a matrix by $[\mathrm{L}] = [l_{ij}]$. A square matrix is one that has the same number of rows as columns. An $n \times n$ matrix is said to be of order n. The elements of a square matrix for which the row number and the column number are the same (i.e., l_{ij} for $i = j$) are called diagonal elements or simply the diagonal.

A square matrix is defined as a diagonal matrix if all the off-diagonal elements are zero. An identity matrix, denoted by $[\mathbf{I}]$, is a diagonal matrix whose elements are all 1. Examples of a diagonal $[\mathbf{P}]$ and an identity matrix $[\mathbf{I}]$ are as follows:

$$[\mathbf{P}] = \begin{bmatrix} P_{11} & 0 & 0 \\ 0 & P_{22} & 0 \\ 0 & 0 & P_{33} \end{bmatrix}, \quad [\mathbf{I}] = \begin{bmatrix} 1 & 0 & 0 \\ 0 & 1 & 0 \\ 0 & 0 & 1 \end{bmatrix}. \tag{2.3.5}$$

If the matrix has only one row or one column, we normally use only a single subscript to designate its elements. For example,

$$\mathbf{X} = \begin{pmatrix} X_1 \\ X_2 \\ X_3 \end{pmatrix}, \quad \mathbf{Y} = \begin{pmatrix} Y_1 & Y_2 & Y_3 \end{pmatrix}. \tag{2.3.6}$$

$\mathbf{X}$ denotes a column matrix, and $\mathbf{Y}$ denotes a row matrix. Row and column matrices can be used to represent the components of a vector.

2.3.2 *Matrix Properties*

We assume $\mathbf{A}$ and $\mathbf{B}$ here are 3×3 matrices, and their components are A_{ij} and B_{ij}:

$$[\mathbf{A}] = \begin{bmatrix} A_{11} & A_{12} & A_{13} \\ A_{21} & A_{22} & A_{23} \\ A_{31} & A_{32} & A_{33} \end{bmatrix} \quad \text{and} \quad [\mathbf{B}] = \begin{bmatrix} B_{11} & B_{12} & B_{13} \\ B_{21} & B_{22} & B_{23} \\ B_{31} & B_{32} & B_{33} \end{bmatrix}. \tag{2.3.7}$$

2.3.2.1 *The trace of a matrix*

Another important notation involving matrices is the trace of a matrix. The trace is defined as the sum of the diagonal elements of the matrix. It is denoted by the symbol

$$\mathrm{Tr}[\mathbf{A}] = A_{11} + A_{22} + A_{33} = A_{ii}. \tag{2.3.8}$$

2.3.2.2 *Matrix addition and multiplication of a matrix by a scalar*

The sum of two matrices of the same size is defined as a matrix of the same size obtained by simply adding the corresponding elements. If $[\mathbf{A}]$ is an $m \times n$ matrix and $[\mathbf{B}]$ is an $m \times n$ matrix, their sum is an $m \times n$ matrix, $[\mathbf{C}]$, with

$$C_{ij} = A_{ij} + B_{ij}, \quad i = 1, 2, \ldots, m, \quad j = 1, 2, \ldots, n. \tag{2.3.9}$$

A constant multiple of a matrix is equal to the matrix obtained by multiplying all of its elements by the constant. In other words, the multiplication of a matrix $[\mathbf{A}]$ by a scalar α, denoted as $\alpha[\mathbf{A}]$, results in a matrix in which each element is obtained by multiplying the corresponding element of $[\mathbf{A}]$ by α. The matrix addition has the following properties:

(1) Addition is commutative: $[\mathbf{A}] + [\mathbf{B}] = [\mathbf{B}] + [\mathbf{A}]$.
(2) Addition is associative: $[\mathbf{A}] + ([\mathbf{B}] + [\mathbf{C}]) = ([\mathbf{A}] + [\mathbf{B}]) + [\mathbf{C}]$.
(3) There exists a unique matrix $[\mathbf{0}]$ such that $[\mathbf{A}]+[\mathbf{0}] = [\mathbf{0}]+[\mathbf{A}] = [\mathbf{A}]$. The matrix $[\mathbf{0}]$ is called zero matrix because all its elements are zeros.
(4) For each matrix $[\mathbf{A}]$, there exists a unique matrix $-[\mathbf{A}]$ such that $[\mathbf{A}] + (-[\mathbf{A}]) = [\mathbf{0}]$.
(5) Addition is distributive with respect to scalar multiplication: $\alpha([\mathbf{A}] + [\mathbf{B}]) = \alpha[\mathbf{A}] + \alpha[\mathbf{B}]$.

2.3.2.3 *Matrix transpose*

If $[\mathbf{A}]$ is an $m \times n$ matrix, then the $n \times m$ matrix obtained by interchanging its rows and columns is called the transpose of $[\mathbf{A}]$ and is denoted by $[\mathbf{A}]^{\mathrm{T}}$. For example, the transposes of the matrices $\mathbf{A}$ and $\mathbf{B}$,

$$[\mathbf{A}] = \begin{bmatrix} A_{11} & A_{12} & A_{13} \\ A_{21} & A_{22} & A_{23} \\ A_{31} & A_{32} & A_{33} \\ A_{41} & A_{42} & A_{43} \end{bmatrix} \quad \text{and} \quad [\mathbf{B}] = \begin{bmatrix} B_{11} & B_{12} & B_{13} & B_{14} \\ B_{21} & B_{22} & B_{23} & B_{24} \\ B_{31} & B_{32} & B_{33} & B_{34} \end{bmatrix}, \tag{2.3.10}$$

are, respectively,

$$[\mathbf{A}]^{\mathrm{T}} = \begin{bmatrix} A_{11} & A_{21} & A_{31} & A_{41} \\ A_{12} & A_{22} & A_{32} & A_{42} \\ A_{13} & A_{23} & A_{33} & A_{43} \end{bmatrix} \quad \text{and} \quad [\mathbf{B}]^{\mathrm{T}} = \begin{bmatrix} B_{11} & B_{21} & B_{31} \\ B_{12} & B_{22} & B_{32} \\ B_{13} & B_{23} & B_{33} \\ B_{14} & B_{24} & B_{34} \end{bmatrix}. \tag{2.3.11}$$

An additional basic property is $([\mathbf{A}]^{\mathrm{T}})^{\mathrm{T}} = [\mathbf{A}]$.

2.3.2.4 *Matrix multiplication*

Consider a vector $\mathbf{A} = A_1\mathbf{e}_1 + A_2\mathbf{e}_2 + A_3\mathbf{e}_3$ in the Cartesian system; we can represent $\mathbf{A}$ as a product of a row matrix with a column matrix:

$$\mathbf{A} = \begin{pmatrix} A_1 & A_2 & A_3 \end{pmatrix} \begin{pmatrix} \mathbf{e}_1 \\ \mathbf{e}_2 \\ \mathbf{e}_3 \end{pmatrix}. \tag{2.3.12}$$

Note that the vector $\mathbf{A}$ is obtained by multiplying the ith element in the row matrix with the ith element in the column matrix and adding them.

Let $\mathbf{X}$ and $\mathbf{Y}$ be the vectors (matrices with one column). First, it can be seen that the dot product of two vectors can be represented by $\mathbf{X}^{\mathrm{T}} \cdot \mathbf{Y}$:

$$\mathbf{X} = \begin{pmatrix} x_1 \\ x_2 \\ \vdots \\ x_m \end{pmatrix}, \quad \mathbf{Y} = \begin{pmatrix} y_1 \\ y_2 \\ \vdots \\ y_m \end{pmatrix}. \tag{2.3.13}$$

We can define $\mathbf{X}^{\mathrm{T}} \cdot \mathbf{Y} = \mathbf{Y}^{\mathrm{T}} \cdot \mathbf{X}$, and the product is a scalar.

More generally, let $[\mathbf{A}] = [A_{ij}]$ be an $m \times n$ matrix and $[\mathbf{B}] = [B_{ij}]$ be an $n \times p$ matrix. The product of $[\mathbf{A}][\mathbf{B}]$ is defined as an $m \times p$ matrix $[\mathbf{C}] = [C_{ij}]$, with components given by

$$C_{ij} = \{i\text{th row of } [\mathbf{A}]\} \begin{Bmatrix} j\text{th} \\ \text{column} \\ \text{of } [\mathbf{B}\ ] \end{Bmatrix} = (A_{i1}A_{i2}\cdots A_{in}) \begin{pmatrix} B_{1j} \\ B_{2j} \\ \vdots \\ B_{nj} \end{pmatrix}$$

$$= A_{i1}B_{1j} + A_{i2}B_{2j} + \cdots + A_{in}B_{nj} = \sum_{1}^{n} A_{ik}B_{kj}. \tag{2.3.14}$$

The following remarks concerning matrix multiplication are in order, where $[\mathbf{A}]$ represents an $m \times n$ matrix and $[\mathbf{B}]$ represents a $p \times q$ matrix:

(1) The product $[\mathbf{A}][\mathbf{B}]$ is defined only if the number of columns n in $[\mathbf{A}]$ is equal to the number of rows p in $[\mathbf{B}]$ (i.e., $p = n$). Similarly, the product $[\mathbf{B}][\mathbf{A}]$ is defined only if $q = m$.
(2) If $[\mathbf{A}][\mathbf{B}]$ is defined (i.e., $p = n$), $[\mathbf{B}][\mathbf{A}]$ may (when $q = m$) or may not (when $q \neq m$) be defined. If both $[\mathbf{A}][\mathbf{B}]$ and $[\mathbf{B}][\mathbf{A}]$ are defined (i.e., $p = n$ and $q = m$), it is not necessary that they be of the same size. For example, $[\mathbf{A}][\mathbf{B}]$ can be an $m \times n$ matrix, while $[\mathbf{B}][\mathbf{A}]$ is an $n \times n$ matrix.
(3) The products $[\mathbf{A}][\mathbf{B}]$ and $[\mathbf{B}][\mathbf{A}]$ are of the same size if and only if both $[\mathbf{A}]$ and $[\mathbf{B}]$ are square matrices of the same size (i.e., $m = n = p = q$).
(4) The products $[\mathbf{A}][\mathbf{B}]$ and $[\mathbf{B}][\mathbf{A}]$ are, in general, not equal: $[\mathbf{A}][\mathbf{B}] = [\mathbf{B}][\mathbf{A}]$ (even if they are of equal size). This means that matrix multiplication is not commutative.
(5) For any real square matrix $[\mathbf{A}]$, $[\mathbf{A}]$ is said to be normal if $[\mathbf{A}][\mathbf{A}]^T = [\mathbf{A}]^T[\mathbf{A}]$. The product $[\mathbf{A}][\mathbf{A}]^T$ is always symmetric: $([\mathbf{A}][\mathbf{A}]^T)^T = [\mathbf{A}][\mathbf{A}]^T$.
(6) If $[\mathbf{A}]$ is a square matrix, the powers of $[\mathbf{A}]$ are defined by $[\mathbf{A}]^2 = [\mathbf{A}][\mathbf{A}]$, $[\mathbf{A}]^3 = [\mathbf{A}][\mathbf{A}]^2 = [\mathbf{A}]^2[\mathbf{A}]$, and so on.
(7) Matrix multiplication is associative: $([\mathbf{A}][\mathbf{B}])[\mathbf{C}] = [\mathbf{A}]([\mathbf{B}][\mathbf{C}])$.
(8) The product of any square matrix with the identity matrix is the matrix itself, i.e., $[\mathbf{A}][\mathbf{I}] = [\mathbf{A}]$.
(9) The transpose of the product is $([\mathbf{A}][\mathbf{B}])^T = [\mathbf{B}]^T[\mathbf{A}]^T$.

2.3.2.5 *Symmetric and skew-symmetric matrices*

A square matrix $[\mathbf{A}]$ of real numbers is considered symmetric if $[\mathbf{A}]^T = [\mathbf{A}]$, and it is considered skew symmetric if $[\mathbf{A}]^T = -[\mathbf{A}]$. In terms of the elements of $[\mathbf{A}]$, $[\mathbf{A}]$ is symmetric if and only if $A_{ij} = A_{ji}$ for all i and j, and it is skew symmetric if and only if $A_{ij} = -A_{ji}$. Note that the diagonal elements of a skew-symmetric matrix are always zero because $A_{ij} = -A_{ji}$ implies $A_{ij} = 0$ for $i = j$.

Every square matrix $[\mathbf{A}]$ can be expressed as a sum of a symmetric matrix $([\mathbf{A}] + [\mathbf{A}]^T)$ and a skew-symmetric matrix $([\mathbf{A}] - [\mathbf{A}]^T)$:

$$[\mathbf{A}] = \frac{\mathbf{1}}{\mathbf{2}}([\mathbf{A}] + [\mathbf{A}]^T) + \frac{\mathbf{1}}{\mathbf{2}}([\mathbf{A}] - [\mathbf{A}]^T). \tag{2.3.15}$$

2.3.2.6 *Inverse and determinant of a matrix*

Consider two $n \times n$ matrices, $[\mathbf{A}]$ and $[\mathbf{B}]$, and the identity matrix $[\mathbf{I}]$, then $[\mathbf{B}]$ is the inverse of $[\mathbf{A}]$ if and only if $[\mathbf{A}][\mathbf{B}] = [\mathbf{B}][\mathbf{A}] = [\mathbf{I}]$. If the inverse of $[\mathbf{A}]$ exists, it is unique, which follows from the associative law. The inverse of $[\mathbf{A}]$ is denoted by $[\mathbf{A}]^{-1}$. A procedure for computing the inverse will be presented shortly.

A matrix is said to be singular if it does not have an inverse. If $[\mathbf{A}]$ is nonsingular, then the transpose of the inverse is equal to the inverse of the transpose: $([\mathbf{A}]^{-1})^T = ([\mathbf{A}]^T)^{-1} = [\mathbf{A}]^{-T}$.

Let $[\mathbf{A}] = [A_{ij}]$ be an $n \times n$ matrix. We wish to associate a scalar with $[\mathbf{A}]$ that measures the "size" of $[\mathbf{A}]$ and indicates whether $[\mathbf{A}]$ is nonsingular. The determinant of the matrix $[\mathbf{A}]$ is defined to be a scalar $\det[\mathbf{A}] = |\mathbf{A}|$ and is computed according to the rule

$$\det[\mathbf{A}] = |\mathbf{A}| = \sum_{1}^{n} (-1)^{i+1} A_{i1} |A_{\mathrm{ij}}|, \tag{2.3.16}$$

where $|A_{ij}|$ is the determinant of the $(n-1) \times (n-1)$ matrix that remains after deleting the ith row and jth column of $[\mathbf{A}]$. For convenience, we define the determinant of a zeroth-order matrix to be unity. For 1×1 matrices, the determinant is defined according to $|\boldsymbol{a}_{11}| = a_{11}$. For a 2×2 matrix $[\mathbf{A}]$, the determinant is defined by

$$[\mathbf{A}] = \begin{bmatrix} A_{11} & A_{12} \\ A_{21} & A_{22} \end{bmatrix},$$

$$\det[\mathbf{A}] = |\mathbf{A}| = \begin{vmatrix} A_{11} & A_{12} \\ A_{21} & A_{22} \end{vmatrix} = A_{11}A_{22} - A_{12}A_{21}. \tag{2.3.17}$$

In the above definition, special attention is given to the first column of the matrix $[\mathbf{A}]$. We call it the expansion of $|\mathbf{A}|$ according to the first column of $[\mathbf{A}]$. One can expand $|\mathbf{A}|$ according to any column or row:

$$\det[\mathbf{A}] = |\mathbf{A}| = \sum_{1}^{n} (-1)^{i+j} A_{ij} |A_{\mathrm{ij}}|, \tag{2.3.18}$$

for a fixed j or i.

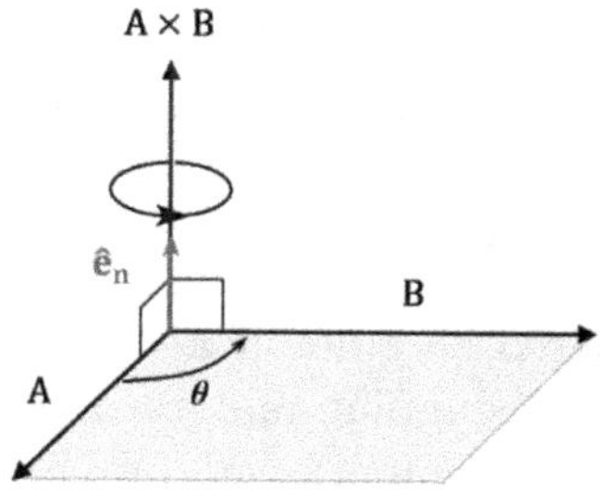

Figure 2.3.1 The cross product of two vectors.

A matrix is considered singular if its determinant is zero. There exists a connection between the inverse and the determinant of a matrix, which we will see shortly. Let's consider a numerical example to illustrate the calculation of a determinant.

Let $\mathbf{A} = A_i \mathbf{e}_{\mathrm{I}}$, $\mathbf{B} = B_i I$, and $\mathbf{C} = C_i \mathbf{e}_{\mathrm{i}}$. Then, the cross product of vectors $\mathbf{A}$ and $\mathbf{B}$ (Figure 2.3.1) can be expressed as the determinant

$$\mathbf{A} \times \mathbf{B} = |\mathbf{A}||\mathbf{B}| \sin\theta \, \hat{\mathbf{e}}_{\mathrm{n}} = \begin{vmatrix} \mathbf{e}_1 & \mathbf{e}_2 & \mathbf{e}_3 \\ A_1 & A_2 & A_3 \\ B_1 & B_2 & B_3 \end{vmatrix}, \tag{2.3.19}$$

and the scalar triple product can be expressed as the determinant

$$\mathbf{A} \cdot (\mathbf{B} \times \mathbf{C}) = \begin{vmatrix} A_1 & A_2 & A_3 \\ B_1 & B_2 & B_3 \\ C_1 & C_2 & C_3 \end{vmatrix}. \tag{2.3.20}$$

Consequently, the determinant of the 3×3 matrix $[\mathbf{A}]$ can be expressed as $\det[\mathbf{A}] = |\mathbf{A}| = e_{ijk} A_{1i} A_{2j} A_{3k}$. The determinants of square matrices have the following properties:

(1) $\det([\mathbf{A}][\mathbf{B}]) = \det[\mathbf{A}] \cdot \det[\mathbf{B}]$.
(2) $\det([\mathbf{A}]^{\mathrm{T}}) = \det[\mathbf{A}]$.
(3) $\det(\alpha[\mathbf{A}]) = \alpha^n \det[\mathbf{A}]$, where α is a scalar and n is the order of $[\mathbf{A}]$.
(4) If $\mathbf{A}'$ is a matrix obtained from $[\mathbf{A}]$ by multiplying a row (or column) of $[\mathbf{A}]$ by a scalar α, then $\det([\mathbf{A}']) = \alpha \det[\mathbf{A}]$.
(5) If $\mathbf{A}'$ is the matrix obtained from $[\mathbf{A}]$ by interchanging any two rows (or columns) of $[\mathbf{A}]$, then $\det([\mathbf{A}']) = -\det[\mathbf{A}]$.

(6) If [**A**] has two linearly dependent rows (or columns), i.e., one row (or column) is a scalar multiple of another, $\det[\mathbf{A}] = 0$.
(7) If $\mathbf{A}'$ is the matrix obtained from [**A**] by adding a multiple of one row (or column) to another, then $\det([\mathbf{A}']) = \det[\mathbf{A}]$.

A matrix is considered singular if and only if its determinant is zero. This means that a singular matrix does not have an inverse. According to property (6) mentioned previously, the determinant of a matrix is zero if its rows (or columns) are linearly dependent, indicating that the matrix is singular.

For an $n \times n$ matrix [**A**], the determinant of the $(n-1) \times (n-1)$ sub-matrix of [**A**] obtained by deleting row i and column j of [**A**], is called the minor of A_{ij} and is denoted by $M_{ij}([\mathbf{A}])$. The quantity $\mathrm{cof}_{ij}([\mathbf{A}]) = (-1)^{i+j} M_{ij}([\mathbf{A}])$ is called the cofactor of A_{ij}. The determinant of [**A**] can be cast in terms of the minor and cofactor of A_{ij}:

$$\begin{aligned} \det[\mathbf{A}] = |\mathbf{A}| &= \sum_{1}^{n} (-1)^{i+j} A_{ij} M_{ij}([\mathbf{A}]) \\ &= \sum_{1}^{n} A_{ij} \mathrm{cof}_{ij}([\mathbf{A}]), \end{aligned} \tag{2.3.21}$$

for any fixed value of j.

The adjunct (also called adjoint) of a matrix [**A**] is the transpose of the matrix obtained from [**A**] by replacing each element by its cofactor. The adjunct of [**A**] is denoted by Adj[**A**].

Now, we have the essential tools to compute the inverse of a matrix. If [$\boldsymbol{A}$] is nonsingular (i.e., $\det[\mathbf{A}] \neq 0$), the inverse $[\mathbf{A}]^{-1}$ of [$\boldsymbol{A}$] can be computed according to

$$[\mathbf{A}]^{-1} = \frac{1}{\det[\mathbf{A}]} \mathrm{Adj}[\mathbf{A}]. \tag{2.3.22}$$

2.3.2.7 *Positive-definite and orthogonal matrices*

A symmetric real matrix [**A**] is considered positive or positive-definite if, for all nonzero vector **X**,

$$\mathbf{X}^T [\mathbf{A}] \mathbf{X} > 0. \tag{2.3.23}$$

For example, for the matrix $[\mathbf{A}] = \begin{bmatrix} 1 & -23 \\ -2 & 6 \end{bmatrix}$, $(x_1, x_2)\begin{bmatrix} 1 & -2 \\ -2 & 6 \end{bmatrix}\begin{pmatrix} x_1 \\ x_2 \end{pmatrix} = x_1^2 + 4x_1x_2 + 6x_2^2$, which is positive for all nonzero vectors.

A nonsingular matrix $[\mathbf{Q}]$ is said to be orthogonal if the following condition holds:

$$[\mathbf{Q}]^T[\mathbf{Q}] = [\mathbf{Q}][\mathbf{Q}]^T = [\mathbf{I}], \quad \text{or} \quad [\mathbf{Q}]^T = [\mathbf{Q}]^{-1}. \tag{2.3.24}$$

For a matrix example $\begin{bmatrix} 1 & 0 & 0 \\ 0 & 1 & 0 \\ 0 & 1 & 1 \end{bmatrix}$, we find that $[\mathbf{A}] = [\mathbf{T}]^T[\mathbf{T}] = [\mathbf{T}][\mathbf{T}]^T = \begin{bmatrix} 1 & 0 & 0 \\ 0 & 2 & 1 \\ 0 & 1 & 1 \end{bmatrix}$. According to a previous definition, we can find that $[\mathbf{A}]$ is positive; however, $[\mathbf{T}]$ is not an orthogonal matrix since $[\mathbf{A}] = [\mathbf{T}]^T[\mathbf{T}] = [\mathbf{T}][\mathbf{T}]^T \neq \begin{bmatrix} 1 & 0 & 0 \\ 0 & 1 & 0 \\ 0 & 0 & 1 \end{bmatrix}$.

Example 2.3.1

Determine the inverse of the matrix $[\mathbf{A}]$, where $[\mathbf{A}] = \begin{bmatrix} 2 & 5 & -1 \\ 1 & 4 & 3 \\ 2 & -3 & 5 \end{bmatrix}$.

Solution:

We first compute the determinant of the matrix:

$$\begin{aligned} |\mathbf{A}| &= \sum_{i=1}^{3}(-1)^{i+1}a_{i1}|A_{i1}| = a_{11}\begin{vmatrix} 4 & 3 \\ -3 & 5 \end{vmatrix} - a_{21}\begin{vmatrix} 5 & -1 \\ -3 & 5 \end{vmatrix} + a_{31}\begin{vmatrix} 5 & -1 \\ 4 & 3 \end{vmatrix} \\ &= 2(20+9) - (25-3) + 2(15+4) = 74. \end{aligned}$$

Then, we compute the minors M_{ij}:

$$M_{11}([\mathbf{A}]) = \begin{vmatrix} 4 & 3 \\ -3 & 5 \end{vmatrix}, \quad M_{12}([\mathbf{A}]) = \begin{vmatrix} 1 & 3 \\ 2 & 5 \end{vmatrix}, \quad M_{13}([\mathbf{A}]) = \begin{vmatrix} 1 & 4 \\ 2 & -3 \end{vmatrix};$$

$$\begin{aligned} \mathrm{cof}_{11}([\mathbf{A}]) &= (-1)^2 M_{11}([\mathbf{A}]) = 29, \\ \mathrm{cof}_{12}([\mathbf{A}]) &= (-1)^3 M_{12}([\mathbf{A}]) = 1, \\ \mathrm{cof}_{13}([\mathbf{A}]) &= (-1)^4 M_{13}([\mathbf{A}]) = -11, \end{aligned}$$

and so on, we can get other cofactors. Then,

$$\mathrm{Adj}([\mathbf{A}]) = \begin{bmatrix} \mathrm{cof}_{11}([\mathbf{A}]) & \mathrm{cof}_{12}([\mathbf{A}]) & \mathrm{cof}_{13}([\mathbf{A}]) \\ \mathrm{cof}_{21}([\mathbf{A}]) & \mathrm{cof}_{22}([\mathbf{A}]) & \mathrm{cof}_{23}([\mathbf{A}]) \\ \mathrm{cof}_{31}([\mathbf{A}]) & \mathrm{cof}_{32}([\mathbf{A}]) & \mathrm{cof}_{33}([\mathbf{A}]) \end{bmatrix}^T$$

$$= \begin{bmatrix} 29 & -22 & 19 \\ 1 & 12 & 19 \\ -11 & 16 & 3 \end{bmatrix}.$$

The inverse of $\mathbf{A}$ can now be computed using the definition:

$$[\mathbf{A}]^{-1} = \frac{\mathrm{Adj}([\mathbf{A}])}{|\mathbf{A}|} = \frac{1}{74}\begin{bmatrix} 29 & -22 & 19 \\ 1 & 12 & 19 \\ -11 & 16 & 3 \end{bmatrix}.$$

2.4 Vector Calculus

2.4.1 *Differentiation of a Vector with Respect to a Scalar*

A vector function defines a vector field, while a scalar function defines a scalar field. Examples of vector fields include the field of tangent vectors of a curve, the field of normal vectors of a surface, the velocity field of a rotating body, and the gravitational field. Scalar fields include the temperature field in a body and the pressure field of the air in the Earth's atmosphere.

In the context of a vector function given as a function of a scalar variable t, denoted as $\mathbf{A} = \mathbf{A}(t)$, the vector $\mathbf{A}$ will have different magnitudes and directions for different values of t. This is depicted schematically in Figure 2.4.1(a), where the tails of the vectors are located at the same point, but the tips trace out a trajectory as t varies. Figure 2.4.1(b) shows a schematic drawing of the field of normal vectors of a surface. Each normal vector corresponds to a specific point on the surface.

Now, let's consider two values of t that differ by an infinitesimal amount, denoted as t and $t + \Delta t$. The variation of the vector field between these two values is shown in Figure 2.4.2(a), and the resulting variation is depicted in Figure 2.4.2(b).

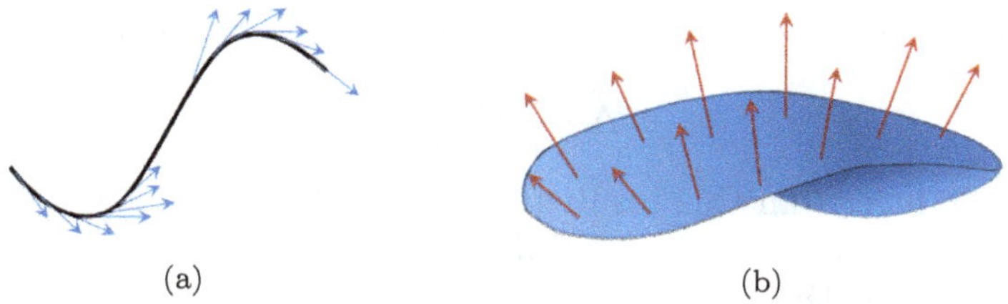

Figure 2.4.1 (a) The field of tangent vectors of a curve and (b) the field of normal vectors of a surface.

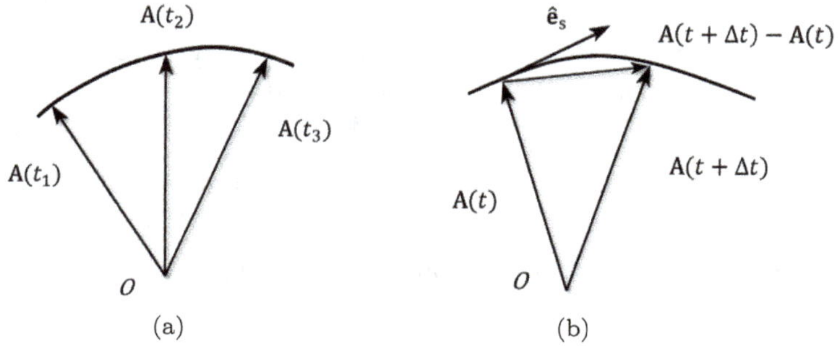

Figure 2.4.2 (a) Variation of a vector as a function of a scalar t and (b) differential change in a vector $\mathbf{A}(t)$.

Figure 2.4.2 visualizes the definition of the derivative of a vector with respect to t:

$$\frac{\mathrm{d}\mathbf{A}}{\mathrm{d}t} = \lim_{\Delta s \to 0} \frac{\Delta \mathbf{A}}{\Delta s} \frac{\Delta s}{\Delta t}, \tag{2.4.1}$$

where $\Delta s = |\Delta \mathbf{A}|$, so that s is the distance measured along the trajectory. In the limit, $\Delta \mathbf{A}/\Delta s$ is a unit vector that is tangent to the trajectory, say $\hat{\mathbf{e}}_s$. In the limit, therefore, we have

$$\frac{\mathrm{d}\mathbf{A}}{\mathrm{d}t} = \frac{\mathrm{d}s}{\mathrm{d}t}\hat{\mathbf{e}}_s. \tag{2.4.2}$$

The derivative of a vector differs in direction and magnitude from the vector itself. The magnitude of the derivative $\mathrm{d}s/\mathrm{d}t$ represents the rate of change of distance s with respect to time t along the trajectory. Observe that the distance s has the same dimensions as the vector $\mathbf{A}$ itself.

When $\mathbf{A}$ has a constant length, then $\mathrm{d}\mathbf{A}/\mathrm{d}t = 0$, and we have

$$\mathbf{A} \cdot \frac{\mathrm{d}\mathbf{A}}{\mathrm{d}t} = 0. \tag{2.4.3}$$

We can deduce from this result that either $\mathbf{A} = \mathbf{0}$, or $\mathrm{d}\mathbf{A}/\mathrm{d}t = 0$, or $\mathbf{A}$ is perpendicular to $\mathrm{d}\mathbf{A}/\mathrm{d}t$. If $\mathrm{d}\mathbf{A}/\mathrm{d}t = 0$, then the vector has not only a constant length but also a constant direction. If the direction of $\mathbf{A}$ varies while its magnitude remains constant, then the derivative $\mathrm{d}\mathbf{A}/\mathrm{d}t$ is perpendicular to $\mathbf{A}$.

In the general case, consider a vector-valued function of a scalar, for example the time-dependent displacement of a particle $\mathbf{A} = \mathbf{A}(t) = A_i\mathbf{e}_i$. In this case, the derivative is defined in the usual way:

$$\frac{\mathrm{D}\mathbf{A}}{\mathrm{d}t} = \frac{\mathrm{d}A_1}{dt}\mathbf{e}_1 + \frac{\mathrm{d}A_2}{dt}\mathbf{e}_2 + \frac{\mathrm{d}A_3}{dt}\mathbf{e}_3. \tag{2.4.4}$$

Partial derivatives can also be defined in the usual way. For example, if $\mathbf{A}$ is a function of the coordinates, $\mathbf{A} = \mathbf{A}(\mathbf{x}) = \mathbf{A}(x_1, x_2, x_3)$, then

$$\frac{\partial \mathbf{A}}{\partial x_1} = \lim_{\Delta x_1 \to 0} \frac{\mathbf{A}(x_1 + \Delta x_1, x_2, x_3) - \mathbf{A}(x_1, x_2, x_3)}{\Delta x_1}, \tag{2.4.5}$$

$$\mathbf{A}' = \frac{\mathrm{d}\mathbf{A}}{\mathrm{d}x} = \lim_{\Delta x \to 0} \frac{\mathbf{A}(x + \Delta x) - \mathbf{A}(x)}{\Delta x}. \tag{2.4.6}$$

Using differential notation, the differentiability condition can be written as

$$\mathrm{d}\mathbf{A} = \mathbf{A}'\mathrm{d}x. \tag{2.4.7}$$

Given a basis $\mathbf{e}_i$ that is independent of x, i.e., $\mathrm{d}\mathbf{e}_i/\mathrm{d}x = 0$, vector differentiation is performed component wise, i.e.,

$$\mathrm{D}\mathbf{A} = \mathbf{A}'\mathrm{d}x = A_i'(x)\mathbf{e}_i. \tag{2.4.8}$$

Suppose that the components of a vector function $\mathbf{A}$, $\mathbf{A}(t) = A_1(t_1, t_2, \ldots, t_n)\mathbf{e}_1 + A_2(t_1, t_2, \ldots, t_n)\mathbf{e}_2 + A_3(t_1, t_2, \ldots, t_n)\mathbf{e}_3$ are differentiable functions of n variables $t_1, t_2, \ldots, t_n$. Then the partial derivative of $\mathbf{A}$ with respect to t_m is denoted by $\partial\mathbf{A}/\partial t_m$ and is defined as the vector function

$$\frac{\partial \mathbf{A}}{\partial t_m} = \frac{\partial A_1}{\partial t_m}\mathbf{e}_1 + \frac{\partial A_2}{\partial t_m}\mathbf{e}_2 + \frac{\partial A_3}{\partial t_m}\mathbf{e}_3. \tag{2.4.9}$$

Similarly, the second partial derivatives are

$$\frac{\partial^2 \mathbf{A}}{\partial t_l \partial t_m} = \frac{\partial^2 A_1}{\partial t_l \partial t_m}\mathbf{e}_1 + \frac{\partial^2 A_2}{\partial t_l \partial t_m}\mathbf{e}_2 + \frac{\partial^2 A_3}{\partial t_l \partial t_m}\mathbf{e}_3. \tag{2.4.10}$$

2.4.2 *Derivative of a Scalar Function of a Vector*

To simplify the problem, we assume that the following calculus operations are applicable to rectangular Cartesian coordinate systems with the same Cartesian local basis for vector components. This means that we can use standard calculus techniques, such as differentiation and integration, when dealing with vectors in Cartesian coordinates. The components of vectors can be treated as functions of the coordinates, and the rules of calculus can be applied accordingly.

2.4.2.1 *The Nabla operator*

Gradient operator: The gradient operator implies differentiation by a vector, and its components are written as

$$\nabla(\cdot) = \mathbf{e}_{\mathrm{i}}\frac{\partial}{\partial x_i} = \frac{\partial}{\partial x_1}\mathbf{e}_1 + \frac{\partial}{\partial x_2}\mathbf{e}_2 + \frac{\partial}{\partial x_3}\mathbf{e}_3, \tag{2.4.11}$$

and it is called the "Nabla" operator. The Nabla operator is a vector differential operator, and the "components" appear as covariant components. The symbolic vector operator $\nabla = \mathbf{e}_{\mathrm{i}}\frac{\partial}{\partial x_i} = \frac{\partial}{\partial x_1}\mathbf{e}_1 + \frac{\partial}{\partial x_2}\mathbf{e}_2 + \frac{\partial}{\partial x_3}\mathbf{e}_3$ is also called the Nabla operator.

2.4.2.2 *Gradient of scalar field*

If $\varphi = \varphi(\mathbf{x})$ is a scalar field, then its gradient of $\varphi = \varphi(\mathbf{x})$ is a vector field defined by

$$\nabla\varphi = \mathbf{e}_{\mathrm{i}}\frac{\partial\varphi}{\partial x_i} = \frac{\partial\varphi}{\partial x_1}\mathbf{e}_1 + \frac{\partial\varphi}{\partial x_2}\mathbf{e}_2 + \frac{\partial\varphi}{\partial x_3}\mathbf{e}_3 \equiv \frac{\partial\varphi}{\partial\mathbf{x}}. \tag{2.4.12}$$

The gradient $\nabla\varphi$ is of considerable importance because if one takes the dot product of $\nabla\varphi$ with $\mathrm{d}\mathbf{x}$, it gives the increment in φ:

$$\begin{aligned}\nabla\varphi\cdot\mathrm{d}\mathbf{x} &= \frac{\partial\varphi}{\partial x_i}\mathbf{e}_i\cdot\mathrm{d}x_j\mathbf{e}_j\\ &= \frac{\partial\varphi}{\partial x_i}\mathrm{d}x_i = \mathrm{d}\varphi = \varphi(\mathbf{x}+\mathrm{d}\mathbf{x}) - \varphi(\mathrm{d}\mathbf{x}).\end{aligned} \tag{2.4.13}$$

For a scalar field $\varphi = \varphi(\mathbf{x})$, its gradient is a vector field, and the gradient of a scalar function and its physical meaning are shown in Figure 2.4.3.

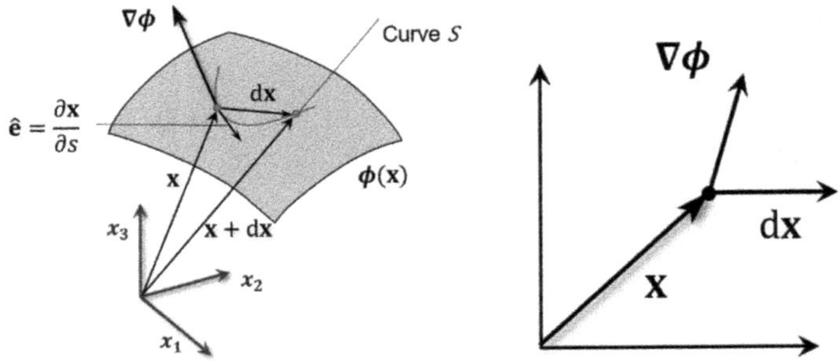

Figure 2.4.3 The gradient of a scalar function and its physical meaning.

If we write $d\mathbf{x}$ as $|d\mathbf{x}|\hat{\mathbf{e}}$, where $\hat{\mathbf{e}}$ is a unit vector in the direction of $d\mathbf{x}$, then

$$\nabla\varphi\cdot\hat{\mathbf{e}} = \left(\frac{d\varphi}{\partial x_i}\right)_{\text{in }\hat{\mathbf{e}}\text{ direction}} \equiv \frac{d\varphi}{\partial\mathbf{n}}. \tag{2.4.14}$$

The quantity $\mathbf{n}$ is called the directional derivative of φ, in the direction of $\hat{\mathbf{e}}$. The gradient of a scalar field is also called the scalar gradient to distinguish it from the vector gradient and is also denoted by

$$\text{grad}\varphi = \nabla\varphi. \tag{2.4.15}$$

The dot product of $\mathbf{n}$ and the gradient of φ is called the normal derivative of φ and is denoted by

$$\frac{\partial\varphi}{\partial\mathbf{n}} = \mathbf{n}\cdot\nabla\varphi. \tag{2.4.16}$$

In a Cartesian system, this becomes

$$\frac{\partial\varphi}{\partial\mathbf{n}} = \frac{\partial\varphi}{\partial x_1}n_{x1} + \frac{\partial\varphi}{\partial x_2}n_{x2} + \frac{\partial\varphi}{\partial x_3}n_{x3}, \tag{2.4.17}$$

where n_{x1}, n_{x2}, n_{x3} are the direction cosines of the unit normal $\mathbf{e}_{\mathrm{i}}$:

$$\mathbf{n} = n_{x1}\mathbf{e}_1 + n_{x2}\mathbf{e}_2 + n_{x3}\mathbf{e}_3. \tag{2.4.18}$$

For a scalar function φ, we will have the following properties:

(i) □ $\nabla\varphi$ □ points in the direction normal to the surface (or curve in two dimensions) $\varphi = \text{const}$.

(ii) The direction of maximum rate of change of φ is in the direction of $\nabla\varphi$.
(iii) The direction of zero $d\varphi$ is in the direction perpendicular to $\nabla\varphi$.

Example of gradient application: In engineering, many physical laws are given in terms of the gradient of a scalar field. For example, Fourier's law of heat conduction relates the heat flux $\mathbf{q}$ (the rate at which heat flows through a surface of unit area) to the temperature gradient through the following relation:

$$\mathbf{q} = -k\nabla\theta, \tag{2.4.19}$$

where k is the thermal conductivity of the material, so that heat flows along the direction normal to the isotherms.

2.4.2.3 *The divergence of a vector field*

One can generalize the idea of the gradient of a scalar field by defining the dot product and the cross product of the vector operator ∇ "Nabla" with a vector field $\mathbf{A}(\boldsymbol{x})$. The dot product of the Nabla operator with a vector is called the divergence of the vector, and it represents a scalar field. The divergence of a vector field $\mathbf{A}(\boldsymbol{x})$ is denoted by $\nabla \cdot \mathbf{A}$ is given by the following expression:

$$\begin{aligned}\operatorname{div}\mathbf{A} = \nabla\cdot\mathbf{A} &= \left(\mathbf{e}_\mathrm{i}\frac{\partial}{\partial x_i}\right)\cdot(A_j\mathbf{e}_\mathrm{j}) = \frac{\partial A_i}{\partial x_i}\\ &= \frac{\partial A_1}{\partial x_1} + \frac{\partial A_2}{\partial x_2} + \frac{\partial A_3}{\partial x_3}.\end{aligned} \tag{2.4.20}$$

If we take the divergence of the gradient of a scalar function φ, we have

$$\mathrm{Div}\,(\mathrm{grad}\varphi) = \nabla\cdot\nabla\varphi = (\nabla\cdot\nabla)\varphi = \nabla^2\varphi. \tag{2.4.21}$$

The notation $\nabla^2 = \nabla\cdot\nabla$ is called the Laplacian operator. In Cartesian systems, this reduces to the simple form

$$\nabla^2\varphi = \frac{\partial^2\varphi}{\partial x_1^2} + \frac{\partial^2\varphi}{\partial x_2^2} + \frac{\partial^2\varphi}{\partial x_3^2}. \tag{2.4.22}$$

The Laplacian of a scalar appears frequently in the partial differential equations governing physical phenomena.

Now, we consider the vector function of the Laplacian operator. If $\mathbf{u} = \mathbf{u}(\mathbf{x})$ is a displacement vector field, then its Laplacian has the components

$$\nabla^2\mathbf{u} = \frac{\partial^2 u_k}{\partial x_i \partial x_i}\mathbf{e}_\mathrm{k} = u_{k,ii}\mathbf{e}_\mathrm{k}. \tag{2.4.23}$$

2.4.2.4 *Curl of a vector field*

The curl of a vector is defined as the Nabla operator operating on a vector using the cross product:

$$\mathrm{curl}\mathbf{A} = \nabla \times \mathbf{A} = e_{ijk}\mathbf{e}_i\frac{\partial A_k}{\partial x_j}. \tag{2.4.24}$$

It can also be expressed in the matrix form:

$$\begin{aligned}\mathrm{curl}\,\mathbf{A} = \nabla \times \mathbf{A} &= \begin{vmatrix} \mathbf{e}_1 & \mathbf{e}_2 & \mathbf{e}_3 \\ \dfrac{\partial}{\partial x_1} & \dfrac{\partial}{\partial x_2} & \dfrac{\partial}{\partial x_3} \\ A_1 & A_2 & A_3 \end{vmatrix} \\ &= e_{ijk}\mathbf{e}_i\frac{\partial A_k}{\partial x_j} = e_{ijk}\mathbf{e}_k\frac{\partial A_j}{\partial x_i} = e_{ijk}\mathbf{e}_j\frac{\partial A_i}{\partial x_k}.\end{aligned} \tag{2.4.25}$$

For a physical interpretation of the curl, we can consider a particle with a position vector $\mathbf{r}$ and moving with a velocity vector $\mathbf{v} = \boldsymbol{\omega} \times \mathbf{r}$. If the particle has an angular velocity $\boldsymbol{\omega}$, then the curl of the velocity field represents the local rotational behavior of the fluid, or the rate at which the fluid is rotating around a given point. The curl of the velocity field is denoted by $\nabla \times \mathbf{v}$ and is given by the following expression:

$$\mathrm{curl}\,\mathbf{v} = \nabla \times (\boldsymbol{\omega} \times \mathbf{r}) = 2\boldsymbol{\omega}. \tag{2.4.26}$$

Therefore, the curl of a vector field is associated with its rotational properties. In the case of a velocity field $\mathbf{v}$ representing a moving fluid, if the curl of the velocity field ($\nabla \times \mathbf{v}$) is nonzero in a region, it indicates the presence of rotation or swirling motion. In this case, if a small paddle wheel is placed in the fluid, it would tend to rotate (Figure 2.4.4). This type of velocity field is called a vortex field.

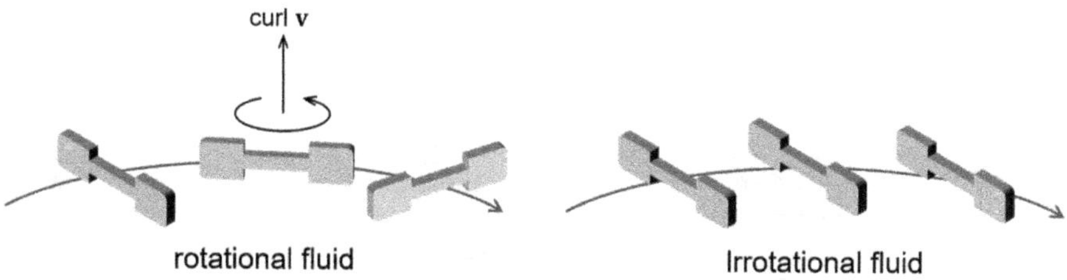

Figure 2.4.4 A schematic drawing of a paddle wheel placed in a fluid.

On the other hand, if the curl of the velocity field is zero curl $\mathbf{v} = 0 (\nabla \times \mathbf{v} = 0)$ in a region, it indicates that the fluid flow is smooth and lacks rotational motion. In such regions, if a paddle wheel is placed in the fluid, it will remain stationary. This type of velocity field is called an irrotational field.

These concepts are illustrated schematically in Figure 2.4.4, which demonstrates the difference between a vortex field and an irrotational field.

2.4.2.5 *Gradient, divergence, and curl theorems*

The relationship between volume integrals and surface integrals can establish integral identities involving the gradient, divergence, and curl of a vector. These identities are valuable tools in various fields of physics and engineering, particularly when deriving equations for continuous media. These integral identities enable us to interchange between volume integrals, which involve the properties of the vector field within a region, and surface integrals, which involve the properties of the vector field on the boundary of the region.

These identities will prove particularly useful in subsequent chapters when we derive equations to describe the behavior of continuous media, such as fluid dynamics, electromagnetism, and elasticity. They provide a way to connect the local properties of vector fields within a region to the fluxes and sources of those fields at the region's boundaries.

By employing these integral identities, we can derive important equations and conservation laws that govern the behavior of physical systems.

Let Ω denote a region in a body bounded by the closed surface Γ (Figure 2.4.5). Let ds be a differential element of surface, $\mathbf{n}$ be the

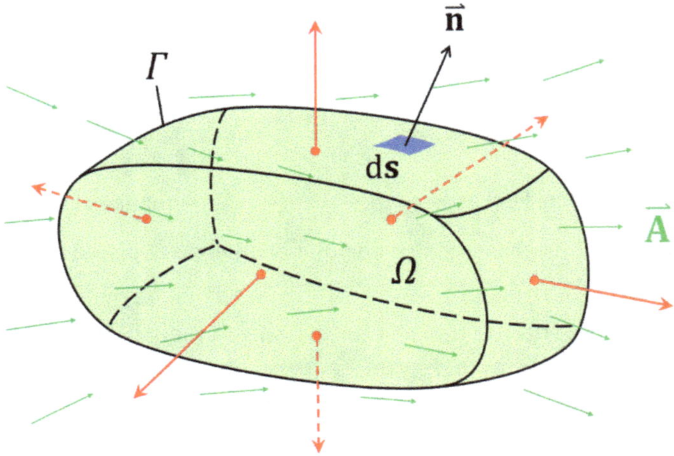

Figure 2.4.5 A schematic drawing of divergence of a vector field.

unit outward normal, and $\mathrm{d}x$ be a differential volume element in Ω. For vector $\mathbf{A}$ and a scalar function φ, the following relations, known from advanced calculus, hold

$$\int_\Omega \nabla\varphi \,\mathrm{d}x = \oint_\Gamma \mathbf{n}\,\varphi \,\mathrm{d}s \qquad \text{Gradient theorem,} \tag{2.4.27}$$

$$\int_\Omega \nabla\cdot\mathbf{A} \,\mathrm{d}x = \oint_\Gamma \mathbf{n}\cdot\mathbf{A} \,\mathrm{d}s \qquad \text{Divergence theorem,} \tag{2.4.28}$$

$$\int_\Omega \nabla\cdot\mathbf{A} \,\mathrm{d}x = \oint_\Gamma \mathbf{n}\times\mathbf{A} \,\mathrm{d}s \qquad \text{Curl theorem.} \tag{2.4.29}$$

The combination $\mathbf{n}\cdot\mathbf{A}\,\mathrm{d}s$ is called the outflow of $\mathbf{A}$ through the differential surface $\mathrm{d}s$. The integral is called the total or net outflow through the surrounding surface Δs. This is easier to see if one imagines that $\mathbf{A}$ is a velocity vector and the outflow is the amount of fluid flow. In the limit, as the region shrinks to a point, the net outflow per unit volume is therefore associated with the divergence of the vector field. The integral forms presented in Equations (2.4.27)–(2.4.29) are known as invariant forms because they do not depend on the coordinate system.

Note that grad $\varphi = \nabla\varphi$ measures the rate and direction of change in a scalar field, and it maps scalar fields to vector fields. For divergence div $\mathbf{A} = \nabla\cdot\mathbf{A}$, it measures the magnitude of a source or sink at a given point in a vector field and maps vector fields to scalar fields. In the case of curl, curl $\mathbf{A} = \nabla \times \mathbf{A}$, it measures the tendency to rotate about a point in a vector field and maps vector fields to vector fields.

Example 2.4.1

For scalar functions F and G and for vector functions $\mathbf{A}$ and $\mathbf{B}$, which are the functions of position x with continuous first and second derivatives, establish the following identities using index notation (we use the notations $x = r$ and $|x| = r$):

(a) $\nabla(\mathbf{r}) = \frac{\mathbf{r}}{r}$;
(b) $\nabla \times (\nabla F) = 0$.

Solution:

(a) Note that $\frac{\partial x_j}{\partial x_i} = \delta_{ij}$ and $\frac{\partial i}{\partial x_i} = \delta_{ii} = 3$.

$$\nabla(\mathbf{r}) = \mathbf{e}_\mathrm{i}\frac{\partial r}{\partial x_i} = \mathbf{e}_\mathrm{i}\frac{\partial}{\partial x_i}(x_j x_j)^{\frac{1}{2}} = \tfrac{1}{2}\mathbf{e}_\mathrm{k}(r^2)^{\left(\frac{1}{2}-1\right)}\left(\frac{\partial x_j}{\partial x_i}x_j + \frac{\partial x_j}{\partial x_i}x_j\right)$$

$$= x_i\mathbf{e}_\mathrm{i}(r^2)^{-\frac{1}{2}} = \frac{\mathbf{x}}{r} = \frac{\mathbf{r}}{r},$$

From which we also note the identity $\frac{\partial r}{\partial x_i} = \frac{x_i}{r}$.

(b) Consider the expression

$$\nabla \times (\nabla F) = \left(\mathbf{e}_\mathrm{i}\frac{\partial}{\partial x_i}\right) \times \left(\mathbf{e}_\mathrm{j}\frac{\partial F}{\partial x_j}\right) = e_{ijk}\mathbf{e}_\mathrm{k}\frac{\partial^2 F}{\partial x_i \partial x_j}.$$

Note that $\frac{\partial^2 F}{\partial x_i \partial x_j}$ is symmetric in i and j. Consider the kth component of the vector $\nabla \times (\nabla F)$:

$$e_{ijk}\frac{\partial^2 F}{\partial x_i \partial x_j} = -e_{jik}\frac{\partial^2 F}{\partial x_i \partial x_j} = -e_{ijk}\frac{\partial^2 F}{\partial x_j \partial x_i} = -e_{ijk}\frac{\partial^2 F}{\partial x_i \partial x_j}.$$

Thus, the expression is equal to its own negative, implying that it is zero.

It is convenient to use index notation when establishing vector identities and simplifying vector expressions. A list of vector operations in both vector and Cartesian component forms is presented in following:

(a) $\mathbf{A} \cdot \mathbf{B} \quad A_i B_i$.
(b) $\mathbf{A} \times \mathbf{B} \quad e_{ijk} A_i B_j \mathbf{e}_\mathrm{k}$.
(c) $\mathbf{A} \cdot (\mathbf{B} \times \mathbf{C}) \quad e_{ijk} A_i B_i C_k$.
(d) $\mathbf{A} \times (\mathbf{B} \times \mathbf{C}) = \mathbf{B}(\mathbf{A} \cdot \mathbf{C}) + \mathbf{C}(A \cdot \mathbf{B}) \quad e_{ijk} e_{klm} A_j B_l C_m \mathbf{e}_\mathrm{i}$.
(e) $\nabla \cdot \mathbf{A} \quad \frac{\partial A_i}{\partial x_i}$.
(f) $\nabla \times \mathbf{A} e_{ijk} \quad \frac{\partial A_j}{\partial x_i} \mathbf{e}_k$.
(g) $(\mathbf{A} \cdot \nabla)\mathbf{B} A_j \quad \frac{\partial B_i}{\partial x_j} \mathbf{e}_\mathrm{i}$.
(h) $\mathbf{A}(\nabla \cdot \mathbf{B}) A_i \mathbf{e}_\mathrm{i} \quad \frac{\partial B_j}{\partial x_j}$.

2.5 Tensors

2.5.1 *Second-Order Tensor: Dyads and Dyadics*

In solid mechanics, some quantities, such as stress and strain, may have two or three directions. Therefore, it is necessary to define a quantity with respect to multiple directions. For instance, stress, which represents force per unit area, depends not only on the orientation of the plane on which it acts but also on the direction of the force, as shown in Figure 2.5.1. Thus, specifying stress at a point requires two vectors: one to indicate the plane (through a vector perpendicular to the plane) on which the force acts, and the other to indicate the direction of the force. Another example is the expression for the gradient of a vector, which involves the tensor product of two basis vectors. This notation signifies that the entity is characterized by two directions: one originating from the gradient (vector) operator and the other from the vector itself.

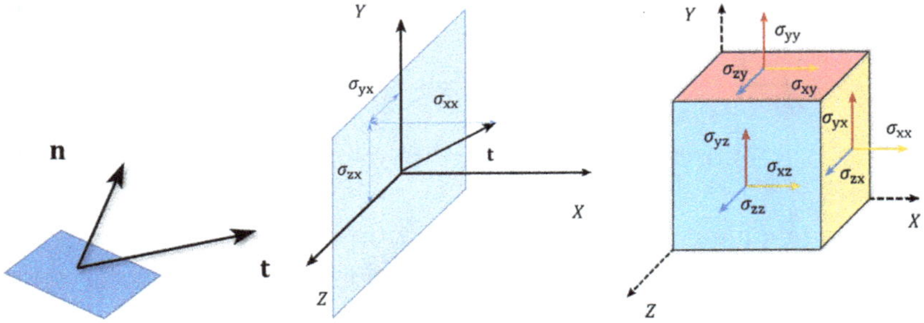

Figure 2.5.1 Stress tensor, and stress acting on a plane.

For example, consider the del operator, ∇, with a vector $\mathbf{A}$:

$$\nabla \mathbf{A} = \left(\mathbf{e}_{\rm i}\frac{\partial}{\partial x_i}\right)(A_j\mathbf{e}_{\rm j}) = \frac{\partial A_j}{\partial x_i}\mathbf{e}_{\rm i}\mathbf{e}_{\rm j} = \frac{\partial A_j}{\partial x_i}\mathbf{e}_{\rm i} \otimes \mathbf{e}_{\rm j}. \tag{2.5.1}$$

Objects that consist of two vectors positioned side by side without any vector operation between them are referred to as dyads or second-order tensors. In this context, a dyad is defined as two vectors placed together and treated as a single entity. A linear combination of dyads is known as a dyadic. The symbolic representation for two vectors positioned side by side is denoted by the operator symbol $\otimes$.

Let $\mathbf{A}$ and $\mathbf{B}$ be arbitrary vectors. Then, the following linear combination, denoted $\mathbf{S}$, constitutes a dyadic:

$$\mathbf{S} = \mathbf{AB} = \mathbf{A} \otimes \mathbf{B} = A_i B_j \mathbf{e}_{\rm i} \otimes \mathbf{e}_{\rm j}. \tag{2.5.2}$$

The transpose of a dyadic is defined as the result obtained by the interchange of the two vectors in each of the dyads:

$$\mathbf{S}^{\rm T} = \mathbf{BA}. \tag{2.5.3}$$

One of the properties of a dyadic is defined by the dot product with a vector $\mathbf{V}$:

$$\mathbf{S} \cdot \mathbf{V} = \mathbf{A}(\mathbf{B} \cdot \mathbf{V}), \mathbf{V} \cdot \mathbf{S} = (\mathbf{V} \cdot \mathbf{A})\mathbf{B},$$
$$\mathbf{S} \cdot \mathbf{V} = \mathbf{V} \cdot \mathbf{S}^T, \mathbf{V} \cdot \mathbf{S} = \mathbf{S}^T \cdot \mathbf{V}. \tag{2.5.4}$$

A dyadic refers to a second-order tensor. Tensors come in different orders, including zeroth-order, first-order, second-order, and higher-order tensors. While the zeroth- and first-order tensors are significant, the second-order tensors hold particular importance from a practical standpoint. They play a crucial role in fields such as continuum mechanics, relativity, electromagnetism, and quantum theory. Therefore, we can summarize as follows:

(1) A tensor of order zero is equivalent to a scalar, represented by a single value, a.
(2) A first-order tensor is equivalent to a vector, represented by $\mathbf{V}$.

Note that the vector can also be defined as a mapping $\mathbf{U}$ that acts on a vector $\mathbf{V}$, resulting in a scalar a, expressed as $\mathbf{U} \cdot \mathbf{V} = a$. This transformation, known as the dot product, is linear. Consequently, a first-order tensor (vector) maps a first-order tensor to a zeroth-order tensor (scalar), while a second-order tensor maps a first-order tensor to a first-order tensor, as represented by $(\mathbf{U} \otimes \mathbf{V})\mathbf{W} = \mathbf{U}(\mathbf{W} \cdot \mathbf{V})$. Similarly, a third-order tensor maps a first-order tensor to a second-order tensor, and so on.

For any vector $\mathbf{V}$, two tensors $\mathbf{T}$ and $\mathbf{S}$ are considered equal if and only if their components satisfy this equation

$$\mathbf{SV} = \mathbf{TV}. \tag{2.5.5}$$

To illustrate, let us consider the angular momentum and the moment of inertia tensor of a rigid body undergoing rotational motion, where each particle in the body moves in a circular path around a fixed axis in space, as shown in Figure 2.5.2. The angular velocity of the body is represented by the vector $\boldsymbol{\omega}$, which has a magnitude equal to the angular speed ω and a direction along the axis of rotation.

The linear velocity of a particle in the body can be expressed as linear velocity, $\mathbf{v} = \boldsymbol{\omega} \times \mathbf{r}$, where $\mathbf{v}$ is the linear velocity, $\boldsymbol{\omega}$ is the angular velocity vector, $\mathbf{r}$ is the position vector of the particle from a fixed point O on the axis, and $\times$ denotes the cross product.

The angular momentum of a particle about point O is defined as $\mathbf{h} = m\mathbf{v} \times \mathbf{r}$, where m is the mass of the particle. The angular momentum of the rigid body can be obtained by summing up the angular momenta of all the particles in the body. It can be written in vector form as

$$\mathbf{h} = \hat{\mathbf{I}}\boldsymbol{\omega}, \hat{\mathbf{I}} = m(|\mathbf{r}|^2\mathbf{I} - \mathbf{r} \otimes \mathbf{r}), \tag{2.5.6}$$

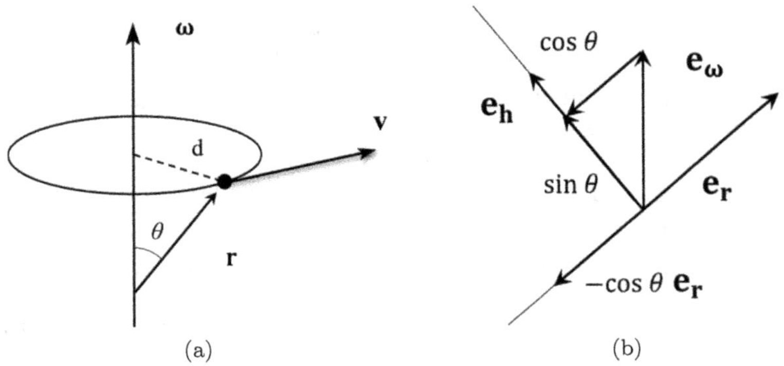

Figure 2.5.2 (a) A particle in motion about an axis and (b) Geometry of unit vectors for angular momentum calculation.

where $\hat{\mathbf{I}}$, a second-order tensor, is the moment of inertia of the particle about the point O, given by $\mathbf{I}$, where $\mathbf{I}$ is the identity tensor, i.e., $\mathbf{IA} = \mathbf{A}$ for all vectors $\mathbf{A}$.

2.5.2 *The Properties of Second-Order Tensors*

Consider a dyad $\mathbf{S} = \mathbf{AB}$ which will be represented in a given basis system. In the Cartesian system, we can write $\mathbf{A} = A_i\mathbf{e}_\mathrm{i}$ and $\mathbf{B} = B_j\mathbf{e}_\mathrm{j}$, with summations on i and j as implied by the repeated indices. Then, we can express the second-order tensor as $\mathbf{S} = \mathbf{AB} = A_iB_j\mathbf{e}_\mathrm{i}\otimes \mathbf{e}_\mathrm{j} = S_{ij}\mathbf{e}_\mathrm{i} \otimes \mathbf{e}_\mathrm{j}$.

We can display all of the components of a dyad or second-order tensor $\mathbf{S}$ in the rectangular Cartesian basis $\mathbf{e}_\mathrm{i}$ as $\mathbf{S} = S_{ij}\mathbf{e}_\mathrm{i} \otimes \mathbf{e}_\mathrm{j} = S_{ij}\mathbf{e}_\mathrm{i}\mathbf{e}_\mathrm{j}$ by letting the index j run to the right and the index i run downward:

$$\begin{aligned}\mathbf{S} = s_{ij}\mathbf{e}_\mathrm{i}\mathbf{e}_\mathrm{j} &= s_{11}\mathbf{e}_1\mathbf{e}_1 + s_{12}\mathbf{e}_1\mathbf{e}_2 + s_{13}\mathbf{e}_1\mathbf{e}_3\\ &+ s_{21}\mathbf{e}_1\mathbf{e}_2 + s_{22}\mathbf{e}_2\mathbf{e}_2 + s_{23}\mathbf{e}_2\mathbf{e}_3\\ &+ s_{31}\mathbf{e}_3\mathbf{e}_1 + s_{32}\mathbf{e}_3\mathbf{e}_2 + s_{33}\mathbf{e}_3\mathbf{e}_3. \end{aligned} \tag{2.5.7}$$

This form is known as the notation form of the second-order tensor $\mathbf{S}$, which demonstrates that a dyadic in 3D space generally has nine independent components. Each component is associated with a specific dyad pair and is therefore considered ordered. To simplify notation, the explicit representation of the second-order tensor can be omitted, and the dyadic can be expressed as a matrix:

$$[\mathbf{S}] = \begin{bmatrix} s_{11} & s_{12} & s_{13}\\ s_{21} & s_{22} & s_{23}\\ s_{31} & s_{32} & s_{33}\end{bmatrix}, \tag{2.5.8}$$

$$\mathbf{S} = \begin{pmatrix} e_1\\ e_2\\ e_3\end{pmatrix}^T [\mathbf{S}] \begin{pmatrix} e_1\\ e_2\\ e_3\end{pmatrix}. \tag{2.5.9}$$

The determinant of a second-order tensor $\mathbf{S}$ is the determinant of the matrix of its components, $\det[\mathbf{S}] = |\mathbf{S}|$. The determinant of $\mathbf{S}$ can be expressed in the form

$$\mathrm{Det}[\mathbf{S}] = |\mathbf{S}| = e_{ijk}s_{1i}s_{2j}s_{3k}. \tag{2.5.10}$$

It is important to note that although the definition of the determinant in terms of the components of a matrix involves a specific coordinate system, the value of the determinant is actually independent of the coordinate system chosen (we will discuss this later).

The unit dyad or unit second-order tensor is defined in terms of the Cartesian components δ_{ij} as

$$\mathbf{I} = \delta_{ij}\mathbf{e}_\mathrm{i}\mathbf{e}_\mathrm{j} = \mathbf{e}_1\mathbf{e}_1 + \mathbf{e}_2\mathbf{e}_2 + \mathbf{e}_3\mathbf{e}_3 \tag{2.5.11}$$

and

$$\mathbf{I} = \begin{pmatrix} e_1 \\ e_2 \\ e_3 \end{pmatrix}^T [\mathbf{I}] \begin{pmatrix} e_1 \\ e_2 \\ e_3 \end{pmatrix}, \quad [\mathbf{I}] = \begin{bmatrix} 1 & 0 & 0 \\ 0 & 1 & 0 \\ 0 & 0 & 1 \end{bmatrix}. \tag{2.5.12}$$

From the above equations, it is obvious that the unit second-order tensor $\mathbf{I}$ is symmetric.

2.5.3 *Double Contraction*

Before defining double contraction, first we need to define the dot product of tensors.

For a vector $\mathbf{A}$ and tensors $\mathbf{S}$ and $\mathbf{T}$, we can define the dot product as follows:

(1) Dot product of a vector and a tensor: The dot product of a vector $\mathbf{A}$ with a tensor $\mathbf{S}$, denoted as $\mathbf{A} \cdot \mathbf{S}$, is defined as the sum of the products of the corresponding components of $\mathbf{A}$ and $\mathbf{S}$.
(2) Dot product of two tensors: The dot product of two tensors $\mathbf{S}$ and $\mathbf{T}$, denoted as $\mathbf{S} \cdot \mathbf{T}$, is defined as the sum of the products of the corresponding components of $\mathbf{S}$ and $\mathbf{T}$.

These definitions enable us to perform dot products between vectors and tensors, as well as between two tensors, and obtain scalar results:

$$\mathbf{A} \cdot \mathbf{T} = A_i T_{jk}\mathbf{e}_\mathrm{i} \cdot \mathbf{e}_\mathrm{j} \otimes \mathbf{e}_\mathrm{k} = A_i T_{ik}\mathbf{e}_\mathrm{k}, \tag{2.5.13}$$

$$\mathbf{S} \cdot \mathbf{T} = S_{ij} T_{kl} \mathbf{e}_{\mathrm{i}} \otimes \mathbf{e}_{\mathrm{j}} \cdot \mathbf{e}_{\mathrm{k}} \otimes \mathbf{e}_{\mathrm{l}} \\ = S_{ij} T_{jl} \mathbf{e}_{\mathrm{i}} \otimes \mathbf{e}_{\mathrm{l}}, \tag{2.5.14}$$

$$\mathbf{T} \cdot \mathbf{T}^{-1} = \mathbf{T}^{-1} \cdot \mathbf{T} = \mathbf{I}. \tag{2.5.15}$$

Double contraction, as the name implies, contracts the tensors twice as much as a simple contraction. Thus, while the sum of the orders of two tensors is reduced by two in a simple contraction, the sum of the orders is reduced by four in a double contraction. Two types of "double-dot products" between two second-order tensors are useful in solid mechanics. We define the horizontal double-dot product and the vertical double-dot product between a dyad (**AB**) and another dyad (**CD**) (where **A**, **B**, **C**, and **D** are vectors) as scalars.

The double contraction or vertical double-dot product is denoted by a colon (:), e.g., $\mathbf{S} : \mathbf{T}$, then we define the double contraction of simple tensors (dyads) through

$$(\mathbf{AB}) : (\mathbf{CD}) = (\mathbf{A} \cdot \mathbf{C})(\mathbf{B} \cdot \mathbf{D}). \tag{2.5.16}$$

Therefore, in double contraction, one takes the scalar product of four vectors that are adjacent to each other, according to the same rule. The double-dot products, by this definition, are commutative, for example,

$$\mathbf{S} : \mathbf{T} = (s_{ij} \mathbf{e}_{\mathrm{i}} \mathbf{e}_{\mathrm{j}}) : (t_{mn} \mathbf{e}_{\mathrm{m}} \mathbf{e}_{\mathrm{n}}) \\ = s_{ij} t_{mn} (\mathbf{e}_{\mathrm{i}} \cdot \mathbf{e}_{\mathrm{m}})(\mathbf{e}_{\mathrm{j}} \cdot \mathbf{e}_{\mathrm{n}}), \\ = s_{ij} t_{mn} \delta_{im} \delta_{jn} = s_{ij} t_{ij} \tag{2.5.17}$$

which is, as expected, a scalar.

Similarly, the horizontal double-dot product can be defined as

$$(\mathbf{AB}) \cdot \cdot (\mathbf{CD}) = (\mathbf{B} \cdot \mathbf{C})(\mathbf{A} \cdot \mathbf{D}). \tag{2.5.18}$$

The double-dot product between two dyads **S** and **T** in a rectangular Cartesian system is

$$\mathbf{S} \cdot \cdot \mathbf{T} = (s_{ij} \mathbf{e}_{\mathrm{i}} \mathbf{e}_{\mathrm{j}}) \cdot \cdot (t_{mn} \mathbf{e}_{\mathrm{m}} \mathbf{e}_{\mathrm{n}}) \\ = s_{ij} t_{mn} (\mathbf{e}_{\mathrm{j}} \cdot \mathbf{e}_{\mathrm{m}})(\mathbf{e}_{\mathrm{i}} \cdot \mathbf{e}_{\mathrm{n}}) \\ = s_{ij} t_{mn} \delta_{jm} \delta_{in} = s_{ij} t_{ji}. \tag{2.5.19}$$

The trace of a second-order tensor (i.e., the sum of the diagonal terms of the matrix representing the tensor) is defined to be the double-dot product of the tensor with the unit tensor:

$$\mathrm{tr}\,\mathbf{S} = \mathbf{S} : \mathbf{I} = \mathbf{S} \cdot \cdot \mathbf{I}. \tag{2.5.20}$$

2.5.4 *Eigenvalues, Eigenvectors, and Invariants of a Tensor*

Certain combinations of a tensor's components remain unchanged regardless of the coordinate system used. These quantities, which involve sums and products of the tensor's components, are known as invariants. Invariants are important because they are independent of coordinate transformations and provide valuable information about the tensor's properties.

For instance, the determinant of a tensor is an invariant, meaning it has the same value in all coordinate systems. The determinant represents a scalar quantity that encapsulates important information about the tensor's overall behavior. Similarly, the trace of the matrix representing a tensor is also an invariant. The trace is obtained by summing the diagonal elements of the matrix and provides another scalar measure of the tensor's characteristics.

Among the various invariants of a tensor, three special invariants, known as principal invariants, are particularly significant. These principal invariants play a crucial role in determining the eigenvalues of the tensor. For example, in the case of a stress tensor, which is a second-order tensor, these principal invariants capture important information about the tensor's behavior and provide insights into the material's response to external forces or deformation.

Consider a second-order tensor $\mathbf{T}$. Suppose that one can find a scalar λ and a (nonzero) normalized, i.e., unit vector $\hat{\mathbf{n}}$ such that

$$\mathbf{T}\hat{\mathbf{n}} = \lambda\hat{\mathbf{n}} \tag{2.5.21}$$

In other words, a transformation takes the vector $\hat{\mathbf{n}}$ and transforms it into a vector that is parallel to itself, as depicted in Figure 2.5.3. If such a transformation is possible, the associated scalars are referred to as the eigenvalues or principal values of the tensor, while the vectors themselves are known as the eigenvectors, principal directions, or principal axes of the tensor. It is observed that

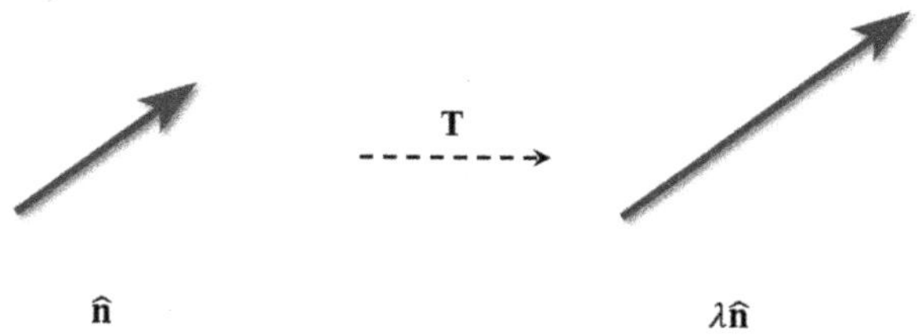

Figure 2.5.3 The action of a tensor $\mathbf{T}$ on a unit vector.

there are three vectors $\hat{\mathbf{n}}$ (each associated with a specific scalar λ) that satisfy this condition. To determine the eigenvalues and eigenvectors, we can solve the problem by rewriting it in the following form:

$$(\mathbf{T} - \lambda \mathbf{I})\hat{\mathbf{n}} = 0, \tag{2.5.22}$$

or, in terms of a Cartesian coordinate system,

$$\begin{aligned} T_{ij}(\mathbf{e}_\mathrm{i} \otimes \mathbf{e}_\mathrm{j})\hat{n}_k \mathbf{e}_\mathrm{k} - \lambda \delta_{pq}(\mathbf{e}_\mathrm{p} \otimes \mathbf{e}_\mathrm{q})\hat{n}_m \mathbf{e}_\mathrm{m} &= 0, \\ \text{or} \quad T_{ij}\hat{n}_j \mathbf{e}_\mathrm{i} - \lambda \hat{n}_k \mathbf{e}_\mathrm{k} &= 0, \\ \text{or} \quad (T_{ij}\hat{n}_j - \lambda \hat{n}_i)\mathbf{e}_\mathrm{i} &= 0, \end{aligned} \tag{2.5.23}$$

or

$$\begin{aligned} [(T_{11} - \lambda)\hat{n}_1 + T_{12}\hat{n}_2 + T_{13}\hat{n}_3]\mathbf{e}_1 &= 0, \\ [T_{21}\hat{n}_1 + (T_{22} - \lambda)\hat{n}_2 + T_{23}\hat{n}_3]\mathbf{e}_2 &= 0, \\ [T_{31}\hat{n}_1 + T_{32}\hat{n}_2 + (T_{33} - \lambda)\hat{n}_3]\mathbf{e}_3 &= 0. \end{aligned} \tag{2.5.24}$$

Dividing out the base vectors, this is a set of three homogeneous equations in three unknowns (if one treats λ as known). From basic linear algebra, this system has a solution (apart from $\hat{n}_k = 0$) if and only if the determinant of the coefficient matrix is zero, i.e., if

$$\det(\mathbf{T} - \lambda \mathbf{I}) = \det \begin{bmatrix} T_{11} - \lambda & T_{12} & T_{13} \\ T_{21} & T_{22} - \lambda & T_{23} \\ T_{31} & T_{32} & T_{33} - \lambda \end{bmatrix} = 0. \tag{2.5.25}$$

Evaluating the determinant, one has the following cubic characteristic equation of $\mathbf{T}$:

$$\lambda^3 - I_1\lambda^2 + I_2\lambda - I_3 = 0, \tag{2.5.26}$$

where

$$\begin{gathered} I_1 = T_{ii} = \mathrm{tr}\mathbf{T}, \\ I_2 = \frac{1}{2}(T_{ii}T_{jj} - T_{ji}T_{ij}) = \frac{1}{2}[(\mathrm{tr}\mathbf{T})^2 - \mathrm{tr}(\mathbf{T})^2], \\ I_3 = e_{ijk}T_{1i}T_{2j}T_{3k} = \det\mathbf{T}. \end{gathered} \tag{2.5.27}$$

It can be seen that there are three roots, $\lambda_1, \lambda_2, \lambda_3$, to the characteristic equation. Solving for λ, one finds that

$$\begin{gathered} I_1 = \lambda_1 + \lambda_2 + \lambda_3, \\ I_2 = \lambda_1\lambda_2 + \lambda_2\lambda_3 + \lambda_3\lambda_1, \\ I_3 = \lambda_1\lambda_2\lambda_3. \end{gathered} \tag{2.5.28}$$

The eigenvalues (principal values) λ_i must be independent of any coordinate system, and it follows that the functions I_1, I_2, I_3 are also independent of any coordinate system. They are called the principal scalar invariants (or simply invariants) of the tensor. For example, physically, the stress state of one point is invariant, which is not dependent on the selection of coordinate system.

Once the eigenvalues are found, the eigenvectors (principal directions) can be found by solving

$$\begin{aligned} (T_{11} - \lambda)\hat{n}_1 + T_{12}\hat{n}_2 + T_{13}\hat{n}_3 = 0, \\ T_{21}\hat{n}_1 + (T_{22} - \lambda)\hat{n}_2 + T_{23}\hat{n}_3 = 0, \\ T_{31}\hat{n}_1 + T_{32}\hat{n}_2 + (T_{33} - \lambda)\hat{n}_3 = 0, \end{aligned} \tag{2.5.29}$$

for the three components of the principal direction vector $\hat{n}_1, \hat{n}_2, \hat{n}_3$, in addition to the condition that $\hat{\mathbf{n}} \cdot \hat{\mathbf{n}} = 1$. There will be three vectors $\hat{\mathbf{n}} = \hat{n}_i\mathbf{e}_{\mathrm{i}}$, one corresponding to each of the three principal values.

The eigenvector $\hat{\mathbf{n}}^{(j)} = \mathbf{x}^{(j)}$ associated with any particular eigenvalue λ_j is calculated using Equation (2.5.29), which gives only two independent relations among the three components $\mathbf{x}^{(j)}$, i.e., $x_1^{(j)}$, $x_2^{(j)}$ and $x_3^{(j)}$. Thus, two of the three components can be written in terms of the third, whose value is arbitrary (but nonzero). In other words, we can determine the eigenvectors only within a multiplicative constant. If the eigenvector is normalized such that it is a unit vector, we can use the following additional (i.e., third) condition to determine all three components:

$$\left(x_1^{(j)}\right)^2 + \left(x_2^{(j)}\right)^2 + \left(x_3^{(j)}\right)^2 = 1. \tag{2.5.30}$$

For example, if $x_1^{(j)}$ and $x_2^{(j)}$ are expressed in terms of $x_3^{(j)}$, say $x_1^{(j)} = \alpha x_3^{(j)}$ and $x_2^{(j)} = \beta x_3^{(j)}$, then Equation (2.5.30) yields

$$\left(x_3^{(j)}\right)^2 = \frac{1}{\alpha^2 + \beta^2 + 1} \quad \text{or} \quad x_3^{(j)} = \pm\left(\frac{1}{\sqrt{\alpha^2 + \beta^2 + 1}}\right), \tag{2.5.31}$$

and the normalized eigenvector is

$$\begin{pmatrix} x_1^{(j)} \\ x_2^{(j)} \\ x_3^{(j)} \end{pmatrix} = \pm\left(\frac{1}{\sqrt{\alpha^2 + \beta^2 + 1}}\right)\begin{pmatrix} \alpha \\ \beta \\ 1 \end{pmatrix}. \tag{2.5.32}$$

The sign $\pm$ on the three eigenvectors should be selected such that we have a right-hand coordinate system (when the eigenvectors are orthonormal):

$$\mathbf{x}^{(3)} = \mathbf{x}^{(1)} \times \mathbf{x}^{(2)} \tag{2.5.33}$$

In two-dimensional problems of solid mechanics, the matrix under consideration is normally of order 2×2, and the characteristic equation is of the form

$$\text{Det}(\mathbf{T} - \lambda\mathbf{I}) = \det\begin{bmatrix} T_{11} - \lambda & T_{12} \\ T_{21} & T_{22} - \lambda \end{bmatrix} = 0, \tag{2.5.34}$$

$$\lambda^2 - I_1\lambda + I_3 = 0, \tag{2.5.35}$$

where

$$\begin{aligned} I_1 &= T_{ii} = T_{11} + T_{22}, \\ I_3 &= T_{11}T_{22} - T_{12} + T_{21}. \end{aligned} \tag{2.5.36}$$

Therefore, the roots of this quadratic equation are

$$\lambda_1 = \frac{1}{2}\left(I_1 - \sqrt{I_1^2 - 4I_1I_3}\right), \quad \lambda_2 = \frac{1}{2}\left(I_1 + \sqrt{I_1^2 - 4I_1I_3}\right). \tag{2.5.37}$$

Therefore, the eigenvector $\mathbf{x}^{(j)}$ associated with λ_j $(j = 1, 2)$ is determined from

$$\begin{bmatrix} T_{11} - \lambda_j & T_{12} \\ T_{21} & T_{22} - \lambda_j \end{bmatrix} \begin{pmatrix} x_1^{(j)} \\ x_2^{(j)} \end{pmatrix} = \begin{pmatrix} 0 \\ 0 \end{pmatrix}. \tag{2.5.38}$$

This matrix equation gives only one independent relation between $x_1^{(j)}$ and $x_2^{(j)}$. One can arbitrarily select the value of one of the two components and determine the other. Alternatively, one can use the normalization $(x_1^{(j)})^2 + (x_2^{(j)})^2 = 1$ to determine the vector $\mathbf{x}^{(j)}$. The computational procedure can be understood through the following examples.

In the general framework developed so far, scalars are considered to be zeroth-order tensors, vectors are first-order tensors, and dyads are second-order tensors. The order of a tensor can be determined by counting the number of basis vectors in its representation. Therefore, the magnitude of a vector can be regarded as an invariant of first-order tensors.

Example 2.5.1

Determine the eigenvalues and eigenvectors of the matrix $[\mathbf{T}] = \begin{bmatrix} 5 & -1 \\ 3 & 1 \end{bmatrix}$.

Solution:
The eigenvalue problem associated with the matrix $[\mathbf{T}]$ is $\mathbf{TX} - \lambda\mathbf{X} = 0$:

$$\begin{bmatrix} 5 - \lambda & -1 \\ 3 & 1 - \lambda \end{bmatrix} \begin{pmatrix} x_1 \\ x_2 \end{pmatrix} = \begin{pmatrix} 0 \\ 0 \end{pmatrix}.$$

The characteristic equation is obtained from $\lambda^2 - I_1\lambda + I_3 = \lambda^2 - 6\lambda + 8 = 0$.

The two roots of the quadratic equation are

$$\lambda_1 = \frac{1}{2}\left(I_1 - \sqrt{I_1^2 - 4I_1I_3}\right) = 2, \quad \lambda_2 = \frac{1}{2}\left(I_1 + \sqrt{I_1^2 - 4I_1I_3}\right) = 4.$$

To find the eigenvectors, we substitute $\lambda_1 = 2$ for each of the eigenvalues and solve the resulting algebraic equations:

$$\begin{bmatrix} 5-2 & -1 \\ 3 & 1-2 \end{bmatrix} \begin{pmatrix} x_1 \\ x_2 \end{pmatrix} = \begin{pmatrix} 0 \\ 0 \end{pmatrix}.$$

Since each row of the matrix equation above yields the same condition, the eigenvector is given by $\begin{pmatrix} x_1^{(1)} \\ x_2^{(1)} \end{pmatrix} = \binom{1}{3}, x_1^{(1)}$ and $x_2^{(1)} \neq 0$, but arbitrary.

Usually, we take $x_1^{(1)} = 1$, as we are interested in the direction of the vector $(x_1^{(1)}, x_2^{(1)})^{\mathrm{T}}$ rather than its magnitude. One may also normalize the eigenvector by using the condition $(x_1^{(1)})^2 + (x_2^{(1)})^2 = 1$.

Then, we can obtain the following normalized eigenvector:

$$\begin{pmatrix} \hat{x}_1^{(1)} \\ \hat{x}_2^{(1)} \end{pmatrix} = \pm\frac{1}{\sqrt{10}} \begin{pmatrix} 1 \\ 3 \end{pmatrix} = \pm \begin{pmatrix} 0.31621 \\ 0.9487 \end{pmatrix}.$$

For $\lambda_2 = 4$, using the same procedure, we can determine the eigenvector

$$\begin{pmatrix} \hat{x}_1^{(2)} \\ \hat{x}_2^{(2)} \end{pmatrix} = \pm\frac{1}{\sqrt{2}} \begin{pmatrix} 1 \\ 1 \end{pmatrix} = \pm \begin{pmatrix} 0.707 \\ 0.707 \end{pmatrix}.$$

Note that, because the matrix under consideration is not symmetric, we do not expect the eigenvectors to be orthogonal.

Example 2.5.2

Determine the eigenvalues and eigenvectors of the following matrix: $[\mathbf{S}] = \begin{bmatrix} 2 & 1 & 0 \\ 1 & 4 & 1 \\ 0 & 1 & 2 \end{bmatrix}$.

Solution:

The characteristic equation of the matrix is $-\lambda^3 + I_1\lambda^2 - I_2\lambda + I_3 = 0$ with $I_1 = 2+4+2 = 8$, $I_2 = \frac{1}{2}(8^2 - 2^2 - 4^2 - 2^2 - 2 \times 1^2 - 2 \times 1^2) = 18$, and $I_3 = |\mathbf{S}| = 12$.

Thus, the characteristic equation is

$$-\lambda^3 + 8\lambda^2 - 18\lambda + 12 = 0, \text{ or } (2-\lambda)(\lambda^2 - 6\lambda + 6) = 0.$$

The roots of this cubic equation are

$$\lambda_1 = 3 + \sqrt{3} = 4.7321, \quad \lambda_2 = 2, \quad \text{and} \quad \lambda_3 = 3 - \sqrt{3} = 1.2679.$$

The eigenvector corresponding to $\lambda_1 = 3 + \sqrt{3}$ is calculated, and we have

$$\begin{bmatrix} 2-(3+\sqrt{3}) & 1 & 0 \\ 1 & 4-(3+\sqrt{3}) & 1 \\ 0 & 1 & 2-(3+\sqrt{3}) \end{bmatrix} \begin{pmatrix} x_1^1 \\ x_2^1 \\ x_3^1 \end{pmatrix} = \begin{pmatrix} 0 \\ 0 \\ 0 \end{pmatrix}.$$

This gives the following independent relations:

$$-(1+\sqrt{3})x_1^1 + x_2^1 = 0,$$
$$x_2^1 - (1+\sqrt{3})x_3^1 = 0 \Rightarrow x_1^1 = x_3^1 = \frac{1}{(1+\sqrt{3})}x_2^1.$$

Hence, we have the following eigenvector:

$$\mathbf{X} = \frac{1}{(1+\sqrt{3})}\begin{pmatrix} 1 \\ 1+\sqrt{3} \\ 1 \end{pmatrix} x_2^1 = \begin{pmatrix} 0.366 \\ 1 \\ 0.366 \end{pmatrix} x_2^1,$$

for any nonzero value; for example, for $x_2^1 = 1$, the vector can be the form

$$\mathbf{X} = \frac{1}{(1+\sqrt{3})}\begin{pmatrix} 1 \\ 1+\sqrt{3} \\ 1 \end{pmatrix} = \begin{pmatrix} 0.366 \\ 1 \\ 0.366 \end{pmatrix}.$$

Using the condition of normalizing the vector, $(x_1^{(1)})^2 + (x_2^{(1)})^2 + (x_3^{(1)})^2 = 1$, we can obtain

$$\hat{\mathbf{X}}^{(1)} = \pm\frac{1}{\sqrt{(6+2\sqrt{3})}}\begin{pmatrix} 1 \\ 1+\sqrt{3} \\ 1 \end{pmatrix} = \pm\begin{pmatrix} 0.325 \\ 0.888 \\ 0.325 \end{pmatrix}.$$

Similarly, we can obtain the other two normalized eigenvectors as

$$\hat{\mathbf{X}}^{(2)} = \pm \begin{pmatrix} -0.707 \\ 0.000 \\ 0.707 \end{pmatrix}, \quad \hat{\mathbf{X}}^{(3)} = \pm \begin{pmatrix} 0.628 \\ -0.460 \\ 0.628 \end{pmatrix}.$$

2.5.5 *Higher-Order Tensors*

Third-order tensors can be viewed as those derived from triads, or three vectors standing side by side. A tensor $\mathbf{T}$ of any order n is a quantity defined by 3^n components, which may be written as $T_{ijk\ldots n}$, provided the components transform according to the rule

$$\bar{t}_{pq\ldots\ldots s} = l_{pi}l_{qj}\cdots\cdots - l_{sn}t_{ijk\cdots n}. \tag{2.5.39}$$

For example, the components of third- and fourth-order tensors, $\mathbf{T}$ and $\mathbf{C}$, transform according to the rules

$$\bar{t}_{ijk} = l_{im}l_{jn}l_{kp}t_{mnp}, \quad \bar{c}_{ijkl} = l_{im}l_{jn}l_{kp}l_{lq}c_{mnpq}. \tag{2.5.40}$$

Tensors of various orders, especially first-order, second-order, and fourth-order tensors, will be utilized in the analysis of continuous media. As we will explore in later chapters, the tensor characterizing the material constitution is a fourth-order tensor. Tensors whose components remain the same in all coordinate systems, meaning they are invariant under coordinate transformations, are referred to as isotropic tensors. By definition, all zeroth-order tensors (i.e., scalars) are isotropic, and the only isotropic tensor of first order is the zero vector $\mathbf{0}$. Every isotropic second-order tensor $\mathbf{T}$ can be expressed as $\mathbf{T} = \lambda\mathbf{I}$, and the components C_{ijkl} of every isotropic fourth-order tensor $\mathbf{C}$ can be represented as

$$C_{ijkl} = \lambda\delta_{ij}\delta_{kl} + \mu(\delta_{ik}\delta_{jl} + \delta_{il}\delta_{jk}) + \kappa(\delta_{ik}\delta_{jl} - \delta_{il}\delta_{jk}), \tag{2.5.41}$$

where λ, μ, and κ are scalars.

In general, tensors of all orders obey the following rules:

$$\alpha(\mathbf{T}) = (\alpha\mathbf{T}) = T\alpha,$$
$$\alpha(\mathbf{T}_1 + \mathbf{T}_2) = \alpha\mathbf{T}_1 + \alpha\mathbf{T}_2,$$
$$\mathbf{T}_1 + \mathbf{T}_2 = \mathbf{T}_2 + \mathbf{T}_1,$$

$$\mathbf{T_1} + (\mathbf{T_2} + \mathbf{T_3}) = (\mathbf{T_1} + \mathbf{T_2}) + \mathbf{T_3}, \tag{2.5.42}$$
$$\mathbf{T_1} \cdot (\mathbf{T_2} + \mathbf{T_3}) = \mathbf{T_1} \cdot \mathbf{T_2} + \mathbf{T_1} \cdot \mathbf{T_3},$$
$$\mathbf{T_1} \times (\mathbf{T_2} + \mathbf{T_3}) = \mathbf{T_1} \times \mathbf{T_2} + \mathbf{T_1} \times \mathbf{T_3}.$$

A higher-order tensor possesses complete symmetry if the interchange of any indices is immaterial, for example if

$$\begin{aligned}\mathbf{S} &= S_{ijk}(\mathbf{e}_\mathrm{i} \otimes \mathbf{e}_\mathrm{j} \otimes \mathbf{e}_\mathrm{k}) \\ &= S_{ikj}(\mathbf{e}_\mathrm{i} \otimes \mathbf{e}_\mathrm{j} \otimes \mathbf{e}_\mathrm{k}) = S_{jik}(\mathbf{e}_\mathrm{i} \otimes \mathbf{e}_\mathrm{j} \otimes \mathbf{e}_\mathrm{k})\end{aligned} \tag{2.5.43}$$

It is symmetric in two of its indices if the interchange of these indices is immaterial. For example, the above tensor $\mathbf{S}$ is symmetric in j and k if

$$\mathbf{S} = S_{ijk}(\mathbf{e}_\mathrm{i} \otimes \mathbf{e}_\mathrm{j} \otimes \mathbf{e}_\mathrm{k}) = S_{ikj}(\mathbf{e}_\mathrm{i} \otimes \mathbf{e}_\mathrm{j} \otimes \mathbf{e}_\mathrm{k}). \tag{2.5.44}$$

A fourth-order tensor $\mathbf{C}$ possesses the minor symmetries if

$$C_{ijkl} = C_{jikl}, \quad C_{ijkl} = C_{ijlk}, \tag{2.5.45}$$

in which case it has only 36 independent components. The first equality here is for left minor symmetry, and the second is for right minor symmetry.

It possesses the major symmetries if it also satisfies

$$C_{ijkl} = C_{klij}, \tag{2.5.46}$$

in which case it has only 21 independent components.

2.5.6 *Tensor Calculus*

In this section, the concepts from vector calculus are extended to the calculus of higher-order tensors.

2.5.6.1 *Tensor-valued functions*

Tensor-valued functions of a scalar: The most basic type of calculus is that of tensor-valued functions of a scalar, e.g., the time-dependent stress at a point, $\mathbf{S}(t)$. If a second-order tensor $\mathbf{T}$ depends on a scalar t, then the derivative is defined in the usual way:

$$\frac{\mathrm{d}\mathbf{T}}{\mathrm{d}t} = \lim_{\Delta t \to 0} \frac{\mathbf{T}(t+\Delta t) - \mathbf{T}(t)}{\Delta t} \tag{2.5.47}$$

$$\frac{\mathrm{d}\mathbf{T}}{\mathrm{d}t} = \frac{\mathrm{d}T_{ij}}{\mathrm{d}t}\mathbf{e}_{\mathrm{i}} \otimes \mathbf{e}_{\mathrm{j}}. \tag{2.5.48}$$

The derivative is also a tensor, and the usual rules of differentiation apply.

2.5.6.2 *The gradient of vector fields and tensor fields*

In addition to the gradient of scalar fields and the divergence and curl of vector fields, it is also important to consider the gradient of vectors and higher-order tensors, as well as the divergence of higher-order tensors.

First, let us introduce the gradient of a vector field. The gradient of a vector field is defined to be the second-order tensor

$$\mathrm{grad}\,\mathbf{A} = \nabla\mathbf{A} = \left(\mathbf{e}_{\mathrm{j}}\frac{\partial \mathbf{A}}{\partial x_j}\right) = \frac{\partial A_i}{\partial x_j}\mathbf{e}_{\mathrm{j}} \otimes \mathbf{e}_{\mathrm{i}}. \tag{2.5.49}$$

In matrix notation,

$$\mathrm{grad}\,\mathbf{A} = \begin{bmatrix} \dfrac{\partial A_1}{\partial x_1} & \dfrac{\partial A_1}{\partial x_2} & \dfrac{\partial A_1}{\partial x_3} \\ \dfrac{\partial A_2}{\partial x_1} & \dfrac{\partial A_2}{\partial x_2} & \dfrac{\partial A_2}{\partial x_3} \\ \dfrac{\partial A_3}{\partial x_1} & \dfrac{\partial A_3}{\partial x_2} & \dfrac{\partial A_3}{\partial x_3} \end{bmatrix}. \tag{2.5.50}$$

And we have

$$\mathrm{grad}\,\mathbf{A}\cdot\mathrm{d}\mathbf{x} = \frac{\partial A_i}{\partial x_j}\mathbf{e}_{\mathrm{i}} \otimes \mathbf{e}_{\mathrm{j}} \cdot (\mathrm{d}x_k\mathbf{e}_{\mathrm{k}}) = \frac{\partial A_i}{\partial x_j}\mathrm{d}x_j\mathbf{e}_{\mathrm{i}} = \mathrm{d}\mathbf{A}. \tag{2.5.51}$$

Thus, the gradient of a vector field $\mathbf{A}$ is a second-order tensor which transforms a unit vector into a vector describing the gradient of $\mathbf{A}$ in that direction.

The gradient of a tensor field: The gradient of a second-order tensor field $\mathbf{T}$ is defined in a manner analogous to that of the gradient of a vector, which is a third-order tensor:

$$\operatorname{grad}\mathbf{T} = \left(\frac{\partial \mathbf{T}}{\partial x_k} \otimes \mathbf{e}_{\mathrm{k}}\right) = \frac{\partial T_{ij}}{\partial x_k}\mathbf{e}_{\mathrm{i}} \otimes \mathbf{e}_{\mathrm{j}} \otimes \mathbf{e}_{\mathrm{k}}. \tag{2.5.52}$$

This differs from the quantity

$$\nabla \otimes \mathbf{T} = \mathbf{e}_{\mathrm{i}}\frac{\partial}{\partial x_i} \otimes T_{jk}\mathbf{e}_{\mathrm{j}} \otimes \mathbf{e}_{\mathrm{k}} = \frac{\partial T_{jk}}{\partial x_i}\mathbf{e}_{\mathrm{i}} \otimes \mathbf{e}_{\mathrm{j}} \otimes \mathbf{e}_{\mathrm{k}}. \tag{2.5.53}$$

The gradient of a vector, and hence a second-order tensor, can be expressed as the sum of symmetric and skew-symmetric parts by adding and subtracting

$$\nabla \mathbf{A} = \frac{1}{2}[\nabla \mathbf{A} + (\nabla \mathbf{A})^T] + \frac{1}{2}[\nabla \mathbf{A} - (\nabla \mathbf{A})^T], \tag{2.5.54}$$

Or, in rectangular Cartesian component form,

$$\nabla \mathbf{A} = \frac{1}{2}\left(\frac{\partial A_i}{\partial x_j} + \frac{\partial A_j}{\partial x_i}\right)\mathbf{e}_{\mathrm{i}} \otimes \mathbf{e}_{\mathrm{j}} + \frac{1}{2}\left(\frac{\partial A_i}{\partial x_j} - \frac{\partial A_j}{\partial x_i}\right)\mathbf{e}_{\mathrm{i}} \otimes \mathbf{e}_{\mathrm{j}}. \tag{2.5.55}$$

2.5.6.3 *The divergence of a tensor field*

The divergence of a second-order tensor $\mathbf{T}$ is defined to be the vector

$$\operatorname{div}\mathbf{T} = \operatorname{grad}\mathbf{T} : \mathbf{I} = \frac{\partial \mathbf{T}}{\partial x_i}\mathbf{e}_{\mathrm{i}} = \frac{\partial (T_{jk}\mathbf{e}_{\mathrm{j}} \otimes \mathbf{e}_{\mathrm{k}})}{\partial x_i}\mathbf{e}_{\mathrm{i}} = \frac{\partial T_{ij}}{\partial x_j}\mathbf{e}_{\mathrm{i}}. \tag{2.5.56}$$

We also have

$$\nabla \cdot \mathbf{T} = \mathbf{e}_{\mathrm{i}}\frac{\partial}{\partial x_i} \cdot T_{jk}\mathbf{e}_{\mathrm{j}} \otimes \mathbf{e}_{\mathrm{k}} = \frac{\partial T_{ji}}{\partial x_j}\mathbf{e}_{\mathrm{i}}. \tag{2.5.57}$$

Therefore,

$$\operatorname{div}\mathbf{T} = \nabla \cdot \mathbf{T}^T. \tag{2.5.58}$$

Both $(\partial T_{ij}/\partial x_j)\mathbf{e}_{\mathrm{i}}$ and $(\partial T_{ji}/\partial x_j)\mathbf{e}_{\mathrm{i}}$ are commonly used as definitions of the divergence of a tensor. They are distinguished here by labeling the former as $\operatorname{div}\mathbf{T}$ (called here the divergence of $\mathbf{T}$) and the latter as $\nabla \cdot \mathbf{T}$. Note that the operations $\operatorname{div}\mathbf{T}$ and $\nabla \cdot \mathbf{T}$ are equivalent in the case that $\mathbf{T}$ is symmetric.

The Laplacian of a scalar φ is the scalar $\nabla^2\varphi = \nabla \cdot \nabla\varphi$; in component form, $\partial^2\varphi/\partial x_i^2$. Similarly, the Laplacian of a vector $\mathbf{v}$ is $\nabla^2\mathbf{v} = \nabla \cdot \nabla\mathbf{v}$; in component form, $\partial^2 v_i/\partial x_j^2$. The Laplacian of a tensor $\mathbf{T}$ in component form is similarly $\partial^2 T_{ij}/\partial x_k^2$.

2.5.6.4 *Differential of a vector and tensor*

In continuum mechanics, the differentials of vectors, second-order tensors, and fourth-order tensors are often used. If **A** is a vector and **T** is a second-order tensor, the differentials of a vector and a tensor can be expressed as follows:

$$\mathrm{d}\mathbf{A} = \mathrm{grad}\,\mathbf{A} \cdot \mathrm{d}\mathbf{x} = \frac{\partial(A_i)}{\partial x_j}\mathrm{d}x_j\mathbf{e}_{\mathrm{i}} \tag{2.5.59}$$

and

$$\mathrm{d}\mathbf{T} = \mathrm{grad}\,\mathbf{T} \cdot d\mathbf{x} = \frac{\partial(T_{ij})}{\partial x_k}\mathrm{d}x_k\mathbf{e}_{\mathrm{i}} \otimes \mathbf{e}_{\mathrm{j}} = \frac{\partial(T_{ij})}{\partial x_k}\mathrm{d}x_k\mathbf{e}_{\mathrm{i}}\mathbf{e}_{\mathrm{j}}. \tag{2.5.60}$$

Let $\phi = \phi(\mathbf{A})$ be a vector function and $\varphi = \varphi(\mathbf{T})$ be a tensor function.

For vector function $\phi = \phi(\mathbf{A})$, we have

$$\mathrm{d}\phi = \mathrm{d}\phi(\mathbf{A}) = \frac{\partial\phi}{\partial\mathbf{A}} \cdot \mathrm{d}\mathbf{A} = \frac{\partial\phi}{\partial a_i}\mathrm{d}A_i, \quad \frac{\partial\phi}{\partial\mathbf{A}} = \frac{\partial\phi(A_i)}{\partial a_i}\hat{\mathbf{e}}_{\mathrm{i}}. \tag{2.5.61}$$

For tensor function, $\varphi = \varphi(\mathbf{T})$ we have

$$\mathrm{d}\varphi = \mathrm{d}\varphi(\mathbf{T}) = \frac{\partial\varphi}{\partial T_{mn}}\mathrm{d}T_{mn} = \frac{\partial\varphi}{\partial\mathbf{T}} : \mathrm{d}\mathbf{T} \tag{2.5.62}$$

and

$$\frac{\partial\varphi}{\partial\mathbf{T}} = \frac{\partial\varphi}{\partial T_{mn}}\hat{\mathbf{e}}_{\mathrm{m}} \otimes \hat{\mathbf{e}}_{\mathrm{n}}. \tag{2.5.63}$$

If **H** is a second-order tensor and a function of another second-order tensor, i.e., $\mathbf{H} = \mathbf{H}(\mathbf{T})$, the derivative with respect to a second-order tensor can be expressed as

$$\frac{\partial\mathbf{H}}{\partial\mathbf{T}} = \frac{\partial H_{ij}}{\partial T_{kl}}\hat{\mathbf{e}}_{\mathrm{i}} \otimes \hat{\mathbf{e}}_{\mathrm{j}} \otimes \hat{\mathbf{e}}_{\mathrm{k}} \otimes \hat{\mathbf{e}}_{\mathrm{l}} = \frac{\partial H_{ij}}{\partial T_{kl}}\hat{\mathbf{e}}_{\mathrm{i}}\hat{\mathbf{e}}_{\mathrm{j}}\hat{\mathbf{e}}_{\mathrm{k}}\hat{\mathbf{e}}_{\mathrm{l}} \tag{2.5.64}$$

and

$$\mathrm{d}\mathbf{H} = \frac{\partial\mathbf{H}}{\partial\mathbf{T}} : \mathrm{d}\mathbf{T}. \tag{2.5.65}$$

2.5.6.5 *The divergence theorem*

The divergence and curl of vectors have been previously defined. Now, with the introduction of the gradient of a vector, we can redefine the divergence of a vector independent of any coordinate system. It is the scalar field given by the trace of the gradient.

The divergence theorem discussed previously can be extended to the case of higher-order tensors. Consider an arbitrary differentiable tensor field $T_{ij\ldots k}(\mathbf{x}, t)$ defined in some finite region of physical space. Let Γ be a closed surface bounding a volume Ω in this space, and let the outward normal to Γ be $\mathbf{n}$. The divergence theorem of Gauss then states that

$$\int_\Omega \frac{\partial T_{ij\cdots k}}{\partial x_k} \mathrm{d}x = \oint_\Gamma T_{ij\cdots k} n_k \mathrm{d}s \quad \text{Divergence theorem.} \tag{2.5.66}$$

For the second-order tensor,

$$\int_\Omega \mathrm{div} \mathbf{T} \mathrm{d}x = \oint_\Gamma \mathbf{T}\mathbf{n} \mathrm{d}s, \quad \int_\Omega \frac{\partial T_{ij}}{\partial x_j} \mathrm{d}x = \oint_\Gamma T_{ij} n_j \mathrm{d}s. \tag{2.5.67}$$

These formulas will be very useful for the following chapters in continuum mechanics.

Furthermore, one has the following useful identities:

$$\int_\Omega \mathrm{div} \mathbf{T} \mathrm{d}x = \oint_\Gamma \mathbf{T} \cdot \mathbf{n} \mathrm{d}s, \tag{2.5.68}$$

$$\int_\Omega \mathrm{grad}(\mathbf{u}) \mathrm{d}x = \oint_\Gamma (\mathbf{u} \times \mathbf{n}) \, \mathrm{d}s, \tag{2.5.69}$$

$$\int_\Omega \mathrm{div}(\mathbf{T}^\mathbf{T} \mathbf{u}) \mathrm{d}x = \oint_\Gamma (\mathbf{u}\mathbf{T}) \, \mathbf{n} \mathrm{d}s. \tag{2.5.70}$$

2.6 Summary

In this chapter, we thoroughly discussed and reviewed the mathematical preliminaries necessary for this course, including the concepts of vector algebra, vector calculus, matrix theory, tensors, and tensor calculus. We introduced the index notation for representing vectors and tensors in terms of their components, presented transformations of vector and tensor components, and delved into eigenvalue problems associated with second-order tensors. Examples were provided throughout this chapter to illustrate the concepts and definitions introduced. Understanding the material covered in this chapter is essential for comprehending continuum mechanics. Although different books may use various notations, the fundamental concepts remain the same. We strongly encourage students and readers to familiarize themselves with the concepts and notation introduced here. For more comprehensive details on vectors and tensors, we recommend referring to engineering mathematics textbooks.

General References

Liu Z.S. (2014). *Frontiers of Applied Mechanics* (Imperial College Press, London, UK).

Liu Z.S. *et al.* (2022). *Mechanics of Soft Materials: Large Deformation Behavior of Hydrogels* (Xi'an Jiaotong University Press, Xi'an, China).

Oden J.T. (2011). *An Introduction to Mathematical Modeling: A Course in Mechanics* (John Wiley & Sons Inc., New Jersey, USA).

Reddy J.N. (2013). *An Introduction to Continuum Mechanics* (Cambridge University Press, New York, USA).

Reddy J.N. (2017). *Principles of Continuum Mechanics: Conservation and Balance Laws with Applications* (Cambridge University Press, New York, USA).

Problems

2.1. In engineering, which physical quantities are considered scalars, vectors, and tensors? Please list them.

2.2. Validate the following expressions and discuss them:

(a) $A_i = B_j C_i D_i$, (c) $A_i B_j C_j$,

(b) $A_m B_s = C_m(D_s - F_s)$, (d) $A_m B_s = C_m(D_i - F_i)$.

2.3. Expand the equation: $A_{ij}x_i x_j \quad (i, j = 1, 2, 3)$.

2.4. Prove the following expression by using the index notation:

(a) $(\mathbf{A} \times \mathbf{B}) \cdot (\mathbf{C} \times \mathbf{D}) = (\mathbf{A} \cdot \mathbf{C})(\mathbf{B} \cdot \mathbf{D}) - (\mathbf{A} \cdot \mathbf{D})(\mathbf{B} \cdot \mathbf{C})$,

(b) $\mathbf{A} \times (\mathbf{B} \times \mathbf{C}) = (\mathbf{A} \cdot \mathbf{C})\mathbf{B} - (\mathbf{A} \cdot \mathbf{B})\mathbf{C}$,

(c) $(\mathbf{A} \cdot \mathbf{B})^2 + (\mathbf{A} \times \mathbf{B}) \cdot (\mathbf{A} \times \mathbf{B}) = (|\mathbf{A}|)^2(|\mathbf{B}|)^2$,

(d) $\nabla \times (\nabla \times \mathbf{A}) = \nabla(\nabla \cdot \mathbf{A}) - \nabla^2\mathbf{A}$.

2.5. The tetrahedron shown in the following figure can be represented by the three non-coplanar vectors **A**, **B**, and **C**. Prove that the vector sum of the areas of the tetrahedron's sides is zero.

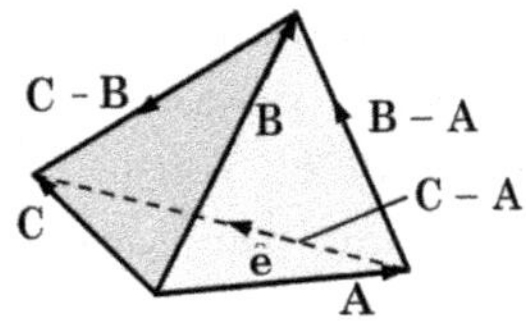

2.6. Find the eigenvalues and eigenvectors of the following matrices:

$$(a)\ \begin{bmatrix} 4 & -4 & 0 \\ -4 & 0 & 0 \\ 0 & 0 & 3 \end{bmatrix}, \quad (b)\ \begin{bmatrix} 3 & 2 & 0 \\ 2 & 0 & 0 \\ 1 & 0 & 2 \end{bmatrix}, \quad (c)\ \begin{bmatrix} -2 & 2 & 10 \\ 2 & -11 & 8 \\ 10 & 8 & -5 \end{bmatrix}.$$

Chapter 3

Kinematics of a Continuum

Table of Contents

3.1 Introduction

Continuum mechanics combines mathematics and physical laws to approximate the macroscopic behavior of matter under mechanical loading. It is an extension of Newtonian particle dynamics, building upon the same foundational assumptions. However, it also introduces additional assumptions to describe the structure of matter.

In the context of continuum mechanics, matter is idealized as a continuum, possessing two key properties. First, it is infinitely divisible, meaning that any given region of the solid can be subdivided as many times as desired. Second, it is locally homogeneous, indicating that if the subdivision is carried out extensively, all resulting sub-regions will exhibit identical properties, such as mass density. Consequently, a continuum can be envisioned as an infinite collection of interconnected, infinitesimally small particles.

Therefore, continuum mechanics involves the mathematical idealizations of both the existence of a Newtonian reference frame and the concept of a continuum. Experimental evidence suggests that the laws of motion based on these assumptions accurately approximate the behavior of most solid and fluid materials at length scales ranging from millimeters to kilometers, as commonly encountered in engineering applications. In some cases, continuum models can also provide reasonable approximations for behavior at much smaller length scales, such as nanomechanics involving volumes of material containing a few thousand atoms. However, at these smaller length scales, models often require different relationships between internal forces and deformation measures in the solid compared to those used for larger volumes.

Materials or matter are composed of discrete molecules, which in turn are made up of atoms. The study of matter at the molecular or atomistic levels, such as through MD simulation, is very useful for understanding a variety of phenomena. However, studies at these scales are not directly applicable to solving common engineering problems. Nonetheless, MD studies can provide valuable information on the mechanical properties of materials at the macroscopic level. Continuum mechanics, on the other hand, is concerned with the study of various forms of matter at the macroscopic level.

The heart of continuum mechanics is the assumption that the discrete nature of matter can be neglected as long as the length scales of interest are large compared to the length scales of discrete molecular structures. Thus, matter at sufficiently large length scales can be treated as a continuum, where all physical quantities of interest, including density, are continuously differentiable almost everywhere. Under the continuum hypothesis, the material being studied, whether it is a solid, liquid, or gas, is assumed to be continuous. In reality, any material is composed of a large number of discrete atoms or molecules. However, continuum mechanics disregards this discontinuous structure and treats matter as if it were continuous. This hypothetical continuous material is referred to as a continuum.

Engineers study continuous systems to understand their behavior under "working conditions," allowing for the proper design and cost-effective production of these systems. The concept of a continuous medium enables us to define quantities such as density, momentum, and energy at each point within the material's domain. Since these quantities are assumed to have a continuous distribution in space, we can use calculus tools, including derivatives and integrals, to formulate the governing equations. It has been observed that theories such as elasticity and fluid mechanics, which are based on the continuum model, provide accurate predictions that closely align with experimental observations. This serves as a strong justification for employing the continuum hypothesis.

However, the continuum hypothesis breaks down when the average distance that atoms or molecules travel between collisions becomes comparable to the characteristic length scale of the flow. This situation typically occurs in low-density or rarefied flows. We will not consider such special situations in this study of continuum mechanics, as they are not the focus.

While the continuum hypothesis overlooks the molecular structure of matter, it does take into account the different behaviors exhibited by materials such as rubber and steel under the same loading conditions. This is accomplished through the use of constitutive equations, which will be discussed in the following chapter. Consequently, in this chapter, we will not specifically distinguish between steel and rubber.

This chapter is dedicated to the study of geometric changes in an equilibrium state of a continuous medium. The examination of geometric changes in a continuum, disregarding the forces causing those changes, is known as kinematics. Kinematics focuses on the analysis of the characteristics of a continuum without considering its dynamics. It involves obtaining results solely from geometrical considerations, without reference to the forces acting on the continuum. These results will later be utilized in formulating the balance laws discussed in subsequent chapters.

3.2 Descriptions of Motion and Deformation

In this preliminary section, we introduce some fundamental concepts that form the basis of the continuum theory of materials. These notions are vital for the continuum modeling of bodies, although they are sometimes used implicitly without extensive discussion.

3.2.1 *Configurations of a Continuous Medium or Body*

In this textbook, our goal is to establish a framework for studying the response of natural objects or bodies to external forces or stimuli, such as thermal, chemical, electrical, optical, and magnetic. To achieve this, we need to construct mathematical models for both the bodies themselves and the external stimuli. Additionally, we define some fundamental assumptions and terminology used in continuum mechanics.

Here, we define the term "body" as a mathematical abstraction representing an object found in nature. We consider a body, denoted as B, with a known geometry in a three-dimensional Euclidean space. B is viewed as a collection of particles, where each particle represents a large group of molecules exhibiting a continuous distribution of matter in space and time.

In a given configuration of the body, each particle is located at a specific point in three-dimensional space. The region occupied by the body or continuum at a particular time t is referred to as a configuration and denoted by B. The geometric changes experienced by the body are accompanied by strains or stresses that are induced within it. If the applied loads are time-dependent, the deformation of the body will vary with time. This means that the geometry of the body B will undergo changes over time.

Suppose that the continuum initially (or at time $t = 0$) occupies a configuration B_0, in which a particle X is located at position $\mathbf{X}$, concerning a right-handed, rectangular Cartesian reference frame (X_1, X_2, X_3). The reference frame has a fixed origin O and orthonormal basis vectors $(\mathbf{E}_1, \mathbf{E}_2, \mathbf{E}_3)$ $(\mathbf{e}_1, \mathbf{e}_2, \mathbf{e}_3)$, as shown in Figure 3.2.1. Here, X is the name of the particle occupying the location $\mathbf{X}$ in configuration B_0; thus, (X_1, X_2, X_3) are referred to as the material coordinates. Following the application of external stimuli (such as loads or heating), the body undergoes geometric changes and assumes a new configuration B, known as the current or deformed configuration. Particle X now occupies position $\mathbf{x}$ in the deformed configuration B, as illustrated in Figure 3.2.1.

The mapping $\chi(\mathbf{X}, t)$ is called the deformation mapping of the body from B_0 to B. The deformation mapping $\mathbf{x} = \chi(\mathbf{X}, t)$ takes

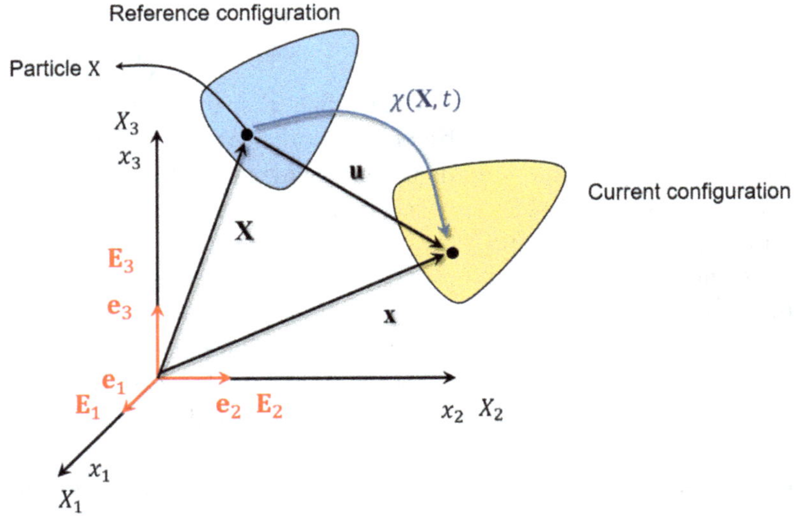

Figure 3.2.1 A body B in the reference and current configurations.

the position vector $\mathbf{X}$ from the reference configuration and places the same point in the deformed configuration as $\mathbf{x} = \chi(\mathbf{X}, t)$. The inverse takes the position vector $\mathbf{x}$ from the deformed configuration B back to the reference configuration B_0, $\mathbf{X} = \chi^{-1}(\mathbf{x}, t)$. Therefore, the mapping relations of two configurations have

$$\mathbf{x} = \chi(\mathbf{X}, t), \tag{3.2.1}$$

$$\mathbf{X} = \chi^{-1}(\mathbf{x}, t). \tag{3.2.2}$$

Thus, $\mathbf{x}$ and $\mathbf{X}$ are the positions of particle in the two configurations under consideration. $\chi(\mathbf{X}, t)$ is also called a deformation of the body from the reference configuration.

Here, a frame of reference is a coordinate system in which a configuration is described or measured. We use the same coordinate system to describe the reference and current configurations. The components X_i and x_i of vectors $\mathbf{X} = X_i\mathbf{E}_{\mathrm{i}}$ and $\mathbf{x} = x_i\mathbf{e}_{\mathrm{i}}$ are along the coordinates used, with the origins of the basis vectors $(\mathbf{E}_1, \mathbf{E}_2, \mathbf{E}_3)$ and $(\mathbf{e}_1, \mathbf{e}_2, \mathbf{e}_3)$ being the same.

3.2.2 *Description of Physical Quantities by Referential and Spatial Forms*

To mathematically describe the deformation of the body, we typically use the following two approaches: (1) the material description, also known as the Lagrangian description, and (2) the spatial description, known as the Eulerian description.

3.2.2.1 *Material description*

First, consider a characteristic, such as the temperature of a particle X. The temperature of particle X in the reference configuration is given by

$$\theta = \theta_0(\mathbf{X}, t), \tag{3.2.3}$$

where the function $\theta = \theta_0(\mathbf{X}, t)$ is defined for all X in B_0. Such a description, though completely rigorous and well-defined, is not especially useful for carrying out calculations since a particle is an abstract entity. It is more useful to describe the temperature as a function of particle position by mapping for $\mathbf{x}$ using Equation (3.2.1):

$$\theta = \theta(\mathbf{x}, t) \stackrel{\text{def}}{=} \theta_0(\chi^{-1}(\mathbf{x}, t)). \tag{3.2.4}$$

The function $\theta(\mathbf{x}, t)$ is defined for all $\mathbf{x}$ in the current configuration. The functions $\theta(\mathbf{x}, t)$ and $\theta_0(\chi^{-1}(\mathbf{x}, t))$ both describe temperature: $\theta_0(\chi^{-1}(\mathbf{x}, t))$ is the temperature of the particle X, while $\theta(\mathbf{x}, t)$ is the temperature of the particle located at $\mathbf{x}$. When $\mathbf{X}$ and $\mathbf{x}$ are related by $\mathbf{x} = \chi(\mathbf{X}, t)$, the two functions $\theta(\mathbf{x}, t)$ and $\theta_0(\chi^{-1}(\mathbf{x}, t))$ have the same value since they both refer to the temperature of the same particle in the same configuration, and they are related by Equation (3.2.4). One usually refers to the representation Equation (3.2.3), which deals directly with the abstract particles, as the material description or the Lagrangian description.

Therefore, in the material description, the motion of the body is referred to as a reference configuration, which is typically selected as the initial configuration. In the Lagrangian description, the current coordinates $\mathbf{x}$ are expressed in terms of the reference coordinates $\mathbf{X}$.

For the deformation of a particle, the relationship between the current and reference coordinates can be expressed using appropriate mathematical equations or transformation functions:

$$\mathbf{x} = \chi(\mathbf{X}, t), \quad \mathbf{X} = \chi(\mathbf{X}, t = 0). \tag{3.2.5}$$

3.2.2.2 *Spatial description*

As discussed in the previous section, the representation given in Equation (3.2.4), which deals with the positions of the particles in the deformed configuration (the configuration in which the physical quantity is being characterized), is called the Eulerian or spatial description. Thus, in the spatial description, the motion is described with respect to the current position $\mathbf{x}$ in space, currently occupied by the material particle $\mathbf{X}$:

$$\theta = \theta(\mathbf{x}, t), \quad \mathbf{X} = \chi^{-1}(\mathbf{x}, t). \tag{3.2.6}$$

A physical field described by a function defined on the body and expressed as a function of $\mathbf{x}$ can easily be expressed through a function defined on the reference and expressed as a function of $\mathbf{X}$ and vice versa.

3.2.3 *Eulerian and Lagrangian Spatial Derivatives*

To be specific, we again consider the temperature field θ in the body in a configuration. We can express this either in the Lagrangian or Eulerian form. For example, $\theta = \theta(\mathbf{X}, t)$, when θ is known in the material description. For $\theta = \theta(\mathbf{X}, t)$, its total time derivative, $\mathrm{D}/\mathrm{D}t$, is simply the partial derivative with respect to time because the material coordinates $\mathbf{X}$ do not change with time:

$$\frac{\mathrm{D}}{\mathrm{D}t}\theta = \frac{\mathrm{D}}{\mathrm{D}t}[\theta(\mathbf{X}, t)] = \frac{\partial}{\partial t}[\theta(\mathbf{X}, t)]\bigg|_{\mathbf{X}\text{ is fixed}} = \frac{\partial \theta}{\partial t}. \tag{3.2.7}$$

However, when θ is known in the spatial description, $\theta = \theta(\mathbf{x}, t)$, its time derivative for a given particle, known as the material derivative, is

$$\frac{\mathrm{D}}{\mathrm{D}t}[\theta(\mathbf{x},t)] = \frac{\partial}{\partial t}[\theta(\mathbf{x},t)] + \frac{\partial}{\partial x_i}[\theta(\mathbf{x},t)]\frac{\mathrm{D}x_i}{\mathrm{D}t}$$
$$= \frac{\partial \theta}{\partial t} + v_i\frac{\partial \theta}{\partial x_i} = \frac{\partial \theta}{\partial t} + \mathbf{v}\cdot\nabla\theta, \tag{3.2.8}$$

where $\mathbf{v}$ is the velocity, $\mathbf{v} = \mathrm{D}\mathbf{x}/\mathrm{D}t = \dot{\mathbf{x}}$. Thus, if the velocity of a particle in the spatial description is $\mathbf{v}(\mathbf{x},t)$, then the acceleration of a particle is

$$\mathbf{a} = \frac{\mathrm{D}\mathbf{v}}{\mathrm{D}t} = \frac{\partial \mathbf{v}}{\partial t} + \mathbf{v}\cdot\nabla\mathbf{v}, \quad \left(a_i = \frac{\partial v_i}{\partial t} + v_j\frac{\partial v_i}{\partial x_j}\right), \tag{3.2.9}$$

where $\nabla\mathbf{v}$ is a second-order tensor.

Suppose that we wish to compute the gradient of the temperature field. If we write this as $\nabla\theta$, we would not know if we were referring to the Lagrangian spatial gradient or to the Eulerian spatial gradient. In order to avoid this confusion, we use the notation "Grad" and "grad" instead of $\nabla\theta$ to represent gradient:

$$\mathrm{Grad}\theta = \nabla\theta(\mathbf{X},t), \quad \mathrm{grad}\theta = \nabla\theta(\mathbf{x},t). \tag{3.2.10}$$

Note that in the study of solid mechanics, the Eulerian description is less useful because the configuration χ is unknown. On the other hand, it is the preferred description for the study of fluid motion because the configuration is known and remains unchanged, and we aim to determine changes in fluid velocities, pressure, density, and so on. Thus, in the Eulerian description, attention is focused on a given region of space rather than a specific body of matter.

3.2.4 *Displacement Field*

Under external stimuli, the body can be deformed and have motion. A motion of a body is a one-parameter family of configurations $\chi(\mathbf{X},t)$, where the parameter t is time

$$\mathbf{x} = \mathbf{x}(\mathbf{X},t) = \chi(\mathbf{X},t). \tag{3.2.11}$$

This motion takes place over the time interval $[0,t]$. During the motion, the body occupies a time-dependent region, and the vector

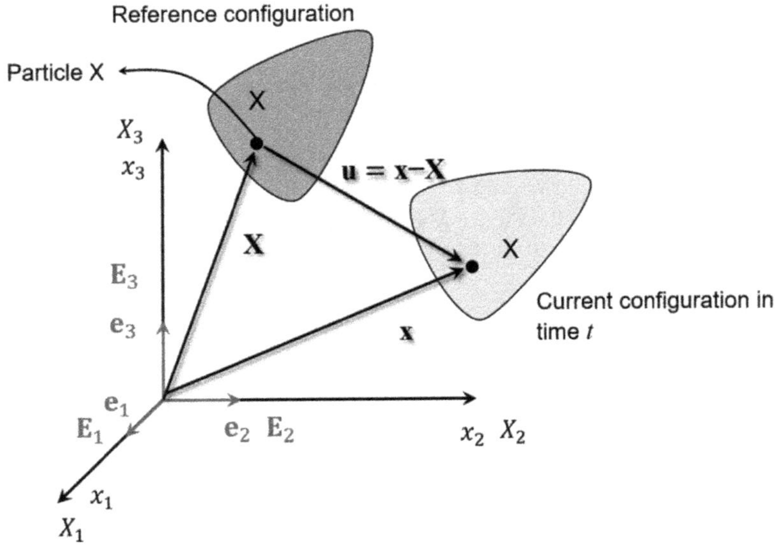

Figure 3.2.2 Position vectors in the initial and current configurations and the displacement of a particle X.

$\mathbf{x}$ is the position occupied by the particle $\mathbf{X}$ at time t, as shown in Figure 3.2.2. For each particle $\mathbf{X}$, Equation (3.2.11) describes the equation of a curve in three-dimensional space, which is the path of this particle.

The phrase "deformation of a body" refers to relative displacements and changes in the geometry experienced by the continuum B under the influence of external stimuli. As shown in Figure 3.2.2, the displacement vector field $\mathbf{u}$ of the particle $\mathbf{X}$ is defined by

$$\mathbf{u} = \mathbf{x} - \mathbf{X}. \tag{3.2.12}$$

In the Lagrangian description, the displacement vector $\mathbf{u}$ is expressed in terms of the material coordinates $\mathbf{X}$:

$$\mathbf{u}(\mathbf{X}, t) = \mathbf{x}(\mathbf{X}, t) - \mathbf{X} = \chi(\mathbf{X}, t) - \mathbf{X}. \tag{3.2.13}$$

On the other hand, in the Eulerian description, the displacements are expressed in terms of the spatial coordinates (or current position) $\mathbf{x}$:

$$\mathbf{u}(\mathbf{x}, t) = \mathbf{x} - \mathbf{X}(\mathbf{x}, t) = \mathbf{x} - \chi^{-1}(\mathbf{x}, t). \tag{3.2.14}$$

Example 3.2.1

Consider a deformation mapping in which we know the deformed position:

$$\mathbf{x} = \mathbf{x}(\mathbf{X}, t) = (X_1 + AtX_2)\mathbf{e}_1 + (X_2 - AtX_1)\mathbf{e}_2 + X_3\mathbf{e}_3$$

Determine the displacement field.

Solution:

$$x_1 = X_1 + AtX_2, \quad x_2 = X_2 - AtX_1, \quad x_3 = X_3$$

Displacement: $u_1 = (X_1 + AtX_2) - X_1 = AtX_2, u_2 = (X_2 - AtX_1) - X_2 = -AtX_1, u_3 = X_3 - X_3 = 0$

Therefore, $\mathbf{u} = \mathbf{u}(\mathbf{X}, t) = (AtX_2)\mathbf{e}_1 + (-AtX_1)\mathbf{e}_2 + (0)\mathbf{e}_3 = AtX_2\mathbf{e}_1 - AtX_1\mathbf{e}_2$.

Thus, there is no displacement in the $\mathbf{e}_3$ direction.

Example 3.2.2

We consider the one-dimensional rod problem with an initial length of 2 units. Assume the rod deforms under force with a mapping of $x_1 = X_1(1 + 0.5t)$, and the inverse mapping is $X_1 = x_1/(1 + 0.5t)$. The rod experiences a temperature distribution $\theta = \theta(\mathbf{X}, t)$ given by the material description $\theta = 2t^2X_1$ or by the spatial description $\theta = 2t^2x_1/(1+0.5t)$, as shown in Figure 3.2.3. Find the displacement of the rod end ($X_1 = 2$) and the deformed length at $t = 1, 2,$ and 3.

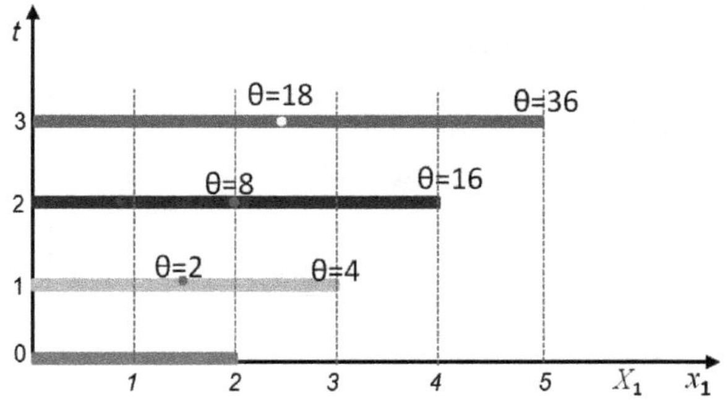

Figure 3.2.3 Material and spatial descriptions of the length and temperature at the middle and end of a rod.

Solution:

Displacement: $u_1 = x_1 - X_1 = X_1(1 + 0.5t) - X_1 = 0.5X_1t$.

The deformed length of the rod: $x_1 = X_1(1 + 0.5t)$.

From Figure 3.2.3, it can be found that at different times, the temperatures are different and the rod deforms at different lengths. For example, when $t = 1$, the rod length of 2 units becomes 3 units. The temperature at the rod end ($X_1 = 2$) is $\theta = 4$. When time is 2 and 3, the rod length becomes 4 and 5 units, and the corresponding temperature at the rod end is 16 and 36, respectively.

In the deformation of a body, a rigid-body motion may occur. A rigid body is one in which the distance between any two material particles remains the same, while a deformable body is one in which the material particles can move relative to each other under the action of external stimuli. Therefore, a rigid-body motion is one in which all material particles of the body undergo the same displacement. In this textbook, we only consider deformed bodies under external stimuli.

3.3 Analysis of Deformation

3.3.1 *Displacement Gradient and Deformation Gradient*

Let $\mathbf{X}$ denote the position of a generic particle of the body in the reference configuration. Questions that we may want to ask, such as "What is the state of stress at this particle?" and "Will the material fracture at this particle?" depend not only on the deformation at $\mathbf{X}$ but also on the deformation of all particles in a small neighborhood of $\mathbf{X}$. Therefore, the deformation in the entire neighborhood of a generic particle plays a crucial role in this subject, and we will focus on this point in the section on deformation.

Thus, we imagine a small ball of material centered at $\mathbf{X}$ and ask what happens to this ball as a result of the deformation. Intuitively, we expect the deformation of the ball (i.e., the local deformation near $\mathbf{X}$) to consist of a combination of a rigid translation, a rigid rotation, and a "straining." To simplify the problem, we now consider a special case: an infinitesimal line element.

Here, the concepts of displacement gradient and deformation gradient are introduced to quantify the change in shape of infinitesimal

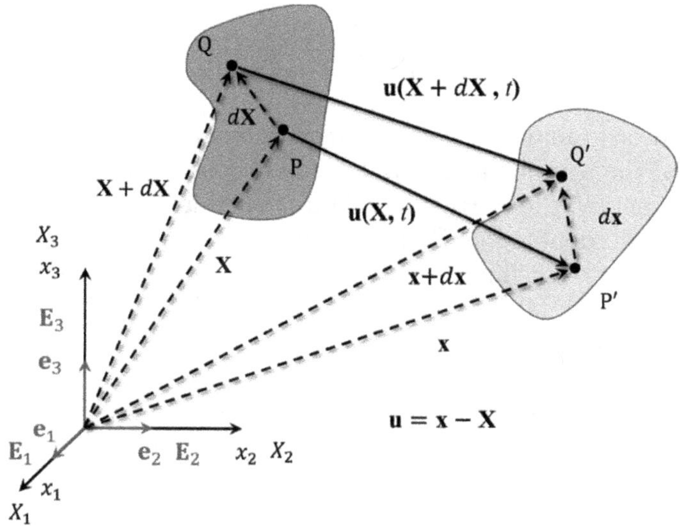

Figure 3.3.1 A body deformation from the reference configuration to the current configuration. An infinitesimal line element $d\mathbf{X}$ in the reference configuration becomes $d\mathbf{x}$ in the deformed configuration.

line elements in a solid body. To illustrate this, let us imagine drawing a straight line on the undeformed configuration or reference configuration of a solid, as shown in Figure 3.3.1. The line would be mapped to a smooth curve in the deformed configuration. However, if we focus our attention on a line segment that is much shorter than the radius of curvature of this curve, as depicted in Figure 3.3.1, the segment would appear straight in the undeformed configuration and also (almost) straight in the deformed configuration. This means that, regardless of how complex the deformation is, infinitesimal line segments are merely subjected to stretching and rotation by the deformation. Figure 3.3.1 demonstrates the relationship between the infinitesimal line segments $d\mathbf{x}$ and $d\mathbf{X}$, as described in the following:

For point P', $\mathbf{x} = \mathbf{X} + \mathbf{u}(\mathbf{X}, t)$ and for point Q', $\mathbf{x} + d\mathbf{x} = \mathbf{X} + d\mathbf{X} + \mathbf{u}(\mathbf{X} + d\mathbf{X}, t)$; thus,

$$\begin{aligned} d\mathbf{x} &= \mathbf{X} + d\mathbf{X} + \mathbf{u}(\mathbf{X} + d\mathbf{X}, t) - \mathbf{x} \\ &= \mathbf{X} + d\mathbf{X} + \mathbf{u}(\mathbf{X} + d\mathbf{X}, t) - (\mathbf{X} + \mathbf{u}(\mathbf{X}, t)) \\ &= d\mathbf{X} + (\mathbf{u}(\mathbf{X} + d\mathbf{X}, t) - \mathbf{u}(\mathbf{X}, t)), \end{aligned} \tag{3.3.1}$$

$$\mathrm{d}\mathbf{x} = \mathrm{d}\mathbf{X} + \operatorname{grad}\mathbf{u} \cdot \mathrm{d}\mathbf{X}, \tag{3.3.2}$$

$$\mathrm{d}\mathbf{x} = \mathrm{d}\mathbf{X} + (\nabla\mathbf{u})\mathrm{d}\mathbf{X} = (\mathbf{I} + \nabla\mathbf{u})\mathrm{d}\mathbf{X}, \tag{3.3.3}$$

where $\nabla\mathbf{u}$ or $\operatorname{grad}\mathbf{u}$ is called the displacement gradient.

One of the key quantities in deformation analysis is the deformation gradient of the current configuration relative to the reference configuration, denoted as $\mathbf{F}$. This quantity describes the relationship between a material line before deformation and the line consisting of the same material after deformation. The deformation gradient is defined as follows:

$$\mathrm{d}\mathbf{x} = (\mathbf{I} + \nabla\mathbf{u})(\mathrm{d}\mathbf{X}) = \mathbf{F}\mathrm{d}\mathbf{X}, \tag{3.3.4}$$

$$\mathrm{d}\mathbf{x} = \mathbf{F} \cdot \mathrm{d}\mathbf{X} \quad \text{or} \quad \mathrm{d}x_i = F_{ij}\mathrm{d}X_j. \tag{3.3.5}$$

Note that this approximation does not assume that the deformation or deformation gradient is small; it only assumes that the two particles, P and Q, are close to each other. The expression for the deformation gradient is as follows:

$$\mathbf{F} = \left(\frac{\partial\mathbf{x}}{\partial\mathbf{X}}\right)^T = \nabla_0(\mathbf{x})^T. \tag{3.3.6}$$

Thus, we call $\mathbf{F}$ as the deformation gradient. This $\mathbf{F}$ carries an infinitesimal undeformed material $\mathrm{d}\mathbf{X}$ into its location $\mathrm{d}\mathbf{x}$ in the deformed configuration.

This means that Equation (3.3.5) must be a one-to-one relation between $\mathrm{d}\mathbf{X}$ and $\mathrm{d}\mathbf{x}$, and thus that $\mathbf{F}$ must be nonsingular. The determinant of $|\mathbf{F}|$ is called the Jacobian of the motion, and it is denoted by $J = |\mathbf{F}|$. Thus, in particular, the Jacobian determinant of J must not vanish:

$$J = \det(\mathbf{F}) \neq 0. \tag{3.3.7}$$

By definition, $\mathbf{F}$ is a function of both position $\mathbf{X}$ and time t. It is sometimes referred to as a two-point tensor, as it represents a linear transformation of points from the small neighborhood of $\mathbf{B}_0$ to the neighborhood of $\mathbf{B}$. This tensor describes the local deformation of a material line element at point $\mathbf{X}$ in the reference configuration, which is transformed to the point in the current configuration. $\mathbf{F}$ generally involves both stretching and rotation.

In the index notation, Equation (3.3.6) can be written as

$$\mathbf{F} = F_{ij}\mathbf{e}_{\mathrm{i}}\mathbf{E}_{\mathrm{j}}, \quad F_{ij} = \frac{\partial x_i}{\partial X_j}, \tag{3.3.8}$$

or, in matrix form,

$$[\mathbf{F}] = \begin{bmatrix} \dfrac{\partial x_1}{\partial X_1} & \dfrac{\partial x_1}{\partial X_2} & \dfrac{\partial x_1}{\partial X_3} \\ \dfrac{\partial x_2}{\partial X_1} & \dfrac{\partial x_2}{\partial X_2} & \dfrac{\partial x_2}{\partial X_3} \\ \dfrac{\partial x_3}{\partial X_1} & \dfrac{\partial x_3}{\partial X_2} & \dfrac{\partial x_3}{\partial X_3} \end{bmatrix}. \tag{3.3.9}$$

As $\mathbf{F}$ is a nonsingular tensor, $J = \det(\mathbf{F}) \neq 0$. Hence, $\mathbf{F}$ has an inverse $\mathbf{F}^{-1}$, and we can write

$$\mathrm{D}\mathbf{X} = \mathbf{F}^{-1} \cdot \mathrm{d}\mathbf{x}, \quad (\mathbf{F}^{-1})^T = \frac{\partial \mathbf{X}}{\partial \mathbf{x}}. \tag{3.3.10}$$

and in index notation,

$$\mathbf{F}^{-1} = F_{ji}^{-1}\mathbf{E}_{\mathrm{j}}\mathbf{e}_{\mathrm{i}}, \quad F_{ji}^{-1} = \frac{\partial X_j}{\partial x_i}, \tag{3.3.11}$$

or, in matrix form,

$$[\mathbf{F}]^{-1} = \begin{bmatrix} \dfrac{\partial X_1}{\partial x_1} & \dfrac{\partial X_1}{\partial x_2} & \dfrac{\partial X_1}{\partial x_3} \\ \dfrac{\partial X_2}{\partial x_1} & \dfrac{\partial X_2}{\partial x_2} & \dfrac{\partial X_2}{\partial x_3} \\ \dfrac{\partial X_3}{\partial x_1} & \dfrac{\partial X_3}{\partial x_2} & \dfrac{\partial X_3}{\partial x_3} \end{bmatrix}. \tag{3.3.12}$$

Example 3.3.1

A continuum body undergoes the deformation described by

$$\mathbf{x} = \mathbf{x}(\mathbf{X}, t) = X_1\mathbf{e}_1 + (X_2 + AX_3)\mathbf{e}_2 + (X_3 + AX_2)\mathbf{e}_3.$$

Determine the deformation gradient.

Solution:

From the deformation mapping, we have $x_1 = X_1$, $x_2 = X_2 + AX_3$, $x_3 = X_3 + AX_2$ and $\mathbf{F} = F_{ij}\mathbf{e}_i\mathbf{E}_j$, $F_{ij} = \frac{\partial x_i}{\partial X_j}$. We can calculate $F_{11} = \frac{\partial x_1}{\partial X_1} = 1$, $F_{12} = \frac{\partial x_1}{\partial X_2} = 0$, $F_{13} = \frac{\partial x_1}{\partial X_3} = 0$, $F_{21} = \frac{\partial x_2}{\partial X_1} = 0$, $F_{22} = \frac{\partial x_2}{\partial X_2} = 1$, $F_{23} = \frac{\partial x_2}{\partial X_3} = A$, and $F_{31} = \frac{\partial x_3}{\partial X_1} = 0$, $F_{32} = \frac{\partial x_3}{\partial X_2} = A$, $F_{33} = \frac{\partial x_3}{\partial X_3} = 1$.

Therefore, $[\mathbf{F}] = \begin{bmatrix} 1 & 0 & 0 \\ 0 & 1 & A \\ 0 & A & 1 \end{bmatrix}$.

Example 3.3.2

For a continuum body undergoing deformation, we consider the following equations of motion in the Lagrangian description described by

$$\mathbf{x} = \mathbf{x}(\mathbf{X}, t) = (X_2t^2 + X_1)\mathbf{e}_1 + (X_3t + X_2)\mathbf{e}_2 + X_3\mathbf{e}_3.$$

Is the motion above possible? If so, find the displacement and its velocity and acceleration fields in the Lagrangian and Eulerian descriptions. Let us consider a particle P that at time $t = 0$ was at the point defined by ($X_1 = 2$, $X_2 = 1$, $X_3 = 3$). Find the velocity of P at time $t = 1$ and $t = 2$.

Solution:

From the deformation mapping, we have $x_1 = X_2t^2 + X_1$, $x_2 = X_3t + X_2$, $x_3 = X_3$,

Or, in matrix form, $\begin{pmatrix} x_1 \\ x_2 \\ x_3 \end{pmatrix} = \begin{bmatrix} 1 & t^2 & 0 \\ 0 & 1 & t \\ 0 & 0 & 1 \end{bmatrix} \begin{pmatrix} X_1 \\ X_2 \\ X_3 \end{pmatrix} = [\mathbf{F}] \begin{pmatrix} X_1 \\ X_2 \\ X_3 \end{pmatrix}$.

Motion is possible if $J = \det(\mathbf{F}) \neq 0$; thus, $J = \det \begin{bmatrix} 1 & t^2 & 0 \\ 0 & 1 & t \\ 0 & 0 & 1 \end{bmatrix} = \begin{vmatrix} 1 & t^2 & 0 \\ 0 & 1 & t \\ 0 & 0 & 1 \end{vmatrix} = 1 \neq 0$.

The displacement vector field is given by the definition in $\mathbf{u} = \mathbf{x} - \mathbf{X}$. Using the equations of motion above, we obtain $\begin{cases} u_1 = x_1 - X_1 = X_2t^2 \\ u_2 = x_2 - X_2 = X_3t \\ u_3 = x_3 - X_3 = 0 \end{cases}$, which are the components of the displacement vector in the Lagrangian description. Here, velocity and acceleration can be evaluated as follows:

$$\text{velocity:}\begin{cases} v_1 = \dfrac{du_1}{dt} = 2X_2t \\ v_2 = \dfrac{du_2}{dt} = X_3 \\ v_3 = \dfrac{du_1}{dt} = 0 \end{cases} \quad \text{and} \quad \text{acceleration:}\begin{cases} a_1 = \dfrac{dv_1}{dt} = 2X_2 \\ a_2 = \dfrac{dv_2}{dt} = 0 \\ a_3 = \dfrac{dv_1}{dt} = 0 \end{cases}.$$

The inverse form of the mapping equation can provide us the equations of motion in the Eulerian description; therefore,

$$\begin{pmatrix} X_1 \\ X_2 \\ X_3 \end{pmatrix} = \begin{bmatrix} 1 & -t^2 & t^3 \\ 0 & 1 & -t \\ 0 & 0 & 1 \end{bmatrix} \begin{pmatrix} x_1 \\ x_2 \\ x_3 \end{pmatrix}$$

$$= [\mathbf{F}]^{-1} \begin{pmatrix} x_1 \\ x_2 \\ x_3 \end{pmatrix} \quad \text{or} \quad \begin{cases} X_1 = x_1 - t^2x_2 + t^3x_3 \\ X_2 = x_2 - tx_3 \\ X_3 = x_3 \end{cases}.$$

Then, the displacement, velocity, and acceleration fields in the Eulerian description can be evaluated by substituting the above equation into the equations just obtained for displacement, velocity, and acceleration.

Thus,

$$\begin{cases} u_1 = X_2t^2 = (x_2 - tx_3)t^2 = u_1(\boldsymbol{x}, t) \\ u_2 = X_3t = x_3t = u_2(\boldsymbol{x}, t) \\ u_3 = 0 = u_3(\boldsymbol{x}, t) \end{cases},$$

$$\begin{cases} v_1 = \dfrac{du_1}{dt} = 2X_2t = 2(x_2 - tx_3)t = v_1(x, t) \\ v_2 = \dfrac{du_2}{dt} = X_3 = x_3 = v_2(x, t) \\ v_3 = \dfrac{du_1}{dt} = v_3(x, t) = 0 \end{cases}, \quad \text{and}$$

$$\begin{cases} a_1 = \dfrac{dv_1}{dt} = 2X_2 = 2(x_2 - tx_3) = a_1(\boldsymbol{x}, t) \\ a_2 = \dfrac{dv_2}{dt} = a_2(\boldsymbol{x}, t) = 0 \\ a_3 = \dfrac{dv_1}{dt} = a_3(\boldsymbol{x}, t) = 0. \end{cases}$$

For $t = 1$ and $X_1 = 2$, $X_2 = 1$, $X_3 = 3$.

Taking the Lagrangian description of velocity into account, the velocity components of particle P for $t = 1$ and $X_1 = 2$, $X_2 = 1$, $X_3 = 3$ will be $v_1 = 2X_2t = 2$, $v_2 = X_3 = 3$, $v_3 = 0$.

We can also obtain the velocity components of the particle P at time $t = 2$ as $v_1 = 2X_2t = 4$, $v_2 = X_3 = 3$, $v_3 = 0$.

3.3.2 *Some Special Deformations*

Now, we can consider the deformation of a body from the reference configuration to the current configuration as a deformation mapping using the deformation gradient. To understand the concept of deformation gradient $\mathbf{F}$, we examine some special deformation cases. Let us consider a body that occupies a unit cube in the reference configuration. We use a fixed orthonormal basis with basis vectors $(\mathbf{e}_1, \mathbf{e}_2, \mathbf{e}_3)$ aligned with the edges of the cube, as shown in Figure 3.3.2. For illustration, we examine a case of pure homogeneous stretching of the cube, assuming that the unit cube in the reference configuration is transformed into an orthorhombic region with dimensions $(\lambda_1 \times \lambda_2 \times \lambda_3)$.

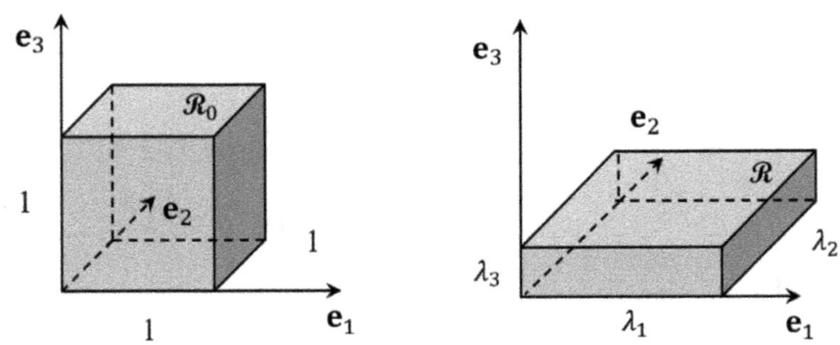

Figure 3.3.2 Pure homogeneous stretching of a cube.

For this deformation, the mapping can be expressed as

$$\mathrm{d}\mathbf{x} = \mathbf{F}\cdot\mathrm{d}\mathbf{X} \quad \text{or} \quad \mathbf{F} = \lambda_1\mathbf{e}_1\otimes\mathbf{e}_1+\lambda_2\mathbf{e}_2\otimes\mathbf{e}_2+\lambda_3\mathbf{e}_3\otimes\mathbf{e}_3, \tag{3.3.13}$$

where the three variables $(\lambda_1, \lambda_2, \lambda_3)$ are positive constants. We define them as stretches.

For example, a bar with an initial length of L is stretched to l under axial loading, and the stretch of the bar is defined as

$$\lambda = \frac{l}{L}. \tag{3.3.14}$$

For the pure homogeneous stretching of the cube, the mapping function or deformation gradient can be expressed as

$$[\mathbf{F}] = \begin{bmatrix} \lambda_1 & 0 & 0 \\ 0 & \lambda_2 & 0 \\ 0 & 0 & \lambda_3 \end{bmatrix}. \tag{3.3.15}$$

The $(1\times1\times1)$ undeformed cube R_0 is transformed by this deformation into an orthorhombic region R, as shown in Figure 3.3.2. The volume of the deformed region is $\lambda_1\lambda_2\lambda_3$. The positive constants λ_1, λ_2, and λ_3 represent the ratios by which the three edges of the cube are stretched in their respective directions $(\mathbf{e}_1, \mathbf{e}_2, \mathbf{e}_3)$. Any material fiber parallel to an edge of the cube in the reference configuration undergoes only a stretch without rotation under this deformation. However, this is not generally true for other material fibers, such as those oriented along a diagonal of a face of the cube, which experience both length change and rotation. We now explore some special deformation cases in the following sections.

3.3.2.1 *Isochoric deformation*

If the deformation is isochoric, i.e., if the volume does not change, then $(\lambda_1 \times \lambda_2 \times \lambda_3)$ must be such that

$$\lambda_1\lambda_2\lambda_3 = 1. \tag{3.3.16}$$

In the general case, if the Jacobian is equal to unity, $J = \det\mathbf{F} = |\mathbf{F}| = 1$, it indicates that the deformation is volume-preserving, meaning that the current and reference configurations coincide. When the volume does not change locally during the deformation, it is referred to as an isochoric deformation at $\mathbf{X}$. If the condition $J = 1$ holds true everywhere in the body $\mathbf{B}$, then the deformation of the body is considered isochoric.

3.3.2.2 *Homogeneous deformation*

In general, the deformation gradient $\mathbf{F}$ is a function of $\mathbf{X}$. If $\mathbf{F} = \mathbf{I}$ holds true everywhere in the body, it indicates that the body is not rotated but may undergo rigid translation. If the deformation gradient has the same value at every material point in a body (i.e., $\mathbf{F}$ is independent of $\mathbf{X}$), then the mapping $\mathbf{x} = \mathbf{x}(\mathbf{X}, t)$ is referred to as a homogeneous motion of the body, and the deformation is considered homogeneous. More generally, at any given time $t > 0$, a mapping $\mathbf{x} = \mathbf{x}(\mathbf{X}, t)$ is classified as a homogeneous motion if and only if it can be expressed as (where $\mathbf{F}$ is a constant tensor)

$$\mathbf{x} = \mathbf{F} \cdot \mathbf{X} + \mathbf{c}, \tag{3.3.17}$$

where the second-order tensor $\mathbf{F}$ and vector $\mathbf{c}$ are functions of time t only. $\mathbf{c}$ represents a rigid-body translation.

Next, we consider several simple forms of homogeneous deformation:

Pure dilatation: Consider a cube of material with edges of length L and $l = L'$ in the reference and current configurations with $\lambda_1 = \lambda_2 = \lambda_3 = \lambda = l/L$, respectively (as shown in Figure 3.3.3. The deformation mapping has the form

$$\mathrm{D}\mathbf{x} = \mathbf{F} \cdot (\mathrm{d}\mathbf{X}) \quad \text{or} \quad \mathbf{F} = \lambda \mathbf{e_1} \otimes \mathbf{e_1} + \lambda \mathbf{e_2} \otimes \mathbf{e_2} + \lambda \mathbf{e_3} \otimes \mathbf{e_3} = \lambda \mathbf{I}, \tag{3.3.18}$$

then $\mathbf{F}$ has the matrix representation

$$[\mathbf{F}] = \begin{bmatrix} \lambda & 0 & 0 \\ 0 & \lambda & 0 \\ 0 & 0 & \lambda \end{bmatrix}. \tag{3.3.19}$$

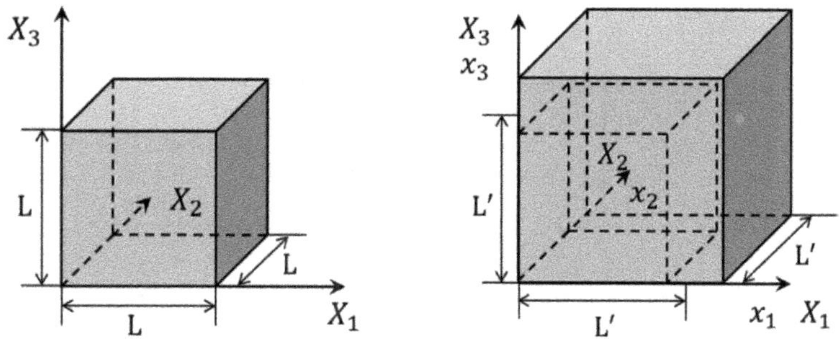

Figure 3.3.3 A homogeneous stretching of a cube under pure dilatation.

If $\lambda_2 = \lambda_3 = 1$, then the body undergoes a uniaxial stretch in the $\mathbf{e}_1$ direction (and no stretch in the $\mathbf{e}_2$ and $\mathbf{e}_3$ directions). In this case,

$$\mathbf{F} = \lambda \mathbf{e}_1 \otimes \mathbf{e}_1 + \mathbf{e}_2 \otimes \mathbf{e}_2 + \mathbf{e}_3 \otimes \mathbf{e}_3 = \mathbf{I} + (\lambda - 1)\mathbf{e}_1 \otimes \mathbf{e}_1. \tag{3.3.20}$$

If $\lambda > 1$, the deformation is an elongation, whereas if $\lambda < 1$, it is a contraction. Note that the terms "tensile" and "compressive" refer to stress, not deformation. $\mathbf{F}$ also has the matrix representation

$$[\mathbf{F}] = \begin{bmatrix} \lambda & 0 & 0 \\ 0 & 1 & 0 \\ 0 & 0 & 1 \end{bmatrix}. \tag{3.3.21}$$

Simple shear: The cube is said to be subjected to a simple shearing deformation if

$$\mathrm{d}\mathbf{x} = \mathbf{F} \cdot \mathrm{d}\mathbf{X} \quad \text{or} \quad \mathbf{F} = \mathbf{I} + k\mathbf{e}_1 \otimes \mathbf{e}_2 \tag{3.3.22}$$

and k is a constant. In terms of components in the basis $(\mathbf{e}_1, \mathbf{e}_2, \mathbf{e}_3)$, the deformation gradient $\mathbf{F}$ reads

$$[\mathbf{F}] = \begin{bmatrix} 1 & k & 0 \\ 0 & 1 & 0 \\ 0 & 0 & 1 \end{bmatrix}. \tag{3.3.23}$$

The simple shear deformation transforms the cube R_0 into the sheared region R, as shown in Figure 3.3.4. It can be observed that the displacement field in this example is given by $\mathbf{u} = \mathbf{FX} - \mathbf{X} = kX_2\mathbf{e}_1$. Consequently, each plane $\mathbf{X}_2$ equaling a constant undergoes a rigid displacement in the $\mathbf{X}_1$-direction, with the amount of

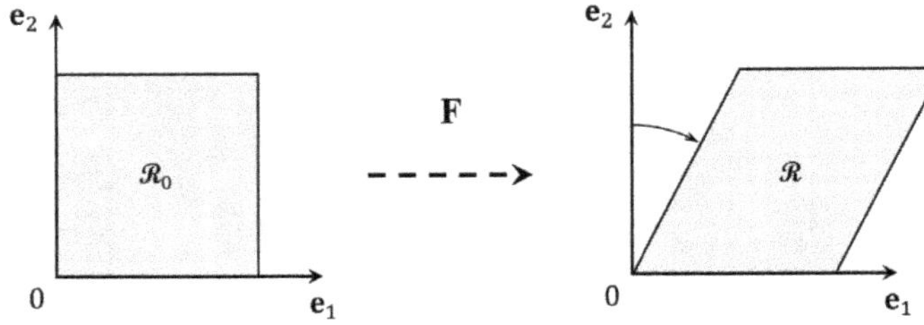

Figure 3.3.4 Simple shear of a cube.

displacement linearly dependent on the value of $\mathbf{X}_2$. A plane $\mathbf{X}_2$ equaling a constant is commonly referred to as a shearing (or glide) plane, while the $\mathbf{X}_1$-direction is known as the shearing direction, and k represents the amount of shear. It can be readily verified that $\det \mathbf{F} = \det(\mathbf{I} + k\mathbf{e}_1 \otimes \mathbf{e}_2) = 1$, indicating that a simple shear deformation automatically preserves volume.

3.3.2.3 *Nonhomogeneous deformation*

A nonhomogeneous deformation is one in which the deformation gradient $\mathbf{F}$ is a function of $\mathbf{X}$. A simple example of an inhomogeneous deformation is

$$\mathbf{x} = X_1(1 + \alpha_1 X_2)\mathbf{e}_1 + X_2(1 + \alpha_2 X_1)\mathbf{e}_2 + X_3\mathbf{e}_3. \tag{3.3.24}$$

The matrix representation of the deformation gradient is

$$[\mathbf{F}] = \begin{bmatrix} 1 + \alpha_1 X_2 & \alpha_1 X_1 & 0 \\ \alpha_2 X_2 & 1 + \alpha_2 X_1 & 0 \\ 0 & 0 & 1 \end{bmatrix}. \tag{3.3.25}$$

3.3.3 *Transformation of Length, Orientation, Angle, Volume and Area*

As previously shown by the definition of the deformation gradient, the tensor $\mathbf{F}(X)$ characterizes all geometric changes in the neighborhood of the particle X. We now examine the deformation of infinitesimal material fibers, surfaces, and regions. Specifically, we calculate quantities such as the local changes in length, angle, volume, and area in terms of $\mathbf{F}(X)$. The change in length is associated with the concept of fiber stretch (or strain), the change in angle relates to

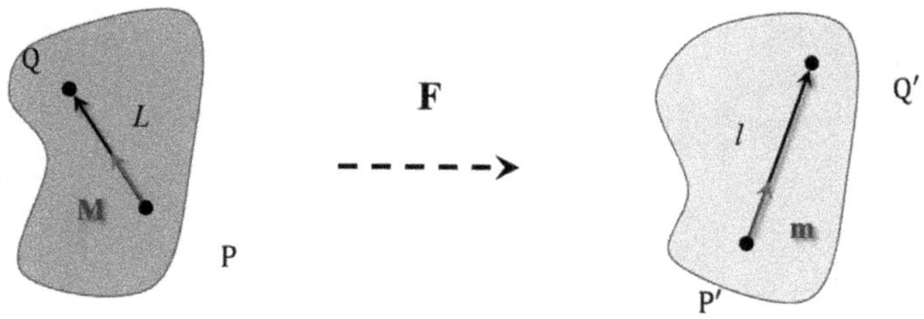

Figure 3.3.5 A segment of a straight line PQ and deformed segment of a straight line $P'Q'$ in the reference and current configurations.

shear strain, and the change in volume corresponds to volumetric (or dilatational) strain. The change in area is crucial for calculating the true stress on a surface.

3.3.3.1 *Change in length and orientation*

A line of material particles: When a body undergoes a homogeneous deformation $\mathbf{F}$ from a reference state to a current state (Figure 3.3.5), we can consider a set of material particles within the body. In the reference state, this set of material particles forms a segment of a straight line with a length L and in the direction of the unit vector $\mathbf{M}$. As the body transitions to the current state, the set of material particles still forms a segment of a straight line, but now the segment stretches and rotates. In the current state, the segment has a length l and is oriented in the direction of the unit vector $\mathbf{m}$.

The deformation gradient $\mathbf{F}$ maps the segment in the reference state to the segment in the current state:

$$l\mathbf{m} = \mathbf{F}(L\mathbf{M}). \tag{3.3.26}$$

The stretch ratio λ at the particle X in the direction $\mathbf{M}$ is defined as the ratio

$$\lambda = \frac{l}{L}. \tag{3.3.27}$$

Recall the definition of the stretch of the line of material particles, $\lambda = l/L$, and we write the above equation as

$$\lambda\mathbf{m} = \mathbf{FM}. \tag{3.3.28}$$

Given a deformation gradient $\mathbf{F}$ and the direction $\mathbf{M}$ of a line of material particles in the reference state, this equation calculates the stretch λ and the direction $\mathbf{m}$ of the line of material particles in the current state.

Therefore, it can be obtained that

$$\lambda^2 = (\mathbf{FM})^T(\mathbf{FM}). \tag{3.3.29}$$

The orientation $\mathbf{m}$ of this fiber in the deformed configuration is found to be

$$\mathbf{m} = \frac{\mathbf{FM}}{|\mathbf{FM}|}. \tag{3.3.30}$$

3.3.3.2 *Change in angle*

For two lines of material particles, let us recall the definition of engineering shear strain that you may have studied in engineering mechanics. Consider two sets of material particles (as shown in Figure 3.3.6). In the reference state, these two sets of material particles form two orthogonal vectors. In the current state, the two sets of material particles still form two vectors, but they are generally no longer orthogonal to each other. The angle between the two lines of material particles in the current state is denoted as $\frac{\pi}{2} - \gamma$. The angle γ is defined as the shear strain, which we will discuss in more detail later for a better understanding.

Consider two sets of material particles. In the reference state, one set of material particles forms a unit vector $\mathbf{M}$, and the other set of material particles forms a unit vector $\mathbf{N}$. We assume the two vectors are orthogonal. After the body undergoes a homogeneous deformation $\mathbf{F}$, the two sets of material particles stretch by $\lambda_{\mathbf{M}}$ and $\lambda_{\mathbf{N}}$, and are in the directions of two vectors $\mathbf{m}$ and $\mathbf{n}$, respectively.

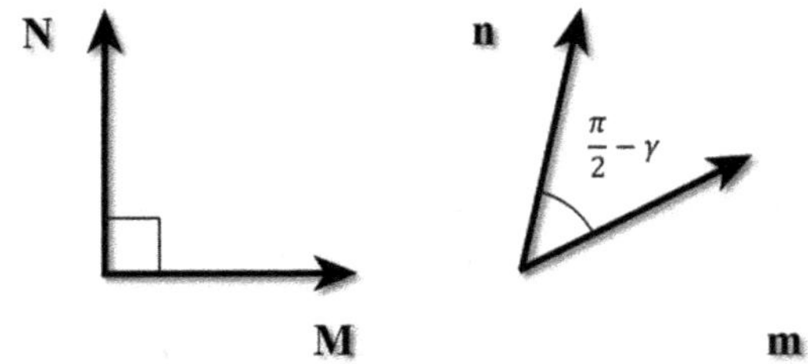

Figure 3.3.6 Two infinitesimal material fibers. In the reference configuration, they have lengths in the directions $\mathbf{M}, \mathbf{N}$, which form two orthogonal vectors.

Each set of material particles is linearly mapped by the deformation

$$\lambda_{\mathbf{M}}\mathbf{m} = \mathbf{FM}$$
$$\lambda_{\mathbf{N}}\mathbf{n} = \mathbf{FN}. \tag{3.3.31}$$

Taking the inner products of the vectors, we obtain that

$$\lambda_{\mathbf{M}}\lambda_{\mathbf{N}}\mathbf{m}^{\mathrm{T}}\mathbf{n} = (\mathbf{FM})^{\mathrm{T}}(\mathbf{FN}). \tag{3.3.32}$$

On the left-hand side, the inner product gives the cosine of the angle between the two vectors:

$$\mathbf{m}^{\mathrm{T}}\mathbf{n} = \cos\left(\frac{\pi}{2} - \gamma\right) = \sin(\gamma). \tag{3.3.33}$$

Consequently, the above expression can be written as

$$\sin(\gamma) = \frac{(\mathbf{FM})^{\mathrm{T}}(\mathbf{FN})}{\lambda_M \lambda_N}. \tag{3.3.34}$$

Given the directions of two orthogonal lines of material particles in the reference state, $\mathbf{M}$ and $\mathbf{N}$, and given the deformation gradient $\mathbf{F}$, the above equation calculates the shear strain associated with the two lines of material particles in the current state. We will discuss later how the change in angle is related to shear strain, as it will be covered in the section on strain.

3.3.3.3 *Change in volume*

Let us once again consider a homogeneous deformation that transforms a unit cube into a parallelepiped (see Figure 3.3.7). The three

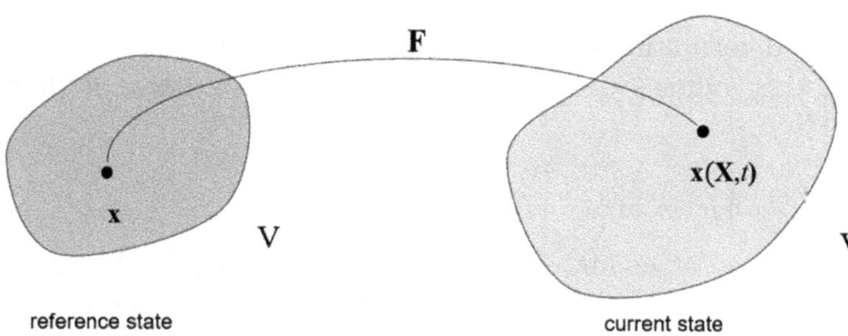

Figure 3.3.7 The volume change of a deformed body.

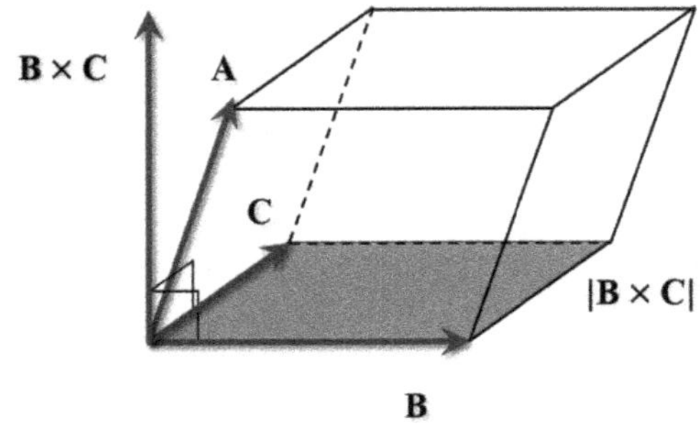

Figure 3.3.8 Scalar triple product representation of the volume of a parallelepiped.

edges of the parallelepiped are represented by the vectors $\mathbf{A}$, $\mathbf{B}$, and $\mathbf{C}$ (as shown in Figure 3.3.8). The volume of the parallelepiped can be calculated using the triple scalar product of these three vectors, which is defined as follows:

$$\mathbf{A} \cdot (\mathbf{B} \times \mathbf{C}) = \mathbf{B} \cdot (\mathbf{C} \times \mathbf{A}) = \mathbf{C} \cdot (\mathbf{A} \times \mathbf{B}). \tag{3.3.35}$$

Recall that the three vectors are the columns of the matrix $\mathbf{F}$. Further, recall that $\det(\mathbf{F}) = \mathbf{A} \cdot (\mathbf{B} \times \mathbf{C})$. Consequently, the volume of the parallelepiped is $\det(\mathbf{F})$.

We now generalize the above result to a homogeneous deformation of a body of any shape. The body occupies a region with a volume V in the reference state and another region with a volume v in the current state. The relationship between the two volumes can be expressed as follows:

$$v = V \det(\mathbf{F}), \quad J = \det(\mathbf{F}) = \frac{v}{V}. \tag{3.3.36}$$

Thus, the deformation gradient is expected to obey $\det(\mathbf{F}) > 0$. The ratio of the volumes in the two states is often written in short as $J = \det(\mathbf{F}) > 0$.

3.3.3.4 *Change in area*

We consider a set of material particles in a plane. In the reference state, the set of material particles lies in a region in the plane with unit normal $\mathbf{N}$ and area $\mathbf{A}$. In the current state, the same set of martial particles lies in a region on another plane with unit normal $\mathbf{n}$

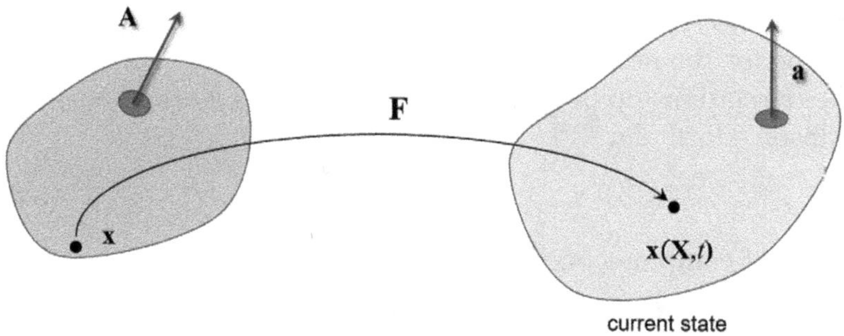

Figure 3.3.9 A plane in the reference configuration deforms, and a new plane is formed in the current configuration.

and area $\mathbf{a}$. The deformation maps the same set of material particles from one region in the reference state to another region in the current state.

The body may undergo a shear deformation relative to the plane. Consider a line of material particles. In the reference state, this line of material particles is normal to the plane of material particles. However, in the current state, the line of material particles may no longer be normal to the plane of material particles. As a result, when the body undergoes shear deformation relative to the plane, the two normal directions $\mathbf{V}$ and $\mathbf{n}$ correspond to two distinct sets of material particles. It is important to note that the use of uppercase and lowercase letters for the same letter in this context is an exception to our convention, as illustrated in Figure 3.3.9.

We aim to establish a relationship between $\mathbf{n}$ and $\mathbf{a}$ to $\mathbf{N}$ and $\mathbf{A}$. Let's define the area vectors $\mathbf{a} = a\mathbf{n}$ and $\mathbf{A} = A\mathbf{N}$. We consider a tilted cone with the plane as its base and an arbitrary point in space as its apex. Select a material particle within the plane. Now, consider the segment of the line of material particles extending from the apex to the chosen point. We denote this segment as vector $\mathbf{Y}$ when the body is in the reference state and as $\mathbf{y}$ when the body is in the current state. The volume of the cone is $V = (\mathbf{Y} \cdot \mathbf{A})/3$ in the reference state and is $v = (\mathbf{y} \cdot \mathbf{a})/3$ in the current state.

Recall that $\mathbf{y} = \mathbf{F}\mathbf{Y}$ and $v = V \det(\mathbf{F})$, so that

$$\mathbf{Y}^T\mathbf{F}^T\mathbf{a} = \det(\mathbf{F})\mathbf{Y}^T\mathbf{A} = J\mathbf{Y}^T\mathbf{A}. \tag{3.3.37}$$

The given expression equates two scalars, each representing an inner product of a vector and another vector $\mathbf{Y}$. Since the equation holds for any choice of material particle in the base of the cone, it must hold true for the arbitrary vector $\mathbf{Y}$. As a result, the above equation implies a relationship between two vectors, which is commonly known as Nanson's formula:

$$\mathbf{F}^T\mathbf{a} = J\mathbf{A}. \tag{3.3.38}$$

In terms of components, this formula is

$$a\, n_i F_{iK} = J\, A\, N_K. \tag{3.3.39}$$

When the deformation gradient $\mathbf{F}$ is known, this equation can be used to calculate $\mathbf{n}$ and $\mathbf{a}$ in terms of $\mathbf{N}$ and $\mathbf{A}$. Equation (3.3.39) provides a relationship between area in the current and reference configurations.

3.4 Decomposition of Deformation Gradient Tensor into Rotation and Stretch

As mentioned multiple times before, the deformation gradient tensor $\mathbf{F}(X)$ fully describes the deformation in the vicinity of the particle X. This deformation can be composed of both rigid rotation and strain. The key question is how to distinguish between the rotation and strain components within $\mathbf{F}(X)$. The answer to this lies in the polar decomposition theorem.

The polar decomposition theorem states that any nonsingular tensor $\mathbf{F}$ with a positive determinant can be uniquely expressed as the product of a proper orthogonal tensor $\mathbf{R}$ and symmetric positive definite tensors $\mathbf{U}$ and $\mathbf{V}$:

$$\mathbf{F} = \mathbf{RU} = \mathbf{VR}. \tag{3.4.1}$$

$\mathbf{R}$ represents the rotational part of $\mathbf{F}$, while $\mathbf{U}$ and $\mathbf{V}$ represent the parts that are not rotational. It is readily seen that $\mathbf{U}$ and $\mathbf{V}$ are given by the positive definite square root

$$\mathbf{U} = \sqrt{\mathbf{F}^T\mathbf{F}}, \quad \mathbf{V} = \sqrt{\mathbf{F}\mathbf{F}^T}, \tag{3.4.2}$$

and

$$\mathbf{R} = \mathbf{F}\mathbf{U}^{-1}, \quad \mathbf{R} = \mathbf{V}^{-1}\mathbf{F}. \tag{3.4.3}$$

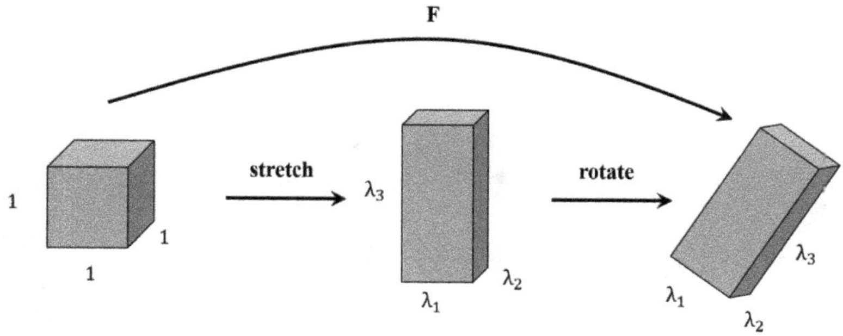

Figure 3.4.1 Schematic diagram of decomposition of deformation gradient.

Therefore, we can write the relationship between the two segments in the reference and current configurations as

$$\text{Dx} = \mathbf{F}\text{d}\mathbf{X} = \mathbf{R}(\mathbf{U}\text{d}\mathbf{X}). \tag{3.4.4}$$

This allows us to view the deformation of the fiber in two steps: First, the fiber $\text{d}\mathbf{X}$ is taken by the deformation to $\mathbf{U}\text{d}\mathbf{X}$, and then, it is rotated rigidly by $\mathbf{R} : \text{d}\mathbf{X} \rightarrow \mathbf{U}\text{d}\mathbf{X} \rightarrow \mathbf{R}(\mathbf{U}\text{d}\mathbf{X}) \rightarrow \text{d}\mathbf{x}$, as shown in Figure 3.4.1.

The key characteristic of $\mathbf{U}$ is that it is a symmetric and positive definite tensor known as the right Cauchy stretch tensor. $\mathbf{V}$, on the other hand, is the symmetric and positive definite left Cauchy stretch tensor, while $\mathbf{R}$ represents the orthogonal rotation tensor. In the general case, the decomposition of the deformation gradient can be visualized in Figure 3.4.2, illustrating the different roles of the components. These tensors possess the following properties:

$$\mathbf{R}^T \cdot \mathbf{R} = \mathbf{I}, \quad \mathbf{U} = \mathbf{U}^T, \quad \mathbf{V} = \mathbf{V}^T. \tag{3.4.5}$$

This decomposition enables a physical interpretation of $\mathbf{U}$ as follows: Due to its symmetry, $\mathbf{U}$ possesses three real eigenvalues λ_1, λ_2, and λ_3, along with a corresponding set of orthonormal eigenvectors. As $\mathbf{U}$ is positive definite, all three eigenvalues are positive. It can be demonstrated that the eigenvalues λ_1, λ_2, and λ_3 of $\mathbf{U}$ are identical to those of $\mathbf{V}$. These shared eigenvalues of $\mathbf{U}$ and $\mathbf{V}$ are referred to as the principal stretches associated with the deformation.

We assume that the eigenvectors of the stretch tensors $\mathbf{U}$ and $\mathbf{V}$ are $(\mathbf{m}_1, \mathbf{m}_2, \mathbf{m}_3)$ and $(\mathbf{n}_1, \mathbf{n}_2, \mathbf{n}_3)$, respectively; thus, the stretch

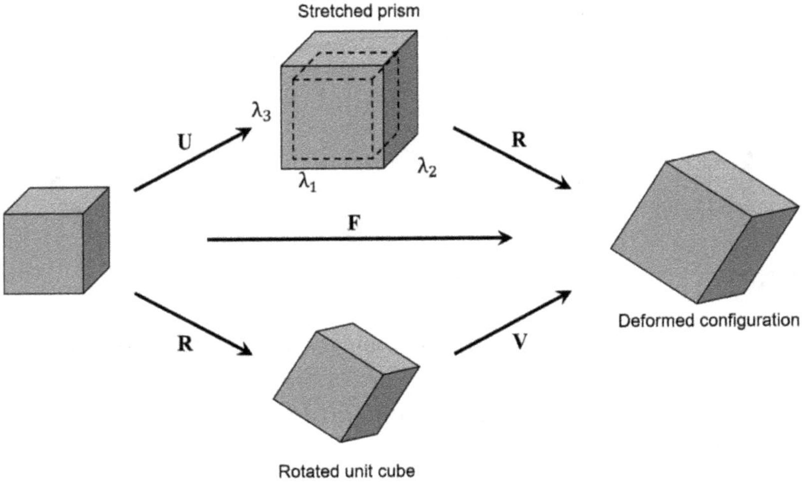

Figure 3.4.2 The roles of $\mathbf{U}, \mathbf{V}$, and $\mathbf{R}$ in stretching and rotating a unit volume of material in the neighborhood of $\mathbf{X}$.

tensors $\mathbf{U}$ and $\mathbf{V}$ can be expressed in terms of their eigenvectors and eigenvalues as

$$\mathbf{U} = \sum_{i=1}^{3} \lambda_i \mathbf{m}_i \otimes \mathbf{m}_i, \quad \mathbf{V} = \sum_{i=1}^{3} \lambda_i \mathbf{n}_i \otimes \mathbf{n}_i, \tag{3.4.6}$$

$$\mathbf{F} = \sum_{i=1}^{3} \lambda_i \mathbf{n}_i \otimes \mathbf{m}_i, \quad \mathbf{R} = \sum_{i=1}^{3} \mathbf{n}_i \otimes \mathbf{m}_i. \tag{3.4.7}$$

Since a rotation does not change the length, angle, area, or volume, we expect that these equations (except the one for orientation) should be independent of the rotation tensor $\mathbf{R}$ in the polar decomposition.

It is quite tedious to calculate the tensors $\mathbf{U} = \sqrt{\mathbf{F}^T\mathbf{F}}$ and $\mathbf{V} = \sqrt{\mathbf{F}\mathbf{F}^T}$. However, since there is a one-to-one relation between $\mathbf{U}$ and $\mathbf{U}^2$ and similarly between $\mathbf{V}$ and $\mathbf{V}^2$, we can just as well use $\mathbf{U}^2$ and $\mathbf{V}^2$ as our measures of stretch. These are usually denoted by $\mathbf{C}$ and $\mathbf{B}$:

$$\mathbf{C} = \mathbf{F}^T\mathbf{F} = \mathbf{U}^2, \quad \mathbf{B} = \mathbf{F}\mathbf{F}^T = \mathbf{V}^2. \tag{3.4.8}$$

$\mathbf{C}$ and $\mathbf{B}$ are referred to as the right and left Cauchy–Green deformation tensors, respectively. Note that the eigenvalues of $\mathbf{C}$ and $\mathbf{B}$ are λ_1^2, λ_2^2, and λ_3^2, where λ_i are the principal stretches and that the eigenvectors of $\mathbf{C}$ and $\mathbf{B}$ are the same as those of $\mathbf{U}$ and $\mathbf{V}$, respectively.

The two Cauchy–Green tensors admit the spectral representations

$$\mathbf{C} = \sum_{i=1}^{3} \lambda_i^2 \mathbf{m}_i \otimes \mathbf{m}_i, \quad \mathbf{B} = \sum_{i=1}^{3} \lambda_i^2 \mathbf{n}_i \otimes \mathbf{n}_i. \tag{3.4.9}$$

The particular scalar-valued functions of $\mathbf{C}$,

$$I_1(\mathbf{C}) = \operatorname{tr}\mathbf{C}, \quad I_2(\mathbf{C}) = \frac{1}{2}(\operatorname{tr}\mathbf{C}^2 - (\operatorname{tr}\mathbf{C})^2), \quad I_3(\mathbf{C}) = \det\mathbf{C}, \tag{3.4.10}$$

are called the principal scalar invariants of $\mathbf{C}$.

Finally, it can be shown that they satisfy the identity for all scalar μ:

$$\operatorname{Det}(\mathbf{C} - \mu\,\mathbf{I}) = -\mu^3 + I_1(\mathbf{C})\mu^2 - I_2(\mathbf{C})\mu + I_3(\mathbf{C}). \tag{3.4.11}$$

The principal scalar invariants can be written in terms of the principal stretches as

$$\begin{aligned} &I_1(\mathbf{C}) = \lambda_1^2 + \lambda_2^2 + \lambda_{31}^2, \quad I_2(\mathbf{C}) = \lambda_1^2\lambda_2^2 + \lambda_2^2\lambda_3^2 + \lambda_3^2\lambda_1^2, \\ &I_3(\mathbf{C}) = \lambda_1^2\lambda_2^2\lambda_3^2. \end{aligned} \tag{3.4.12}$$

The principal scalar invariants of $\mathbf{B}$ and $\mathbf{C}$ also coincide:

$$I_i(\mathbf{C}) = I_i(\mathbf{B}). \quad i = 1, 2, 3. \tag{3.4.13}$$

3.5 Strain Measures

The geometric changes experienced by a continuous medium can be measured in various ways. In this context, we discuss a general measure of deformation for a continuous medium or body that is independent of both translation and rotation.

3.5.1 *Cauchy–Green Deformation Tensors*

Consider two material particles P and Q in the neighborhood of each other, separated by $\mathrm{d}\mathbf{X}$ in the reference configuration, as shown in Figure 3.5.1. In the current (deformed) configuration, the material points P and Q occupy positions P' and Q', and they are separated by $\mathrm{d}\mathbf{x}$. We wish to determine the change in the distance $\mathrm{d}\mathbf{X}$ between the material points P and Q as the body deforms and the material points move to the new locations P' and Q'.

The distances between points P and Q and points P' and Q' are given, respectively, by

$$\begin{aligned}(\mathrm{d}S)^2 &= \mathrm{d}\mathbf{X}\cdot\mathrm{d}\mathbf{X},\\ (\mathrm{d}s)^2 &= \mathrm{d}\mathbf{x}\cdot\mathrm{d}\mathbf{x} = \mathrm{d}\mathbf{X}\cdot(\mathbf{F}^T\cdot\mathbf{F})\cdot\mathrm{d}\mathbf{X} = \mathrm{d}\mathbf{X}\cdot\mathbf{C}\cdot\mathrm{d}\mathbf{X},\end{aligned} \quad (3.5.1)$$

where $\mathbf{C}$ is called the right Cauchy–Green deformation tensor, as defined in Equation (3.4.8):

$$\mathbf{C} = \mathbf{F}^T\cdot\mathbf{F}. \quad (3.5.2)$$

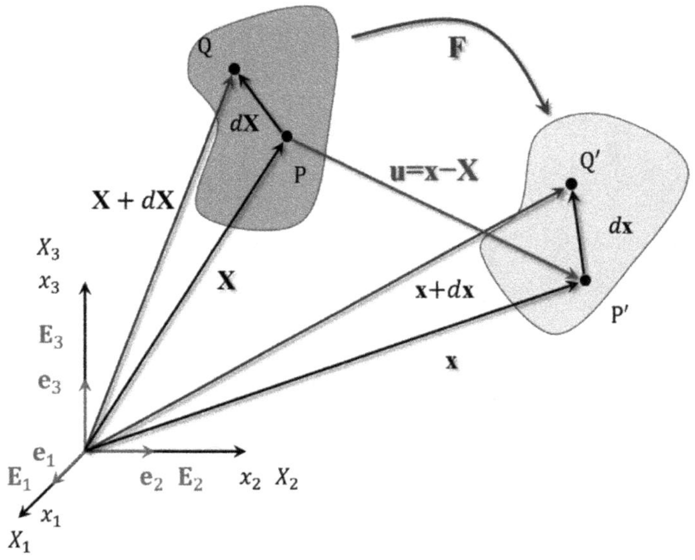

Figure 3.5.1 A distance $\mathrm{d}\mathbf{X}$ in the reference configuration takes up positions in the deformed configuration by distance $\mathrm{d}\mathbf{x}$.

By definition, $\mathbf{C}$ is a symmetric second-order tensor. Similarly, the left Cauchy–Green deformation tensor is defined by

$$\boldsymbol{B} = \boldsymbol{F} \cdot \boldsymbol{F}^T, \tag{3.5.3}$$

which is also a symmetric tensor:

$$\mathbf{C} = \mathbf{F}^T \cdot \mathbf{F} = \mathbf{U}^2, \quad \mathbf{B} = \mathbf{F} \cdot \mathbf{F}^T = \mathbf{V}^2. \tag{3.5.4}$$

From the previous section, we have seen that the deformation gradient tensor $\mathbf{F}$ can be decomposed into the stretch tensors $\mathbf{U}$ and $\mathbf{V}$ and the rotation tensor $\mathbf{R}$. It is evident that $\mathbf{U}$ and $\mathbf{V}$ are the fundamental components that characterize the nonrigid part of the deformation. In the absence of deformation, when the deformed configuration coincides with the reference configuration $\mathrm{d}\mathbf{x} = \mathrm{d}\mathbf{X}$, the deformation is given by $\mathbf{F} = \mathbf{I}$, where $\mathbf{I}$ represents the identity tensor. Consequently, $\mathbf{U} = \mathbf{V} = \mathbf{I}$ becomes equal to the identity tensor in the reference configuration. On the other hand, it is customary for strain to vanish in the reference configuration. Strain is merely an alternative measure for the nonrigid component of deformation, selected in such a way that it becomes zero in the reference configuration (This distinction between stretch and strain is the only tiny difference). For instance, we could define the strain as $\mathbf{E}_\mathbf{U} = \mathbf{U} - \mathbf{I}$, where $\mathbf{E}_\mathbf{U}$ represents the stretch tensor.

Various measures of Lagrangian strain and Eulerian strain are commonly employed in the literature, and we describe some examples in the following. It is important to note that continuum theory does not favor one strain measure over another; each measure is a one-to-one function of the stretch tensor, making all strain measures equivalent. In fact, it is not even necessary to introduce the concept of strain, as the theory could be entirely based on the stretch tensors $\mathbf{U}$ and $\mathbf{V}$.

The various measures of Lagrangian strain used in the literature are all directly related to the stretch tensor $\mathbf{U}$ in a one-to-one manner. Examples of these measures include the Green strain, the generalized Green strain, and the Hencky (or logarithmic) strain, which are defined by the following expressions, respectively:

$$\begin{aligned} \frac{1}{m}(\mathbf{U}^m - \mathbf{I}), &\quad \text{generalized Green strain,} \\ \ln \mathbf{U}, &\quad \text{Hencky strain.} \end{aligned} \tag{3.5.5}$$

Similarly, various measures of the Eulerian strain are used in the literature, all of them being related to the stretch $\mathbf{V}$ in a one-to-one manner. Examples include the Almansi strain, the generalized Almansi strain, and the logarithmic strain, defined by the following respective expressions:

$$\begin{aligned} &\frac{1}{2}(\mathbf{I}-\mathbf{V}^{-2}), \quad \text{Almansi strain,} \\ &\frac{1}{m}(\mathbf{V}^{m}-\mathbf{I}), \quad \text{generalized Almansi strain,} \\ &\ln\mathbf{V}, \quad \text{logarithmic strain,} \end{aligned} \tag{3.5.6}$$

where m is nonzero integer.

3.5.2 *Green–Lagrange Strain Tensor*

The change in the squared lengths that occurs as a body deforms from the reference to the current configuration can be expressed relative to the original length as follows:

$$(\mathrm{d}s)^2-(\mathrm{d}S)^2=\mathrm{d}\mathbf{X}\cdot(\mathbf{F}^T\cdot\mathbf{F})\cdot\mathrm{d}\mathbf{X}-\mathrm{d}\mathbf{X}\cdot\mathrm{d}\mathbf{X}=\mathrm{d}\mathbf{X}\cdot\mathbf{E}\cdot\mathrm{d}\mathbf{X}, \tag{3.5.7}$$

where $\mathbf{E}$ is called the Green–St. Venant (Lagrangian) strain tensor, the Green–Lagrange strain tensor, or simply the Green strain tensor. When we consider the expression $[(\mathrm{d}s)^2-(\mathrm{d}S)^2]/(\mathrm{d}S)^2$, the Green–Lagrange strain tensor can be expressed as

$$\begin{aligned} \mathbf{E} &= \frac{1}{2}[(\mathbf{F}^T\cdot\mathbf{F})-\mathbf{I}] = \frac{1}{2}[\mathbf{C}-\mathbf{I})] \\ &= \frac{1}{2}[(\mathbf{I}+\nabla_0\mathbf{u})^T\cdot(\mathbf{I}+\nabla_0\mathbf{u}))-\mathbf{I}] \\ &= \frac{1}{2}[\nabla_0\mathbf{u}+(\nabla_0\mathbf{u})^T-(\nabla_0\mathbf{u})\cdot(\nabla_0\mathbf{u})^T], \end{aligned} \tag{3.5.8}$$

where we use displacement to express deformation gradient and $\nabla_0\mathbf{u}$ is for reference configuration. By definition, the Green–Lagrange strain tensor is a symmetric second-order tensor. Additionally, the change in the squared lengths is zero if and only if $\mathbf{E}=\mathbf{0}$.

Therefore, the vector form of the Green–Lagrange strain tensor in Equation (3.5.8) allows us to express it in terms of its components in any coordinate system. In the rectangular Cartesian coordinate system $(\mathbf{E}_1, \mathbf{E}_2, \mathbf{E}_3)$ and $(\mathbf{e}_1, \mathbf{e}_2, \mathbf{e}_3)$, the components of $\mathbf{E}$ are given by

$$
\begin{aligned}
E_{ij} &= \frac{1}{2}\left(\frac{\partial x_k}{\partial X_i}\frac{\partial x_k}{\partial X_j} - \delta_{ij}\right),\\
E_{ij} &= \frac{1}{2}\left(\frac{\partial u_i}{\partial X_j} + \frac{\partial u_j}{\partial X_i} + \frac{\partial u_k}{\partial X_i}\frac{\partial u_k}{\partial X_j}\right).
\end{aligned} \tag{3.5.9}
$$

Clearly, the last term in Equations (3.5.8) and (3.5.9) is nonlinear in the displacement gradients. In expanded notation, the Green–Lagrange strain tensor components are given by

$$
\begin{aligned}
E_{11} &= \frac{\partial u_1}{\partial X_1} + \frac{1}{2}\left[\left(\frac{\partial u_1}{\partial X_1}\right)^2 + \left(\frac{\partial u_2}{\partial X_1}\right)^2 + \left(\frac{\partial u_3}{\partial X_1}\right)^2\right],\\
E_{22} &= \frac{\partial u_2}{\partial X_2} + \frac{1}{2}\left[\left(\frac{\partial u_1}{\partial X_2}\right)^2 + \left(\frac{\partial u_2}{\partial X_2}\right)^2 + \left(\frac{\partial u_3}{\partial X_2}\right)^2\right],\\
E_{33} &= \frac{\partial u_3}{\partial X_3} + \frac{1}{2}\left[\left(\frac{\partial u_1}{\partial X_3}\right)^2 + \left(\frac{\partial u_2}{\partial X_3}\right)^2 + \left(\frac{\partial u_3}{\partial X_3}\right)^2\right],
\end{aligned} \tag{3.5.10}
$$

$$
\begin{aligned}
E_{12} &= \frac{1}{2}\left[\frac{\partial u_1}{\partial X_2} + \frac{\partial u_2}{\partial X_1} + \frac{\partial u_1}{\partial X_1}\frac{\partial u_1}{\partial X_2} + \frac{\partial u_2}{\partial X_1}\frac{\partial u_2}{\partial X_2} + \frac{\partial u_3}{\partial X_1}\frac{\partial u_3}{\partial X_2}\right],\\
E_{13} &= \frac{1}{2}\left[\frac{\partial u_1}{\partial X_3} + \frac{\partial u_3}{\partial X_1} + \frac{\partial u_1}{\partial X_1}\frac{\partial u_1}{\partial X_3} + \frac{\partial u_2}{\partial X_1}\frac{\partial u_2}{\partial X_3} + \frac{\partial u_3}{\partial X_1}\frac{\partial u_3}{\partial X_3}\right],\\
E_{23} &= \frac{1}{2}\left[\frac{\partial u_2}{\partial X_3} + \frac{\partial u_2}{\partial X_1} + \frac{\partial u_1}{\partial X_2}\frac{\partial u_1}{\partial X_3} + \frac{\partial u_2}{\partial X_2}\frac{\partial u_2}{\partial X_3} + \frac{\partial u_3}{\partial X_2}\frac{\partial u_3}{\partial X_3}\right].
\end{aligned} \tag{3.5.11}
$$

The components E_{11}, E_{22}, and E_{33} are termed normal strains, and E_{12}, E_{13}, and E_{23} are called shear strains, as shown in Figure 3.5.2.

To understand the physical meaning of the normal strain component E_{11}, consider a line element initially parallel to the $\mathbf{E}_1$-axis, i.e., $\mathrm{d}\mathbf{X} = \mathrm{d}X_1\mathbf{E}_1$ in the reference configuration of the body, as shown in

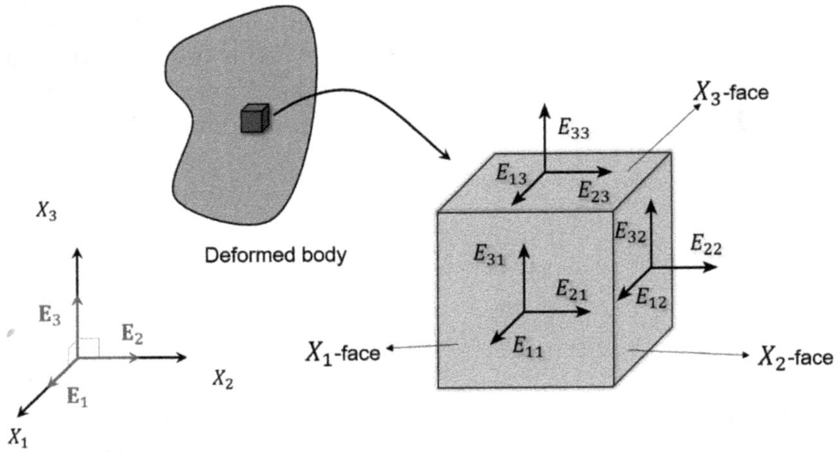

Figure 3.5.2 Green–Lagrange strain tensor components in rectangular Cartesian coordinates.

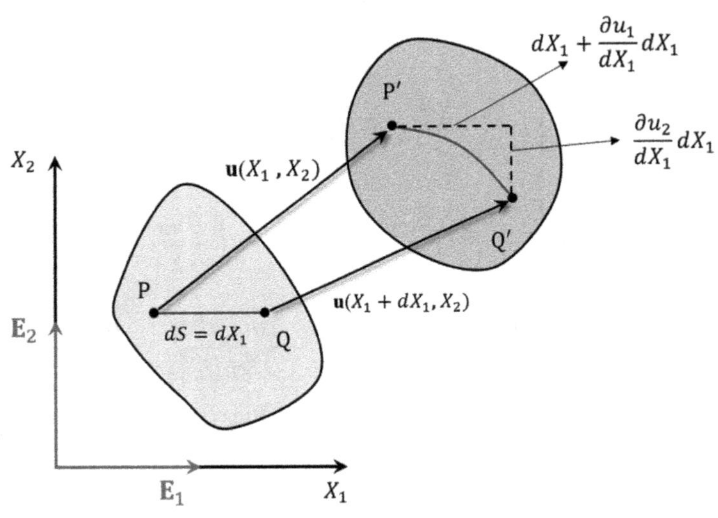

Figure 3.5.3 Physical interpretation of normal strain component E_{11}.

Figure 3.5.3. Then,

$$(\mathrm{d}s)^2 - (\mathrm{d}S)^2 = 2E_{11}\mathrm{d}X_1X_1 = 2E_{11}(\mathrm{d}S)^2 \tag{3.5.12}$$

and

$$E_{11} = \frac{1}{2}\left[\frac{(\mathrm{d}s)^2 - (\mathrm{d}S)^2}{(\mathrm{d}S)^2}\right] = \frac{1}{2}\left[\left(\frac{\mathrm{d}s}{\mathrm{d}S}\right)^2 - 1\right]. \tag{3.5.13}$$

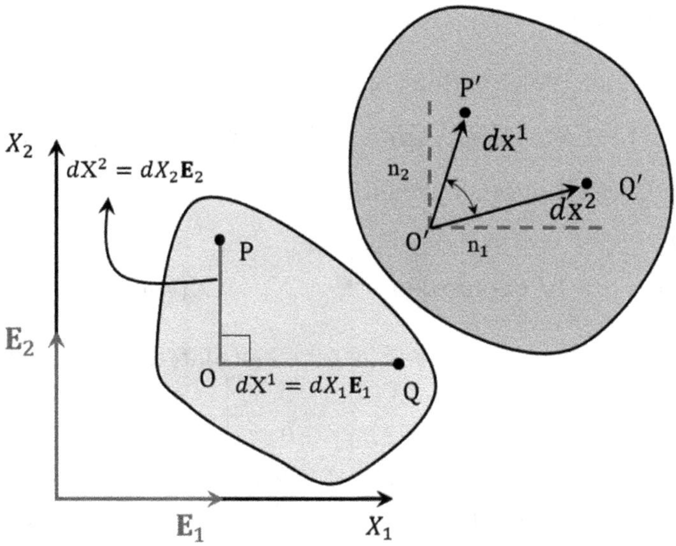

Figure 3.5.4 Physical interpretation of shear strain component E_{12}.

Assuming that λ is the stretch of the line element $\mathrm{d}\mathbf{X} = \mathrm{d}X_1\mathbf{E}_1$, we have

$$E_{11} = \frac{1}{2}\left[\left(\frac{\mathrm{d}s}{\mathrm{d}S}\right)^2 - 1\right] = \frac{1}{2}[(\lambda)^2 - 1], \tag{3.5.14}$$

$$\lambda = \sqrt{2E_{11} + 1}. \tag{3.5.15}$$

The shear strain components E_{12} can be interpreted as a measure of the change in the angle between line elements that were perpendicular to each other in the reference configuration. To see this, let us consider line elements $\mathrm{d}\mathbf{X}^1 = \mathrm{d}X_1\mathbf{E}_1$ and $\mathrm{d}\mathbf{X}^2 = \mathrm{d}X_2\mathbf{E}_2$ in the reference configuration of the body, which are perpendicular to each other, as shown in Figure 3.5.4. In the deformed body, the material line elements $\mathrm{d}\mathbf{X}^1$ and $\mathrm{d}\mathbf{X}^2$ occupy the positions $\mathrm{d}\mathbf{x}^1$ and $\mathrm{d}\mathbf{x}^2$, respectively. The cosine of the angle between the line elements $P'O'Q'$ and in the deformed body is given by θ_{12}. Therefore, $2E_{12}$ is equal to the cosine of the angle between the line elements, θ_{12}, multiplied by the product of the stretches λ_1 and λ_2. It is clear that the finite strain E_{12} depends not only on the angle but also on the stretches of the elements involved.

When the unit extensions and the angle changes are small compared to unity, we find that $2E_{12}$ represents the decrease from $\pi/2$.

Example 3.5.1

Let us consider the equations of motion

$$\mathbf{x} = \mathbf{x}(\mathbf{X}, t) = (X_1 + 4X_1X_2)\mathbf{e}_1 + (X_2 + (X_2)^2)\mathbf{e}_2 + (X_3 + (X_3)^2)\mathbf{e}_3.$$

Find the Green–Lagrange strain tensor.

Solution:

The motion can be expressed as $x_1 = X_1 + 4X_1X_2$, $x_2 = X_2 + (X_2)^2$, $x_3 = X_3 + (X_3)^2$.

The deformation gradient $\mathbf{F}$ can be calculated as $F_{ij} = \partial x_i/\partial X_j$.

Thus, $[\mathbf{F}] = \begin{bmatrix} 1+4X_2 & 4X_1 & 0 \\ 0 & 1+2X_2 & 0 \\ 0 & 0 & 1+2X_3 \end{bmatrix}$,

And the Green–Lagrange strain tensor is $\mathbf{E} = \frac{1}{2}(\mathbf{F}^T \cdot \mathbf{F} - \mathbf{I})$, or $E_{ij} = \frac{1}{2}(F_{ki}F_{kj} - \delta_{ij})$.

Thus, $[\mathbf{E}] = \begin{bmatrix} (1+4X_2)^2-1 & 4X_1(1+4X_2) & 0 \\ 4X_1(1+4X_2) & (4X_1)^2+(1+2X_2)^2-1 & 0 \\ 0 & 0 & (1+2X_3)^2-1 \end{bmatrix}$.

It can be seen that the Green–Lagrange strain is symmetric.

3.5.3 *Cauchy and Euler Strain Tensors*

As discussed in the previous section, the Green–Lagrange strain is defined with respect to the reference configuration. We can also define the strain measure with respect to the current configuration. Thus, returning to the strain measures, the change in the squared lengths that occurs as the body deforms from the initial to the current configuration can be expressed relative to the current length. First, we express $\mathrm{d}S$ in terms of $\mathrm{d}\mathbf{x}$ as

$$(\mathrm{d}S)^2 = \mathrm{d}\mathbf{X} \cdot \mathrm{d}\mathbf{X} = \mathrm{d}\mathbf{x} \cdot (\mathbf{F}^{-\mathrm{T}} \cdot \mathbf{F}^{-1}) \cdot \mathrm{d}\mathbf{x} \equiv \mathrm{d}\mathbf{x} \cdot \tilde{\mathbf{B}} \cdot \mathrm{d}\mathbf{x}, \qquad (3.5.16)$$

where $\tilde{\mathbf{B}}$ is called the Cauchy strain tensor,

$$\tilde{\mathbf{B}} = \mathbf{F}^{-\mathrm{T}} \cdot \mathbf{F}^{-1}, \quad \tilde{\mathbf{B}}^{-1} = \mathbf{B} = \mathbf{F} \cdot \mathbf{F}^{\mathrm{T}}, \qquad (3.5.17)$$

and $\mathbf{B}$ is the left Cauchy–Green tensor or Finger tensor. Similar to the Green–Lagrange strain, we can write

$$(\mathrm{d}s)^2 - (\mathrm{d}S)^2 = \mathrm{d}\mathbf{x} \cdot \mathbf{e} \cdot \mathrm{d}\mathbf{x}, \qquad (3.5.18)$$

where $\mathbf{e}$ is called the Almansi–Hamel (Eulerian) strain tensor or simply the Euler strain tensor, which is defined as

$$\begin{aligned}\mathbf{e} &= \frac{1}{2}[(\mathbf{I} - \mathbf{F}^{-T} \cdot \mathbf{F}^{-1})] = \frac{1}{2}[\mathbf{I} - \tilde{\mathbf{B}})] \\ &= \frac{1}{2}[(\mathbf{I} - (\mathbf{I} - \nabla\mathbf{u}) \cdot (\mathbf{I} - \nabla\mathbf{u})^T)] \\ &= \frac{1}{2}[\nabla\mathbf{u} + (\nabla\mathbf{u})^T - (\nabla\mathbf{u}) \cdot (\nabla\mathbf{u})^T],\end{aligned} \tag{3.5.19}$$

where $\nabla\mathbf{u}$ is for the current configuration. In the rectangular Cartesian coordinate system, the components of the Cauchy strain tensor can be expressed as

$$\begin{aligned}\tilde{\boldsymbol{B}}_{ij} &= \frac{\partial X_k}{\partial x_i}\frac{\partial X_k}{\partial x_j}, \quad e_{ij} = \frac{1}{2}\left(\delta_{ij} - \frac{\partial X_k}{\partial x_i}\frac{\partial X_k}{\partial x_j}\right) \\ &= \frac{1}{2}\left(\frac{\partial u_i}{\partial x_j} + \frac{\partial u_j}{\partial x_i} - \frac{\partial u_k}{\partial x_i}\frac{\partial u_k}{\partial x_j}\right).\end{aligned} \tag{3.5.20}$$

The tensors $\mathbf{E}$ and $\mathbf{e}$ can be expressed in any coordinate system, much like any second-order tensor. For example, in a rectangular Cartesian system, they can be transformed into each other.

3.5.4 *Invariants and Principal Values of Strains*

Similar to the previous definition, the principal invariants of the Green–Lagrange strain tensor $\mathbf{E}$ are

$$I_1(\mathbf{E}) = \operatorname{tr}\mathbf{E}, \quad I_2(\mathbf{E}) = \frac{1}{2}[(\operatorname{tr}\mathbf{E})^2 - (\operatorname{tr}\mathbf{E}^2)], \quad I_3(\mathbf{E}) = \det\mathbf{E}, \tag{3.5.21}$$

where the trace of $\mathbf{E}$, $\operatorname{tr}(\mathbf{E})$, is defined as the double-dot product of $\mathbf{E}$ with the identity tensor $\mathbf{I}$:

$$\operatorname{tr}\mathbf{E} = \mathbf{E} : \mathbf{I}. \tag{3.5.22}$$

In terms of the rectangular Cartesian components, the three principal invariants of $\mathbf{E}$ have the form

$$I_1 = E_{ii}, \quad I_2 = \frac{1}{2}(E_{ii}E_{jj} - E_{ij}E_{ji}), \quad I_3 = \det\mathbf{E} = |\mathbf{E}|. \tag{3.5.23}$$

It is of considerable interest to determine the maximum and minimum values of strain at a point. The eigenvalues of the strain tensor matrix, when ordered from largest to smallest, characterize the maximum and minimum normal strains, while the corresponding eigenvectors represent the planes on which they occur. Once the maximum normal strains are determined, the maximum shear strains can also be determined.

The eigenvalues of a strain tensor are referred to as the principal values of strain, and the corresponding eigenvectors are known as the principal directions of strain.

By following the same procedure as discussed earlier (in Chapter 2 on second-order tensors), the principal values of strain and their associated principal directions can be obtained.

Example 3.5.2

Obtain the principal invariants of $\mathbf{E}$ in terms of the principal invariants of $\mathbf{C}$.

Solution:

The principal invariants of $\mathbf{E}$ are given by

$$I_1(\mathbf{E}) = \operatorname{tr}\mathbf{E}, \quad I_2(\mathbf{E}) = \frac{1}{2}[(\operatorname{tr}\mathbf{E})^2 - (\operatorname{tr}\mathbf{E}^2)], \quad I_3(\mathbf{E}) = \det\mathbf{E}.$$

Referring to the fact that $\mathbf{E} = \frac{1}{2}(\mathbf{C} - \mathbf{I})$, the principal invariants can also be expressed as follows:

the first invariant:

$$\begin{aligned} I_1(\mathbf{E}) = \operatorname{tr}(\mathbf{E}) &= \operatorname{tr}[\frac{1}{2}(\mathbf{C} - \mathbf{I})] = \frac{1}{2}\operatorname{tr}(\mathbf{C} - \mathbf{I}) \\ &= \frac{1}{2}[\operatorname{tr}(\mathbf{C}) - \operatorname{tr}(\mathbf{I})] = \frac{1}{2}(I_1(\mathbf{C}) - 3) \end{aligned}$$

the second invariant:

$$I_2(\mathbf{E}) = \frac{1}{2}[(\operatorname{tr}\mathbf{E})^2 - (\operatorname{tr}\mathbf{E}^2)] = \frac{1}{2}[(I_1(\mathbf{E}))^2 - \operatorname{tr}(\mathbf{E}^2)],$$

where

$$\begin{aligned} (I_1(\mathbf{E}))^2 &= \frac{1}{4}[(I_1(\mathbf{C}))^2 - 6I_1(\mathbf{C}) + 9] \\ \operatorname{tr}(\mathbf{E}^2) &= \operatorname{tr}\left[\frac{1}{2}(\mathbf{C} - \mathbf{I})\right]^2 = \frac{1}{4}\operatorname{tr}[(\mathbf{C} - \mathbf{I})^2] = \frac{1}{4}\operatorname{tr}[(\mathbf{C}^2 - 2\mathbf{C} + \mathbf{I})] \\ &= \frac{1}{4}[\operatorname{tr}(\mathbf{C}^2) - 2\operatorname{tr}(\mathbf{C}) + \operatorname{tr}(\mathbf{I})] = \frac{1}{4}[\operatorname{tr}(\mathbf{C}^2) - 2I_1(\mathbf{C}) + 3]. \end{aligned}$$

The term $\mathrm{tr}(\mathbf{C}^2)$ can be obtained as follows.

As $\mathbf{C}^2 = \mathbf{C}\cdot\mathbf{C}$, we can find $\mathrm{tr}(\mathbf{C}^2) = C_1^2 + C_2^2 + C_3^2$.

It is also true that $(I_1(\mathbf{C}))^2 = (C_1 + C_2 + C_3)^2 = C_1^2 + C_2^2 + C_3^2 + 2(C_1C_2 + C_1C_3 + C_2C_3)$.

Thus, $C_1^2 + C_2^2 + C_3^2 = (I_1(\mathbf{C}))^2 - 2(C_1C_2 + C_1C_3 + C_2C_3) = (I_1(\mathbf{C}))^2 - 2I_2(\mathbf{C})$.

Therefore, we have

$$\mathrm{tr}(\mathbf{E}^2) = \frac{1}{4}[(I_1(\mathbf{C}))^2 - 2I_2(\mathbf{C}) - 2I_1(\mathbf{C}) + 3].$$

Whereupon, the second invariant can also be expressed as

$$I_2(\mathbf{E}) = \frac{1}{2}\left[\frac{1}{4}[(I_1(\mathbf{C}))^2 - 6I_1(\mathbf{C}) + 9] - \frac{1}{4}[(I_1(\mathbf{C}))^2 - 2I_2(\mathbf{C}) - 2I_1(\mathbf{C}) + 3]\right] = \frac{1}{4}(-2I_1(\mathbf{C}) + I_2(\mathbf{C}) + 3).$$

The third invariant:

$$I_3(\mathbf{E}) = \det(\mathbf{E}) = \det\left[\frac{1}{2}(\mathbf{C} - \mathbf{I})\right] = \left(\frac{1}{2}\right)^3 \det(\mathbf{C} - \mathbf{I}).$$

The term $\det(\mathbf{C} - \mathbf{I})$ can be expressed as

$$\det(\mathbf{C} - \mathbf{I}) = \begin{vmatrix} C_1 - 1 & & \\ & C_2 - 1 & \\ & & C_3 - 1 \end{vmatrix} = (C_1 - 1)(C_2 - 1)(C_3 - 1)$$
$$= I_3(\mathbf{C}) - I_2(\mathbf{C}) + I_1(\mathbf{C}) - 1,$$

then

$$I_3(\mathbf{E}) = \frac{1}{8}(I_3(\mathbf{C}) - I_2(\mathbf{C}) + I_1(\mathbf{C}) - 1).$$

Therefore, we have obtained the relationship between the **E**-invariants and **C**-invariants as follows:

$$I_1(\mathbf{E}) = \frac{1}{2}(I_1(\mathbf{C}) - 3), \quad I_2(\mathbf{E}) = \frac{1}{4}(-2I_1(\mathbf{C}) + I_2(\mathbf{C}) + 3)$$
$$I_3(\mathbf{E}) = \frac{1}{8}(I_3(\mathbf{C}) - I_2(\mathbf{C}) + I_1(\mathbf{C}) - 1),$$

$$I_1(\mathbf{C}) = 2I_1(\mathbf{E}) + 3, \quad I_2(\mathbf{C}) = 4I_2(\mathbf{E}) + 4I_1(\mathbf{E}) + 3$$
$$I_3(\mathbf{C}) = 8I_3(\mathbf{E}) + 4I_2(\mathbf{E}) + 2I_1(\mathbf{E}) + 1.$$

Example 3.5.3

For a given Green–Lagrange strain tensor described by $[\mathbf{E}] = \begin{bmatrix} 4 & -4 & 0 \\ -4 & 0 & 0 \\ 0 & 0 & 3 \end{bmatrix}$, determine the principal values and principal plans of strains.

Solution:

For the strain tensor, there are three eigenvalues and three corresponding eigenvectors. To determine the three eigenvalues $\lambda_1, \lambda_2, \lambda_3$, we have $\det([\mathbf{E}] - \lambda[\mathbf{I}]) = 0$.

And we have $[(4-\lambda)\lambda + 16](3-\lambda) = 0$.

Solving the above equations, we obtain $\lambda_1 = 3$, $\lambda_2 = 2(1+\sqrt{5})$, $\lambda_3 = 2(1-\sqrt{5})$.

Solving the equation $([\mathbf{E}] - \lambda[\mathbf{I}])\begin{pmatrix} x_1 \\ x_2 \\ x_3 \end{pmatrix} = 0$, we can obtain three eigenvectors corresponding to three eigenvalues. They are $\mathbf{x}^{(\lambda_1)} = \pm\begin{pmatrix} 0 \\ 0 \\ 1 \end{pmatrix}$, $\mathbf{x}^{(\lambda_2)} = \pm\begin{pmatrix} -0.851 \\ 0.526 \\ 0 \end{pmatrix}$, $\mathbf{x}^{(\lambda_3)} = \pm\begin{pmatrix} 0.526 \\ 0.851 \\ 0 \end{pmatrix}$.

3.6 Infinitesimal Strain Tensor and Rotation Tensor

3.6.1 *Infinitesimal Strain Tensor*

From the displacement definition $\mathbf{u}(\mathbf{X}, t) = \mathbf{x}(\mathbf{X}, t) - \mathbf{X}$, we know the displacement can be expressed as

$$d\mathbf{x} = d\mathbf{X} + \operatorname{grad}\mathbf{u}d\mathbf{X} = d\mathbf{X} + \nabla\mathbf{u}d\mathbf{X} = (\mathbf{I} + \nabla\mathbf{u})d\mathbf{X}. \tag{3.6.1}$$

When all displacement gradients $\nabla(\mathbf{u})$ are small, i.e., $|\nabla(\mathbf{u})| \ll 1$, we may neglect the nonlinear terms in the definition of the Green–Lagrange strain tensor $\mathbf{E}$ and obtain the linearized strain tensor $\boldsymbol{\varepsilon}$, called the infinitesimal strain tensor. To derive $\boldsymbol{\varepsilon}$ from $\mathbf{E}$, we must linearize $\mathbf{E}$ using a measure of smallness.

We introduce the nonnegative function

$$e = \|\nabla \mathbf{u}\|_{\infty}, \tag{3.6.2}$$

where $\nabla \mathbf{u}$ or grad $\mathbf{u}$ is call displacement gradient.

If $\mathbf{E}$ is of the order $O(e)$ in $\nabla \mathbf{u}$, then we mean

$$\frac{\partial u_i}{\partial X_j} = O(e) \quad \text{as} \quad e \to 0. \tag{3.6.3}$$

If terms of the order $O(e^2)$, as $e \to 0$, they can be omitted, and the Green–Lagrange strain tensor $E_{ij} = \frac{1}{2}(\frac{\partial u_i}{\partial X_j} + \frac{\partial u_j}{\partial X_i} + \frac{\partial u_k}{\partial X_i}\frac{\partial u_k}{\partial X_j})$ can be approximated as

$$E_{ij} \approx \frac{1}{2}\left(\frac{\partial u_i}{\partial X_j} + \frac{\partial u_j}{\partial X_i}\right). \tag{3.6.4}$$

We also have $x_i = u_i + X_i$,

$$\begin{aligned} \frac{\partial u_i}{\partial X_j} &= \frac{\partial u_i}{\partial x_k}\frac{\partial x_k}{\partial X_j} = \frac{\partial u_i}{\partial x_k}\left(\frac{\partial u_k}{\partial X_j} + \frac{\partial X_k}{\partial X_j}\right) \\ &= \frac{\partial u_i}{\partial x_k}\delta_{kj} + O(e^2) \quad \text{as} \quad e \to 0. \end{aligned} \tag{3.6.5}$$

Thus, when terms of the order $O(e^2)$, as $e \to 0$, are neglected, it is immaterial whether the partial derivative of the displacement field $\mathbf{u}$ is taken with respect to X_j or x_k so that $\frac{\partial u_i}{\partial X_j} = \frac{\partial u_i}{\partial x_j}$, i.e., $\nabla \mathbf{u} = \nabla_0 \mathbf{u} = O(e)$. In other words, in the case of infinitesimal strains, no distinction is made between the material coordinates X_i and the spatial coordinates x_i, and it is not necessary to distinguish between the Green–Lagrange strain tensor $\mathbf{E}$ and the Eulerian strain tensor $\mathbf{e}$. Thus, the infinitesimal strain tensor $\boldsymbol{\varepsilon}$ is defined as

$$\mathbf{E} \approx \boldsymbol{\varepsilon} = \frac{1}{2}(\nabla_0 \mathbf{u} + (\nabla_0 \mathbf{u})^T). \tag{3.6.6}$$

The rectangular Cartesian components of the infinitesimal strain tensor are

$$\varepsilon_{ij} \approx \frac{1}{2}\left(\frac{\partial u_i}{\partial X_j} + \frac{\partial u_j}{\partial X_i}\right), \tag{3.6.7}$$

or, in expanded form,

$$\begin{aligned}
\varepsilon_{11} &= \frac{\partial u_{1i}}{\partial X_1}, \quad \varepsilon_{22} = \frac{\partial u_2}{\partial X_2}, \quad \varepsilon_{33} = \frac{\partial u_3}{\partial X_3},\\
\varepsilon_{12} &= \frac{1}{2}\left(\frac{\partial u_1}{\partial X_2} + \frac{\partial u_2}{\partial X_1}\right),\\
\varepsilon_{13} &= \frac{1}{2}\left(\frac{\partial u_1}{\partial X_3} + \frac{\partial u_3}{\partial X_1}\right),\\
\varepsilon_{23} &= \frac{1}{2}\left(\frac{\partial u_2}{\partial X_3} + \frac{\partial u_3}{\partial X_2}\right).
\end{aligned} \tag{3.6.8}$$

The strain components $\varepsilon_{11}, \varepsilon_{22}, \varepsilon_{33}$ are the infinitesimal normal strains and $\varepsilon_{12}, \varepsilon_{13}, \varepsilon_{23}$ are the infinitesimal shear strains. The shear strains $\varepsilon_{12} = \varepsilon_{21}$, $\varepsilon_{13} = \varepsilon_{31}$, $\varepsilon_{23} = \varepsilon_{32}$ are called the engineering shear strains.

3.6.2 *Infinitesimal Rotation Tensor*

The displacement gradient tensor can be expressed as the sum of a symmetric tensor and a skew-symmetric tensor. We have

$$(\nabla \mathbf{u})^T = \frac{1}{2}[(\nabla \mathbf{u})^T + \nabla \mathbf{u}] + \frac{1}{2}[(\nabla \mathbf{u})^T - \nabla \mathbf{u}], \tag{3.6.9}$$

where the symmetric part is similar to the infinitesimal strain tensor, and the skew-symmetric part is known as the infinitesimal rotation tensor, and we use $\boldsymbol{\Omega}$ to express it:

$$\boldsymbol{\Omega} = \frac{1}{2}[(\nabla \mathbf{u})^T - \nabla \mathbf{u}]. \tag{3.6.10}$$

We note that there is no restriction placed on the magnitude of $\nabla \mathbf{u}$ in the above equation. $\boldsymbol{\Omega}$ does not have the meaning of infinitesimal strain and infinitesimal rotation tensors unless the deformation is infinitesimal.

From the definition, it follows that $\boldsymbol{\Omega}$ is a skew-symmetric tensor, i.e., $\boldsymbol{\Omega}^T = -\boldsymbol{\Omega}$. In Cartesian component form, we have

$$\Omega_{ij} = \frac{1}{2}(u_{i,j} - u_{j,i}), \quad \Omega_{ij} = -\Omega_{ji}. \tag{3.6.11}$$

Thus, there are only three independent components of $\boldsymbol{\Omega}$.

The matrix form is

$$[\mathbf{\Omega}] = \begin{bmatrix} 0 & \Omega_{12} & \Omega_{13} \\ -\Omega_{12} & 0 & \Omega_{23} \\ -\Omega_{13} & -\Omega_{23} & 0 \end{bmatrix}. \tag{3.6.12}$$

The three components can be used to define the components of a vector $\boldsymbol{\omega}$:

$$\boldsymbol{\omega} = \frac{1}{2}\nabla \times \mathbf{u}, \quad \omega_i = \frac{1}{2} e_{ijk} \frac{\partial u_k}{\partial u_j}. \tag{3.6.13}$$

The infinitesimal displacements of the form $d\mathbf{u} = \mathbf{\Omega} \cdot d\mathbf{X}$, where $\mathbf{\Omega}$ is independent of the position $\mathbf{x}$, are rigid-body rotations. Thus, $\boldsymbol{\omega}$ represents the infinitesimal rotation vector; its magnitude is the angle of rotation, and its direction gives the axis of rotation. We also note that $\nabla \cdot \boldsymbol{\omega} = 0$. Such vectors are called solenoidal. A rigid-body motion is one in which the relative distance between points is preserved.

Certain motions do not produce infinitesimal strains; however, they may produce finite strains. For example, consider the following deformation mapping:

$$\mathbf{x} = (u_1 + X_1 \cos\theta - X_2 \sin\theta)\mathbf{e}_1 + (u_2 + X_1 \sin\theta + X_2 \cos\theta)\mathbf{e}_2 + X_3\mathbf{e}_3, \tag{3.6.14}$$

where u_1 and u_2 denote the horizontal and vertical displacements of the point $(0, 0, 0)$, as shown in Figure 3.6.1.

The components of the deformation gradient $\mathbf{F}$ and right Cauchy–Green deformation tensor $\mathbf{C}$ are

$$[\mathbf{F}] = \begin{bmatrix} \cos\theta & -\sin\theta & 0 \\ \sin\theta & \cos\theta & 0 \\ 0 & 0 & 1 \end{bmatrix}, \quad [\mathbf{C}] = \begin{bmatrix} 1 & 0 & 0 \\ 0 & 1 & 0 \\ 0 & 0 & 1 \end{bmatrix}. \tag{3.6.15}$$

Since $\mathbf{C} = \mathbf{I}$, we have $\mathbf{E} = \mathbf{0}$, indicating that the body does not experience stretching or shearing. The mapping is a rigid-body motion (both rigid-body translation and rigid-body rotation).

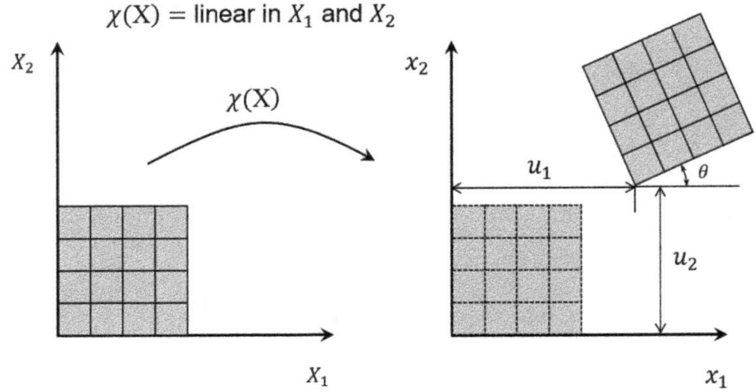

Figure 3.6.1 A mapping that produces nonzero infinitesimal strains but zero finite strains.

3.7 Velocity Gradient and Vorticity Tensors

In fluid mechanics, the velocity vector $\mathbf{v}(\mathbf{x}, t)$ is the variable of interest. Similar to the displacement gradient tensor, we now discuss the velocity gradient tensor $\mathbf{L}$.

3.7.1 *Definitions*

Let $\mathrm{d}\mathbf{X}$ be a material fiber through the particle $\mathbf{X}$ in the reference configuration, and let $\mathrm{d}\mathbf{x}$ be its image at time t. Then, $\mathrm{d}\mathbf{x} = \mathrm{d}(\mathbf{X}, t; \mathrm{d}\mathbf{X}) = \mathbf{F}\mathrm{d}\mathbf{X}$. Differentiating this with respect to t, $\mathbf{v} = \mathrm{D}\mathbf{x}/\mathrm{D}t = \dot{\mathbf{x}}$ or $\mathbf{v} = \mathrm{d}\mathbf{x}/\mathrm{d}t = (\mathrm{d}(\mathbf{F}\mathrm{d}\mathbf{X}))/(\mathrm{d}t) = (\mathrm{d}\mathbf{F}/\mathrm{d}t)\mathrm{d}\mathbf{X}$. Thus, we define a velocity vector as

$$\mathbf{v} = \mathrm{d}\mathbf{x}/\mathrm{d}t = (\mathrm{d}\mathbf{F}/\mathrm{d}t)\mathrm{d}\mathbf{X}. \tag{3.7.1}$$

We can write the velocity gradient tensor $\mathbf{L}$ as the sum of symmetric $\mathbf{D}$ and skew-symmetric $\mathbf{W}$ tensors:

$$\mathbf{L} \equiv (\nabla\mathbf{v})^T = \frac{1}{2}[(\nabla\mathbf{v})^T + \nabla\mathbf{v}] + \frac{1}{2}[(\nabla\mathbf{v})^T - \nabla\mathbf{v}] = \mathbf{D} + \mathbf{W}, \tag{3.7.2}$$

where $\mathbf{D}$ is called the rate-of-deformation tensor (or rate of strain tensor) and $\mathbf{W}$ is called the vorticity tensor or spin tensor:

$$\mathbf{D} = \frac{1}{2}[(\nabla\mathbf{v})^T + \nabla\mathbf{v}], \quad \mathbf{W} = \frac{1}{2}[(\nabla\mathbf{v})^T - \nabla\mathbf{v}] \tag{3.7.3}$$

or

$$\mathbf{D} = \frac{1}{2}[\mathbf{L}^T + \mathbf{L}], \quad \mathbf{W} = \frac{1}{2}[\mathbf{L}^T - \mathbf{L}]. \tag{3.7.4}$$

The skew-symmetric tensor $\mathbf{W}$ (i.e., $\mathbf{W}^T = -\mathbf{W}$) has only three independent scalar components; they can be used to define the scalar components of a vector $\mathbf{w}$, called the axial vector of $\mathbf{W}$, as follows:

$$W_{ij} = e_{ijk}w_k, \quad [\mathbf{W}] = \begin{bmatrix} 0 & -w_3 & w_2 \\ w_3 & 0 & -w_1 \\ -w_2 & w_1 & 0 \end{bmatrix}. \tag{3.7.5}$$

The scalar components of $\mathbf{w}$ can be expressed in terms of the scalar components of $\mathbf{W}$ as

$$w_i = -\frac{1}{2}e_{ijk}W_{jk} = \frac{1}{2}e_{ijk}\frac{\partial v_k}{\partial x_j}, \quad \mathbf{w} = \frac{1}{2}\nabla \times \mathbf{v}. \tag{3.7.6}$$

Thus, $\mathbf{w}$ is also known as the vorticity vector. Note that $\nabla \cdot \mathbf{w} = 0$ by virtue of the vector identity (i.e., the divergence of the curl of a vector is zero). Thus, the vorticity vector is divergence-free.

We can separately calculate the rate of change in length and the rate of change in orientation of the fiber. To this end, let

$$\mathrm{D}\mathbf{x} = \mathbf{n}\mathrm{d}s, \tag{3.7.7}$$

where $\mathrm{d}s(t)$ is the current length of the fiber and the unit vector $\mathbf{n}(t)$ is its current orientation. Taking the material time derivative of $(\mathrm{d}s)^2 = \mathrm{d}\mathbf{x} \cdot \mathrm{d}\mathbf{x}$, we have

$$(\mathrm{d}s)\left(\frac{\mathrm{d}s}{\mathrm{d}t}\right) = \mathrm{d}\mathbf{x} \cdot \left(\frac{\mathrm{d}\mathbf{x}}{\mathrm{d}t}\right) = \mathbf{L}\mathrm{d}\mathbf{x} \cdot \mathrm{d}\mathbf{x}, \tag{3.7.8}$$

$$\left(\frac{\mathrm{d}s}{\mathrm{d}t}\right) \Big/ (\mathrm{d}s) = \mathbf{L}\mathbf{n} \cdot \mathbf{n}. \tag{3.7.9}$$

Using the fact that $\mathbf{L} = \mathbf{D} + \mathbf{W}$ and, furthermore, recalling that $\mathbf{W}\mathbf{n} \cdot \mathbf{n} = 0$, since $\mathbf{W}$ is skew-symmetric, we can write the preceding equation as

$$\left(\frac{\mathrm{d}s}{\mathrm{d}t}\right) \Big/ (\mathrm{d}s) = \mathbf{D}\mathbf{n} \cdot \mathbf{n}. \tag{3.7.10}$$

Consequently, we conclude that the stretching tensor $\mathbf{D}$ characterizes the rate of change in length.

Now, we consider the rate of change of orientation. We have $\frac{\mathbf{n}\mathrm{d}s}{\mathrm{d}t} = \mathbf{L}\mathbf{n}\mathrm{d}s$, which when expanded out reads $\dot{\mathbf{n}} = \mathbf{L}\mathbf{n} - \mathbf{n}((\frac{\mathrm{d}s}{\mathrm{d}t})/(\mathrm{d}s))$. Since $(\frac{\mathrm{d}s}{\mathrm{d}t})/(\mathrm{d}s) = \mathbf{n}\cdot\mathbf{L}\mathbf{n}$, this can be written as

$$\dot{\mathbf{n}} = \mathbf{L}\mathbf{n} - (\mathbf{n}\cdot\mathbf{L}\mathbf{n})\mathbf{n}. \tag{3.7.11}$$

Finally, on using $\mathbf{L} = \mathbf{D} + \mathbf{W}$, this simplifies to

$$\dot{\mathbf{n}} = \mathbf{W}\mathbf{n} + \mathbf{D}\mathbf{n} - (\mathbf{D}\mathbf{n}\cdot\mathbf{n})\mathbf{n}. \tag{3.7.12}$$

We can observe that in a rigid motion, since $\mathbf{D} = \mathbf{0}$, the above equation specializes to $\dot{\mathbf{n}} = \mathbf{W}\mathbf{n}$; thus, in this special case, the vector $\mathbf{n}$ rotates with the spin $\mathbf{W}$. In a general motion, however, we see that $\mathbf{D}\mathbf{n} - (\mathbf{D}\mathbf{n}\cdot\mathbf{n})\mathbf{n}$ represents an additional motion superposed on the rigid spin $\mathbf{W}$.

3.7.2 *Relationship between* D *and* Ė

Note that $\mathbf{W}$ is related to $\dot{\mathbf{E}}$, the time rate of change of the Green–Lagrange strain tensor $\mathbf{E}$, as shown in the following.

Taking the total time derivative of the expression of Green–Lagrange strain tensor, we obtain

$$\frac{\mathrm{d}}{\mathrm{d}t}[(\mathrm{d}s)^2 - (\mathrm{d}S)^2] = \frac{\mathrm{d}}{\mathrm{d}t}[(\mathrm{d}s)^2] = 2\mathrm{d}\mathbf{X}\cdot\frac{\mathrm{d}\mathbf{E}}{\mathrm{d}t}\cdot\mathrm{d}\mathbf{X} \equiv 2\mathrm{d}\mathbf{X}\cdot\dot{\mathbf{E}}\cdot\mathrm{d}\mathbf{X}, \tag{3.7.13}$$

where we used the fact that $\mathrm{d}X$ and $\mathrm{d}S$ are constants. On the other hand, the instantaneous rate of change of the squared length $(\mathrm{d}s)^2$ is

$$\frac{\mathrm{d}}{\mathrm{d}t}[(\mathrm{d}s)^2] = \frac{\mathrm{d}}{\mathrm{d}t}[\mathrm{d}\mathbf{x}\cdot\mathrm{d}\mathbf{x}] = 2\mathrm{d}\mathbf{x}\cdot\frac{\mathrm{d}}{\mathrm{d}t}(\mathrm{d}\mathbf{x}) = 2\mathrm{d}\mathbf{x}\cdot\mathrm{d}\mathbf{v}, \tag{3.7.14}$$

$$\mathbf{L} = (\nabla\mathbf{v})^T \quad\Rightarrow\quad \mathrm{d}\mathbf{v} = \mathbf{L}\cdot\mathrm{d}\mathbf{x}. \tag{3.7.15}$$

Therefore,

$$\frac{\mathrm{D}}{\mathrm{d}t}[(\mathrm{d}s)^2] = 2\mathrm{d}\mathbf{x}\cdot\mathbf{L}\cdot\mathrm{d}\mathbf{x} = 2\mathrm{d}\mathbf{x}\cdot(\mathbf{D}+\mathbf{W})\cdot\mathrm{d}\mathbf{x} = 2\mathrm{d}\mathbf{x}\cdot\mathbf{D}\cdot\mathrm{d}\mathbf{x}. \tag{3.7.16}$$

The second term is zero because of the skew symmetry of $\mathbf{W}$. From the above two equations and using $\mathrm{d}\mathbf{x} = \mathbf{F} \cdot \mathrm{d}\mathbf{X} = \mathrm{d}\mathbf{X} \cdot \mathbf{F}^T$, we can obtain

$$\frac{\mathrm{d}}{\mathrm{d}t}[(\mathrm{d}s)^2] = 2\mathrm{d}\mathbf{X}\cdot\dot{\mathbf{E}}\cdot\mathrm{d}\mathbf{X} = 2\mathrm{d}\mathbf{x}\cdot\mathbf{D}\cdot\mathrm{d}\mathbf{x} = \mathrm{d}\mathbf{X}\cdot\mathbf{F}^T\cdot\mathbf{D}\cdot\mathbf{F}\cdot\mathrm{d}\mathbf{X}. \quad (3.7.17)$$

Thus, we arrive at the result

$$\dot{\mathbf{E}} = \mathbf{F}^T \cdot \mathbf{D} \cdot \mathbf{F}, \quad (3.7.18)$$

And using $\mathrm{d}\mathbf{x} = \mathbf{F} \cdot \mathrm{d}\mathbf{X} = \mathrm{d}\mathbf{X} \cdot \mathbf{F}^T$,

$$\mathrm{d}\mathbf{v} = \frac{\mathrm{d}}{\mathrm{d}t}(\mathrm{d}\mathbf{x}) = \left(\frac{\mathrm{d}\mathbf{F}}{\mathrm{d}t}\right) \cdot \mathrm{d}\mathbf{X} + \mathbf{F} \cdot \frac{\mathrm{d}(\mathrm{d}\mathbf{X})}{\mathrm{d}t} = \dot{\mathbf{F}} \cdot \mathrm{d}\mathbf{X} + 0; \quad (3.7.19)$$

thus,

$$\dot{\mathbf{F}} \cdot \mathrm{d}\mathbf{X} = \mathbf{L} \cdot \mathrm{d}\mathbf{x}. \quad (3.7.20)$$

Finally, we have

$$\dot{\mathbf{F}} = \frac{\mathrm{d}}{\mathrm{d}t}(\nabla_0 \mathbf{x}) = (\nabla_0 \mathbf{v})^T. \quad (3.7.21)$$

Note that $\nabla_0 \mathbf{v}$ is the gradient of the velocity vector $\mathbf{v}$ with respect to the material coordinates X, and it is not the same as $\mathbf{L} = (\nabla \mathbf{v})^T$. From Equation (3.7.20) or (3.7.21) and the identity

$$(\nabla_0 \mathbf{v})^T = \mathbf{L} \cdot \mathbf{F}, \quad (3.7.22)$$

we finally obtain

$$\dot{\mathrm{F}} = \mathbf{L} \cdot \mathbf{F} \quad \text{or} \quad \mathbf{L} = \dot{\mathbf{F}} \cdot \mathbf{F}^{-1}. \quad (3.7.23)$$

Therefore, we obtain the relationship between the time rate of change of the Green–Lagrange strain tensor and the rate-of-deformation tensor (or the rate of strain tensor):

$$\dot{\mathbf{E}} = \mathbf{F}^T \cdot \mathbf{D} \cdot \mathbf{F} \quad \text{and} \quad \dot{\mathbf{F}} = \mathbf{L} \cdot \mathbf{F}. \quad (3.7.24)$$

3.8 Compatibility Equations

3.8.1 *Preliminary Comments*

The task of computing strains (infinitesimal or finite) from a given displacement field is a straightforward exercise. However, sometimes, we encounter the problem of finding the displacements from a given strain field. This is not as straightforward because there are six independent partial differential equations (i.e., strain–displacement relations) for only three unknown displacements. In general, this would overdetermine the solution. To address this issue, we can establish certain conditions, known as Saint-Venant's compatibility equations, which ensure the computation of a unique displacement field from a given strain field.

To understand the concept of strain compatibility, imagine a material body being divided into smaller pieces before deformation, as shown in Figure 3.8.1. Each piece is then subjected to a specific strain. If the strained pieces cannot be reassembled into a single, continuous body without further deformation, it indicates a lack of compatibility between the strains. However, if the strains in each

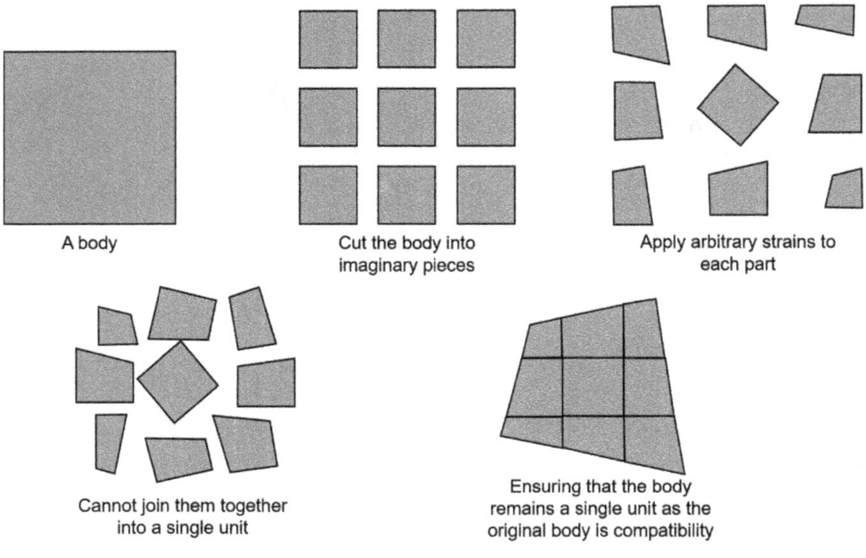

Figure 3.8.1 If the strain in each piece is compatible with the strains in the neighboring pieces, they can be fitted together to form a continuous body.

piece are related to or compatible with the strains in the neighboring pieces, they can be fitted together seamlessly, forming a continuous body. Mathematically, this compatibility is ensured by the six strain–displacement relations that connect the six strain components to the three displacement components, ensuring their consistency.

3.8.2 *Infinitesimal Strains*

The infinitesimal strain tensor $\mathbf{E} \approx \boldsymbol{\varepsilon}$ is defined in terms of the displacement vector $\mathbf{u}$ as

$$\begin{aligned} \mathbf{E} \approx \boldsymbol{\varepsilon} &= \frac{1}{2}[\nabla_0(\mathbf{u}) + (\nabla_0(\mathbf{u}))^T], \\ \varepsilon_{ij} &= \frac{1}{2}\left(\frac{\partial u_i}{\partial X_j} + \frac{\partial u_j}{\partial X_i}\right)\frac{-b \pm \sqrt{b^2 - 4ac}}{2a}. \end{aligned} \tag{3.8.1}$$

We begin with infinitesimal strains in two dimensions. We have the following three strain–displacement relations:

$$\varepsilon_{11} = \frac{\partial u_1}{\partial X_1}; \quad \varepsilon_{22} = \frac{\partial u_2}{\partial X_2}; \quad \varepsilon_{12} = \frac{1}{2}\left(\frac{\partial u_1}{\partial X_2} + \frac{\partial u_2}{\partial X_1}\right). \tag{3.8.2}$$

The compatibility of a given strain field can be established as follows. Differentiate the first equation with respect to X_2 twice, the second equation with respect to X_1 twice, and the third equation with respect to X_1 and X_2 each, and obtain

$$\begin{aligned} \frac{\partial^2 \varepsilon_{11}}{\partial X_2^2} &= \frac{\partial^3 u_1}{\partial X_1 \partial X_2^2}; \\ \frac{\partial^2 \varepsilon_{22}}{\partial X_1^2} &= \frac{\partial^3 u_2}{\partial X_2 \partial X_1^2}; \\ \frac{\partial^3 u_1}{\partial X_1 \partial X_2^2} + \frac{\partial^3 u_2}{\partial X_2 \partial X_1^2} &= 2\frac{\partial^2 \varepsilon_{12}}{\partial X_1 \partial X_2}. \end{aligned} \tag{3.8.3}$$

Using the first two equations in the third equation, we arrive at the following relation among the three strains:

$$\frac{\partial^2 \varepsilon_{11}}{\partial X_2^2} + \frac{\partial^2 \varepsilon_{22}}{\partial X_1^2} = 2\frac{\partial^2 \varepsilon_{12}}{\partial X_1 \partial X_2}. \tag{3.8.4}$$

Equation (3.8.4) is called the strain compatibility condition among the three strains that ensures the integrability to determine the displacement components (u_1, u_2).

A similar procedure can be followed to obtain the strain compatibility equations for the three-dimensional case of

$$\frac{\partial^2 \varepsilon_{mn}}{\partial X_i \partial X_j} + \frac{\partial^2 \varepsilon_{ij}}{\partial X_m \partial X_n} = \frac{\partial^2 \varepsilon_{im}}{\partial X_j \partial X_n} + \frac{\partial^2 \varepsilon_{jn}}{\partial X_i \partial X_m}. \tag{3.8.5}$$

These conditions are both necessary and sufficient to determine a single-valued displacement field. Similar compatibility conditions hold for the rate-of-deformation tensor $\mathbf{D}$.

3.9 Rigid-Body Motions and Material Objectivity

3.9.1 *Introduction and Rigid-Body Motion*

A rigid-body motion refers to a motion that maintains the relative distances between points. Intuitively, when considering the computed strains based on the change in length and orientation of line elements in a small neighborhood of a point, rigid-body motions of the entire body should have no effect on the strain values. In other words, different measures may give various expressions when determining the strains of a body with superposed rigid-body motions; however, the computed values remain independent of the rigid-body motion of the body. Now, let us consider the special case of rigid deformation. A deformation is classified as rigid if the distance between all pairs of particles is preserved throughout the deformation, meaning that the distance $|\mathbf{X}_P - \mathbf{X}_Q|$ between any two particles P and Q in the reference configuration equals the distance $|\mathbf{X}_P - \mathbf{X}_Q|$ between them in the deformed configuration:

$$\begin{aligned} |\mathbf{x}_P - \mathbf{x}_Q|^2 &= (x_i(\mathbf{X}_P) - x_i(\mathbf{X}_Q))(x_i(\mathbf{X}_P) - x_i(\mathbf{X}_Q)) \\ &= ((\mathbf{X}_P)_i - (\mathbf{X}_Q)_i)((\mathbf{X}_P)_i - (\mathbf{X}_Q)_i). \end{aligned} \tag{3.9.1}$$

We may take its derivative with respect to $(\mathbf{X}_P)_j$ to get

$$2F_{ij}(\mathbf{X}_P)(x_i(\mathbf{X}_P) - x_i(\mathbf{X}_Q)) = -2((\mathbf{X}_P)_j - (\mathbf{X}_Q)_j), \tag{3.9.2}$$

where $F_{ij} = \partial x_i(\mathbf{X}_Q)/\partial(\mathbf{X}_Q)_j$ are the components of the deformation gradient tensor. Since Equation (3.9.2) holds for all $\mathbf{X}_P$, we may take its derivative with respect to $(\mathbf{X}_P)_k$ to obtain $F_{ij}(\mathbf{X}_\mathrm{Q})F_{ik}(\mathbf{X}_\mathrm{P}) = \delta_{jk}$; thus,

$$\mathbf{F}(\mathbf{X}_Q)^T\mathbf{F}(\mathbf{X}_P) = \mathbf{I}. \tag{3.9.3}$$

Finally, since the above equation holds for all $\mathbf{X}_P$ and all $\mathbf{X}_Q$, we can take $\mathbf{X}_P = \mathbf{X}_Q$ to get

$$\mathbf{F}(\mathbf{X}_P)^T\mathbf{F}(\mathbf{X}_P) = \mathbf{I}. \tag{3.9.4}$$

Thus, we conclude that $\mathbf{F}$ is an orthogonal tensor at each $\mathbf{X}_P$. In fact, since $\det \mathbf{F} > 0$, it is a proper orthogonal and therefore represents a rotation.

The (possible) dependence of $\mathbf{F}$ on $\mathbf{X}_P$ implies that $\mathbf{F}$ might be a different proper orthogonal tensor at different points $\mathbf{X}_P$ in the body. However, returning to Equation (3.9.3), multiplying both sides of it by $\mathbf{F}(\mathbf{X}_P)$ and recalling that $\mathbf{F}$ is orthogonal gives

$$\mathbf{F}(\mathbf{X}_P) = \mathbf{F}(\mathbf{X}_Q). \tag{3.9.5}$$

This implies that $\mathbf{F}(\mathbf{X}_P)$ is a constant tensor.

In conclusion, the deformation gradient tensor associated with a rigid deformation is a constant rotation tensor. Thus, we can denote $\mathbf{F}(\mathbf{X}) = \mathbf{Q}$, where $\mathbf{Q}$ is a constant proper orthogonal tensor. Thus, necessarily, a rigid deformation has the form

$$\mathbf{x} = \mathbf{QX} + \mathbf{b}, \tag{3.9.6}$$

where $\mathbf{Q}$ is a constant rotation tensor and $\mathbf{b}$ is a constant vector. Conversely, it is easy to verify that the above equation satisfies Equation (3.9.1).

One can easily confirm from Equation (3.9.6) and the results presented in the previous section that in a rigid deformation, the length of every fiber remains unchanged, the angle between any two fibers remains unchanged, the volume of any infinitesimal element remains unchanged, and the unit vectors $\mathbf{n}_0$ and $\mathbf{n}$ that are normal to a surface in the reference and deformed configurations are related simply by the equation

$$\mathbf{n} = \mathbf{Q}\mathbf{n}_0. \tag{3.9.7}$$

3.9.2 *Material Objectivity*

3.9.2.1 *Observer transformation*

The concept of frames of reference should not be confused with that of coordinate systems, as they are not the same. An observer is free to choose any coordinate system that is convenient for observing or analyzing a system's response.

In continuum mechanics, each frame of reference represents an observer, and transformations between moving frames are called observer transformations. The equations of mechanics are used in various problems and locations; therefore, they must be independent of frames of reference, meaning that they should be invariant with respect to observer transformations. A change of observer can be viewed as a certain rigid-body motion superimposed on the current configuration, as illustrated in Figure 3.9.1.

In the analytical description of physical events, the following two requirements must be adhered to:

(1) the invariance of the equations with respect to stationary coordinate frames of reference;
(2) the invariance of the equations with respect to frames of reference that move in arbitrary relative motion.

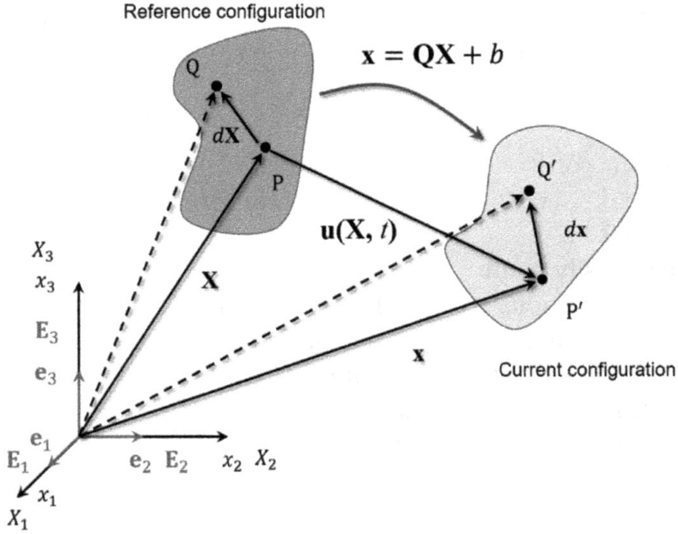

Figure 3.9.1 Deformation by rigid-body motion.

The first requirement is easily satisfied by expressing the equations in vector/tensor form, which is invariant. When we say an equation is in "invariant form," we mean that it is expressed in a vector form that does not depend on the choice of coordinate system. In our study, we assume that the coordinate systems are relatively at rest.

The second requirement is that the invariance property hold for reference frames (or observers) moving arbitrarily with respect to each other. This requirement arises from the necessity for forces and deformations to be consistent regardless of the observers' relative motions. The invariance with respect to changes in the observer is referred to as material frame indifference or material objectivity. This means that certain physical quantities must be independent of the observer.

Observer independence plays a vital role in our subsequent analysis of constitutive relationships in mechanics, and it necessitates that these relationships remain unchanged regardless of the observer.

3.9.2.2 *Objectivity of various kinematic measures*

Let O and O^* be two observers. Suppose that the same event is characterized by the two observers $(\mathbf{x}, t)$ and $(\mathbf{x}^*, t^*)$. The two observers are said to be equivalent if they agree on the distance between every two points, orientation, the time interval between every two instants, and the sense of time. It can be shown that these four requirements hold if and only if $(\mathbf{x}, t)$ and $(\mathbf{x}^*, t^*)$ are related by the following relation:

$$\mathbf{x}^*(\mathbf{X}, t^*) = \mathbf{Q}(t)\mathbf{x} + \mathbf{c}(t), \quad t^* = t + a, \tag{3.9.8}$$

where a is an arbitrary constant, $\mathbf{c}(t)$ is an arbitrary time-dependent vector, and $\mathbf{Q}$ is an arbitrary time-dependent proper orthogonal tensor. Alternatively, given one observer O, we can view Equation (3.9.8) as describing an observer transformation from O to an equivalent observer O^*.

In general, the characterization of a physical quantity associated with a motion depends on the observer. It is important to distinguish between physical quantities that intrinsically depend on the observer and those that do not. A physical quantity is said to be observer-independent or objective (or frame-indifferent) if it remains invariant under all observer transformations. The significance of whether a physical quantity is objective or not will become apparent when we consider constitutive relationships in later chapters.

Specifically, suppose that a certain physical quantity is denoted by the scalar field $\beta(\mathbf{x}, t)$ by observer O and by $\beta^*(\mathbf{x}^*, t^*)$ by observer O^*. Then, we say that this scalar physical quantity is observer-independent or objective if

$$\beta^*(\mathbf{x}^*, t^*) = \beta(\mathbf{x}, t) \tag{3.9.9}$$

for all equivalent observers O and O^*.

Next, consider a physical quantity that is denoted by the vector field $\mathbf{b}(\mathbf{x}, t)$ by observer O, and by $\mathbf{b}^*(\mathbf{x}^*, t^*)$ by observer O^*. Then, we say that this vector physical quantity is objective if

$$\mathbf{b}^*(\mathbf{x}^*, t^*) = \mathbf{Q}(t)\mathbf{b}(\mathbf{x}, t) \tag{3.9.10}$$

for all equivalent observers O and O^*. Physically, this equation ensures that the components associated with an objective vector quantity are unaffected by an observer transformation. For example, consider an orthonormal basis $\mathbf{x} = (\mathbf{e}_1, \mathbf{e}_2, \mathbf{e}_3)$ and a second orthonormal basis $\mathbf{x}^* = (\mathbf{Q}\mathbf{e}_1, \mathbf{Q}\mathbf{e}_2, \mathbf{Q}\mathbf{e}_3)$, as shown in Figure 3.9.2. Suppose that an observer-independent physical quantity is denoted by the vector $\mathbf{b}$ by observer O. The components of $\mathbf{b}$ in the basis $(\mathbf{e}_1, \mathbf{e}_2, \mathbf{e}_3)$ are $b_i = b \cdot \mathbf{e}_i$. If a second observer O^* represents this same physical quantity by the vector $\mathbf{b}^*$, then the components of $\mathbf{b}^*$ in the basis $(\mathbf{Q}\mathbf{e}_1, \mathbf{Q}\mathbf{e}_2, \mathbf{Q}\mathbf{e}_3)$ are $b_i^* = \mathbf{b}^* \cdot \mathbf{Q}\mathbf{e}_i = \mathbf{Q}\mathbf{b} \cdot \mathbf{Q}\mathbf{e}_i = \mathbf{b} \cdot \mathbf{e}_i = b_i$,

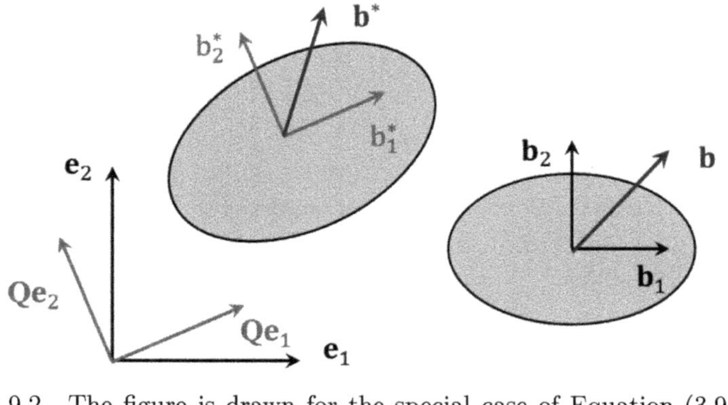

Figure 3.9.2 The figure is drawn for the special case of Equation (3.9.8) with $a = 0$, $c = 0$. At the instant depicted, the two observers see the same particle X to be located at x and $\mathbf{x}^* = \mathbf{Q}\mathbf{x}$, respectively; thus, $\mathbf{b}$ is an objective vector.

i.e., the components of $\mathbf{b}^*$ in the basis $(\mathbf{Q}\mathbf{e}_1, \mathbf{Q}\mathbf{e}_2, \mathbf{Q}\mathbf{e}_3)$ are identical to the components of $\mathbf{b}$ in the basis $(\mathbf{e}_1, \mathbf{e}_2, \mathbf{e}_3)$.

Finally, consider a physical quantity that is denoted by the second tensor field $\mathbf{B}(\mathbf{x}, t)$ by observer O and by $\mathbf{B}^*(\mathbf{x}^*, t^*)$ by observer O^*. Then, we say that this tensor physical quantity is objective if

$$\mathbf{B}^*(\mathbf{x}^*, t^*) = \mathbf{Q}(t)\mathbf{B}(\mathbf{x}, t)\mathbf{Q}^T(t) \tag{3.9.11}$$

for all equivalent observers O and O^*. Similarly, the above equation ensures that the components associated with an objective tensor quantity are unaffected by an observer transformation.

Under the following general rigid-body mapping

$$\mathbf{x}^*(\mathbf{X}, t^*) = \mathbf{Q}(t)\mathbf{x} + \mathbf{c}(t), \quad t^* = t + a \tag{3.9.12}$$

between observer O and O^*, that (if the reference configuration is independent of the observer) the right Cauchy–Green deformation tensor $\mathbf{C}$, and the Green–Lagrange strain tensor $\mathbf{E}$ does not change under the observer transformation, i.e., they are objective:

$$\mathbf{E} = \mathbf{E}^*, \quad \mathbf{C} = \mathbf{C}^*. \tag{3.9.13}$$

In addition, the symmetric part of $\mathbf{L}$, namely $\mathbf{D}$, is also objective:

$$\mathbf{D}^* = \mathbf{Q} \cdot \mathbf{D} \cdot \mathbf{Q}^T. \tag{3.9.14}$$

We have noted that the two observers' perspectives on the velocity and acceleration of a given motion are different, even though the rate of change at a fixed X is the same in each case. Therefore, velocity and acceleration vectors are not objective.

3.10 Summary

In this chapter, we began by introducing the deformation mapping χ, which maps a material point at position $\mathbf{X}$ in the reference configuration to position $\mathbf{X}$ in the current configuration. Two descriptions of motion were discussed: the spatial (Eulerian) description and the material (Lagrange) description of motion. We defined the concept of displacement $\mathbf{u}$ for a material point.

Most importantly, we introduced the deformation gradient $\mathbf{F}$ as a two-point tensor that relates the reference configuration to the current configuration, $\mathbf{F} = (\frac{\partial \mathbf{x}}{\partial \mathbf{X}})^T = \nabla_0(\mathbf{x})^T$. It is important to note that the deformation tensor is nonsingular, hence invertible. We also discussed isochoric, homogeneous, and inhomogeneous deformations in terms of the deformation mapping and the deformation gradient. Additionally, we derived the changes in volume and surface from the reference configuration to the current configuration.

Several strain measures were introduced, including the Green–Lagrange strain tensor $\mathbf{E}$, Cauchy strain tensor $\tilde{\mathbf{B}}$, the Euler or Almansi strain tensor $\mathbf{e}$, the right Cauchy–Green deformation tensor $\mathbf{C}$, and the left Cauchy–Green deformation tensor $\mathbf{B}$. A physical interpretation of the normal and shear strain components was also presented. The determination of principal strains and principal directions of strain was discussed using the eigenvalue problem.

The infinitesimal strain tensor $\boldsymbol{\varepsilon}$ was obtained from $\mathbf{E}$ by retaining the terms of order $|\nabla \mathbf{u}| \ll 1$ and omitting higher-order terms. In the infinitesimal case, the distinction between the Green–Lagrange strain tensor and the Euler strain tensor $\mathbf{e}$ disappears.

The displacement gradient tensor is expressed as the sum of the symmetric strain tensor and the skew-symmetric rotation tensor $\boldsymbol{\Omega}$. Similarly, the rate-of-deformation tensor is expressed as the sum of its symmetric part, the rate-of-deformation tensor, and its skew-symmetric part, the vorticity tensor.

The effect of superposed rigid-body motion and the concept of frame indifference, which ensures independence from the frame of reference in measuring various strain measures, were briefly discussed. It was shown that measures of displacements and various strains adhere to the frame indifference principle, meaning they are independent of the coordinate frame of reference. However, velocities and accelerations depend on the coordinate frame of reference.

General References

Oden, J.T. (2011). *An Introduction to Mathematical Modeling: A Course in Mechanics* (John Wiley & Sons Inc., New Jersey, USA).

Reddy, J.N. (2013). *An Introduction to Continuum Mechanics* (Cambridge University Press, New York, USA).

Reddy, J.N. (2017). *Principles of Continuum Mechanics: Conservation and Balance Laws with Applications* (Cambridge University Press, New York, USA).

Problems

3.1. The motion of a body is described by the following mapping function:

$$\mathbf{x}(\mathbf{X}) = (X_1 + t^2 X_2)\mathbf{e}_1 + (X_2 + t^2 X_1)\mathbf{e}_2 + X_3\mathbf{e}_3, \quad 0 \le t \le \infty.$$

(a) Is the motion above possible?
(b) Determine the components of the displacement.
(c) Determine the velocity and acceleration fields of the motion in the material coordinates and in the spatial description.
(d) Determine the components of the deformation gradient $\mathbf{F}$ and its inverse.
(e) Determine the position $\mathbf{X} = (X_1, X_2, X_3)$ of the particle in the undeformed configuration that occupies the position $(x_1, x_2, x_3) = (9, 6, 1)$ at time $t = 2$ in the deformed configuration.
(f) Determine the position at time $t = 2$ of the particle that will later be located at $\mathbf{x} = (2, 3, 1)$ at time $t = 3$.
(g) Plot the deformed shape of a body at times $t = 0, 1, 2$, and 3, assuming that the body is initially a unit cube.
(h) Determine the Green–Lagrange train tensors in the Cartesian coordinate system.

3.2. The deformation mapping of a body is described by the following mapping function

$$\mathbf{x}(\mathbf{X}) = (X_1 + AX_2)\mathbf{e}_1 + (X_2 + BX_1)\mathbf{e}_2 + X_3\mathbf{e}_3, \quad 0 \le t \le \infty,$$

where A and B are constants.

(a) Determine the displacement components in the material description and in the spatial description.
(b) Determine the components of the Green–Lagrange and Eulerian strain tensors (Almansi–Hamel strain tensor).

3.3. Consider a continuum in which the displacement field is described by the following equations:

$$\mathbf{u}(\mathbf{X}) = (2(X_1)^2 + X_1X_2)\mathbf{e}_1 + (X_2)^2\mathbf{e}_2.$$

By definition, a material curve is always formed by the same particles. Let OP and OT be material lines in the reference configuration, where the point coordinates in the reference configuration are $O(0,0,0)$, $P(1,1,0)$, and $T(1,0,0)$, respectively.

Find the material curves in the current configuration. Also, find the deformation gradient. (Note that to obtain the material curve, one need only substitute the material coordinates with the particles belonging to the line OP in the equations of motion).

3.4. Obtain the principal invariants of the Green–Lagrangian strain $\mathbf{E}$ in terms of the principal invariants of the right Cauchy–Green deformation tensors $\mathbf{C}$.

Chapter 4

Stress Measures

Table of Contents

4.1 Introduction

In Chapter 3, we discussed the kinematics of a continuum body. In engineering, we are aware that a bar may fail or break under a tension force. According to the mechanics of materials, when the stress on a bar exceeds the material thresholds, it can break. Stress, defined as the force per unit area, measures the material's capacity to bear loads. All designs are based on the criterion that the materials used have the capacity to carry the working loads of the system. Stress is also known as the quantification of force intensity within a body undergoing potentially significant deformation. Therefore, it is necessary to determine the state of stress in a material or body.

In this chapter, we study the general concept of stress and its various measures. This chapter involves exploring the different measures of stress that are defined in relation to the alternative configurations discussed in the preceding chapters. For instance, stress can be measured per unit deformed or undeformed area. As we will see shortly, stress at a point in a three-dimensional continuum can be measured in terms of nine quantities on three mutually perpendicular planes at the point, with three quantities per plane. These nine quantities can be viewed as the components of a second-order tensor called a stress tensor.

4.1.1 *Overview of Configurations of Continuum Bodies*

In the previous chapter, we discussed the concepts of different body configurations under deformation, such as the reference and current

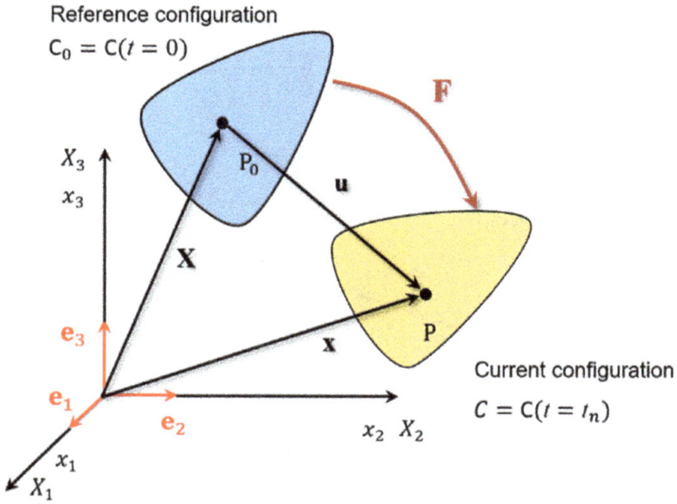

Figure 4.1.1 A body in reference and current configurations.

configurations. We understand that the position of all material particles within the body at a given time t is referred to as the configuration of the body, and a sequence of configurations for all times t defines the motion of the body, as shown in Figure 4.1.1. The deformation of a body or structure is often characterized by a load–displacement diagram, starting from an initial, usually undeformed state at time $t = 0$, referred to as the initial configuration C_0. Each individual point on the equilibrium path corresponds to an instantaneous actual or current (deformed) configuration C_n, at time $t = t_n$. The reference configuration is the configuration to which state variables such as strains and stresses are related. It is important to note that the time "t" is not necessarily the physical time; in this context, "t" should be seen as a state or load parameter, or simply a pseudotime.

As discussed in Chapter 3, position and deformation measurements play a central role in continuum mechanics. Two methods are commonly employed: the Lagrangian method and the Eulerian method.

In the Lagrangian method, particle positions and velocities are measured with respect to a fixed, stationary observer in a coordinate system known as the referential coordinate system. This coordinate system is based on the location of the observer. Therefore, in the

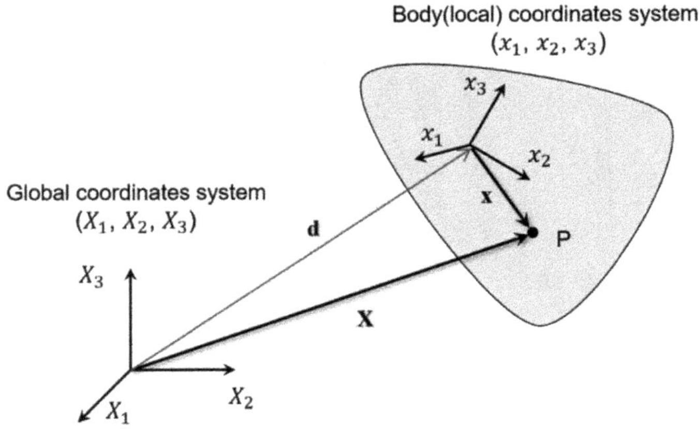

Figure 4.1.2 A body can be observed in global and local positions by observer.

Lagrangian method, the particle state is measured with reference to a global fixed frame of reference.

On the other hand, Eulerian methods utilize a frame of reference attached locally to the area of interest where measurements are to be made. The particle state is then measured relative to this local coordinate system, also known as the body coordinate system. In continuum mechanics, the Lagrangian method is typically used for solid mechanics, while the Eulerian method is often employed in fluid mechanics.

A coordinate transformation gives back the coordinates of a point on a body relative to the global fixed reference frame, given the coordinates of the same point as measured in the local reference frame. This transformation is given by

$$\mathbf{X_g} = \mathbf{Q}\mathbf{X_l} + \mathbf{d}, \tag{4.1.1}$$

where $\mathbf{X_g}$ is the coordinate vector relative to the global frame of reference, $\mathbf{X_l}$ is the coordinate vector relative to the local/body frame of reference, $\mathbf{Q}$ is a 3×3 rotation matrix that represents pure rotation, and $\mathbf{d}$ is an n-dimensional vector that represents pure translation, as shown in Figure 4.1.2.

We now focus on the Lagrangian method. Measurements represented when the body is undeformed are distinguished from those represented when the body is deformed. We use uppercase "$\mathbf{X}$" to denote the coordinates of a point on the body when it is undeformed

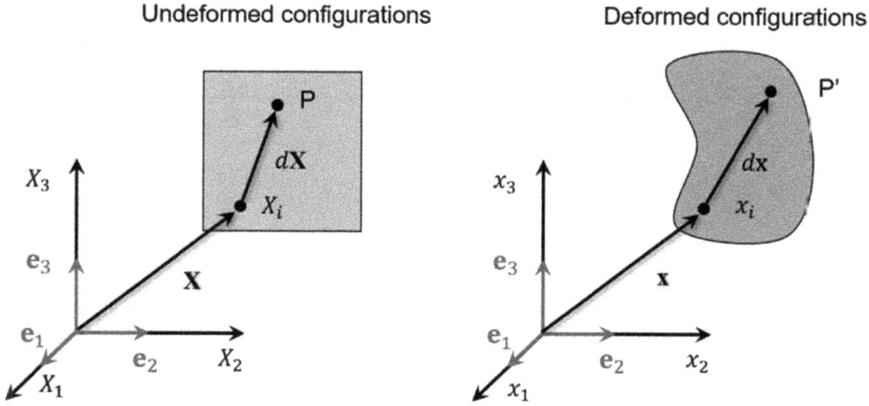

Figure 4.1.3 A body represented in undeformed and deformed configurations.

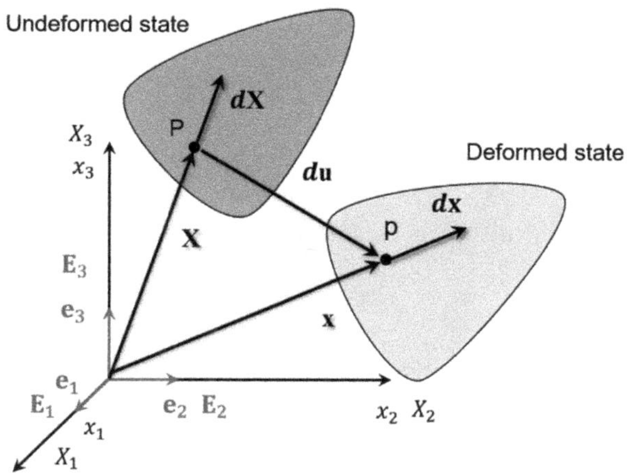

Figure 4.1.4 A body is deformed and can be described in reference and current configurations.

and lowercase "**x**" to represent the coordinates of the same point measured in reference to the same global coordinate system after the body has deformed. The schematic diagram in Figure 4.1.3 illustrates the concept.

4.1.2 *Decomposition Applied on Segment and Area*

As discussed in the previous chapter, a vector d**X** in the reference configuration becomes d**x** after deformation, as shown in Figure 4.1.4.

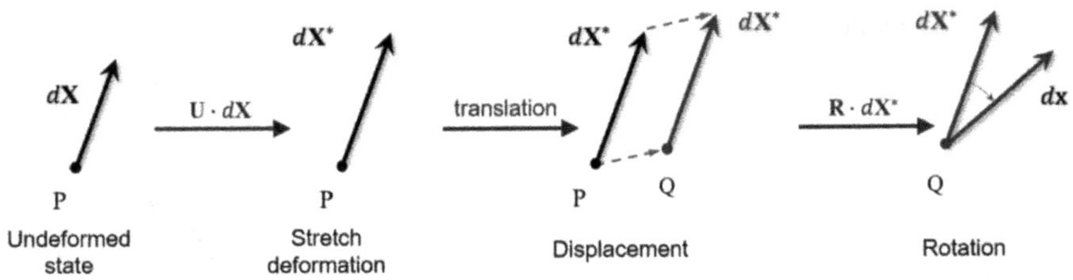

Figure 4.1.5 Deformation can be made of a decomposition into stretch and rotation.

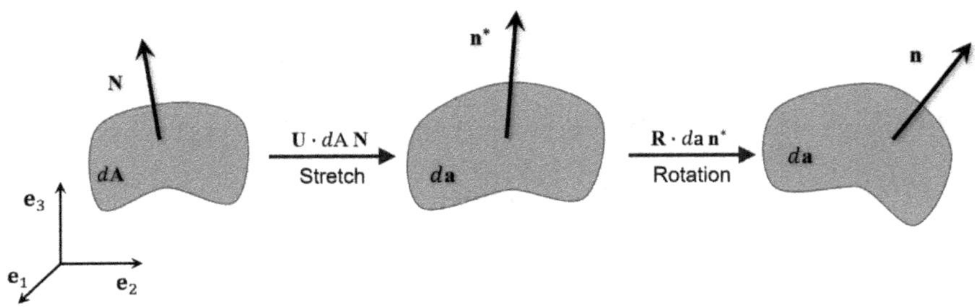

Figure 4.1.6 Polar decomposition applied on an oriented area.

We then have the following relation:

$$\mathrm{D}\mathbf{x} = \mathbf{F}\mathrm{d}\mathbf{X}, \tag{4.1.2}$$

where $\mathbf{F}$ is the deformation gradient that can be decomposed into stretch and rotation deformations, for example,

$$\mathbf{F} = \mathbf{RU}. \tag{4.1.3}$$

This means the effect of applying the deformation gradient tensor $\mathbf{F}$ on a vector $\mathrm{d}\mathbf{X}$ can be considered to have the same result as the effect of first applying a stretch deforming tensor $\mathbf{U}$ (also called the deformation tensor) on $\mathrm{d}\mathbf{X}$, resulting in a vector $\mathrm{d}\mathbf{X}^*$, followed by applying a rotation deforming tensor $\mathbf{R}$ on this new vector $\mathrm{d}\mathbf{X}^*$ to produce the final vector $\mathrm{d}\mathbf{x}$. A schematic diagram illustrating this decomposition is shown in Figure 4.1.5.

An oriented area of a body in the undeformed state is $\mathrm{d}A\,\mathbf{N}$. This area becomes $\mathrm{d}a\,\mathbf{n}^*$ after the application of the stretch tensor $\mathbf{U}$, i.e., $\mathrm{d}a\,\mathbf{n}^* = \mathbf{U} \cdot \mathrm{d}A\,\mathbf{N}$. It is clear whether or not rotation will have an effect on the area $\mathrm{d}a$ itself, but it will rotate the unit vector $\mathbf{n}^*$, which is normal to da, to become the unit vector $\mathbf{n}$. This is illustrated in Figure 4.1.6.

Therefore, we define different stresses in the undeformed and deformed configurations, corresponding to $dA\,\mathbf{N}$ and $da\,\mathbf{n}$, in the following sections.

4.2 Cauchy Stress Tensor and Cauchy's Formula

In this section, we introduce true stress, which is the fundamental concept used in the continuum theory of materials to describe stress. The topics presented in this section were first introduced by Augustin-Louis Cauchy in the 19th century. Cauchy proposed the idea of stress or traction vectors, which represent force vectors per unit area. We also discuss Cauchy's formula and the Cauchy stress tensor.

4.2.1 *Stress Vector*

First, we introduce the true stress, which is the stress measured per unit area of the deformed configuration. Let's consider a continuum body in the current (deformed) configuration that has been divided into two parts by a plane passing through the point P, as shown in Figure 4.2.1. This plane is defined by the point P and the normal vector $\mathbf{n}$ (unit vector). Now, let's consider a deformed area, da, centered at the point P. The internal force acting on this area element is denoted by $\Delta\mathbf{f}$. It's important to note that the surface force acting on a small element of surface area in a continuous medium depends not only on the magnitude of the area but also on its orientation. It is customary to represent the direction of a plane area using a unit vector drawn normal to that plane. The direction of the normal vector is conventionally chosen such that a right-handed screw advances as it is rotated along the boundary curve or contour. We can then define the traction vector (also known as the stress vector) at point P, associated with the normal vector $\mathbf{n}$, as follows:

$$\mathbf{t}(\mathbf{n}) = \lim_{\Delta a \to 0} \frac{\Delta \mathbf{f}}{\Delta a}. \tag{4.2.1}$$

The force vector per unit area is referred to as the "traction vector." The traction vector at a point within a body can be defined by

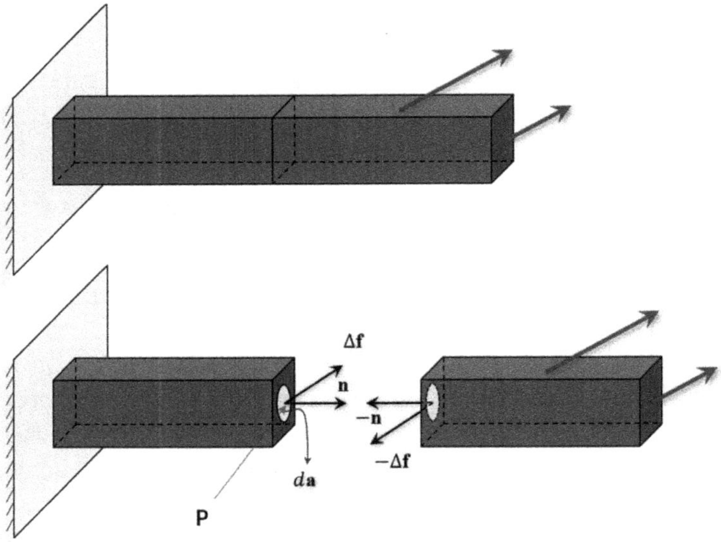

Figure 4.2.1 Traction vector acting at a point in an area with normal vector in the deformed configuration.

removing the adjacent material and considering that a force vector $\Delta\mathbf{f}$ is exerted by the removed material on an area Δa surrounding that point.

We also see that the stress vector $\mathbf{t}(\mathbf{n})$ is a point function of the unit normal vector $\mathbf{n}$, which denotes the orientation of the plane on which $\mathbf{t}$ acts. Because of Newton's third law for action and reaction, we see that $\mathbf{t}(\mathbf{n}) = -\mathbf{t}(-\mathbf{n})$. It is fruitful to establish a relationship between $\mathbf{t}(\mathbf{n})$ and $\mathbf{n}$.

4.2.2 *Cauchy's Formula*

The stress state at a point P is fully described when the traction vector can be determined for any arbitrary plane passing through this point. Cauchy demonstrated that by defining the traction vector on three mutually perpendicular planes passing through the point, we can completely describe the stress state at that point (as shown in Figure 4.2.2).

To establish the relationship between $\mathbf{t}(\mathbf{n})$ and $\mathbf{n}$ for the infinitesimal deformation, we consider an infinitesimal tetrahedron

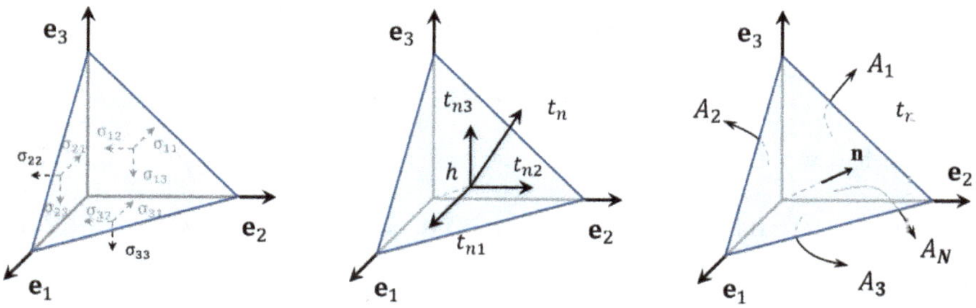

Figure 4.2.2 Cauchy stress tetrahedron: (a) traction components on the faces perpendicular to the basis vectors, (b) components of the traction vector on the inclined face, and (c) areas of the different faces.

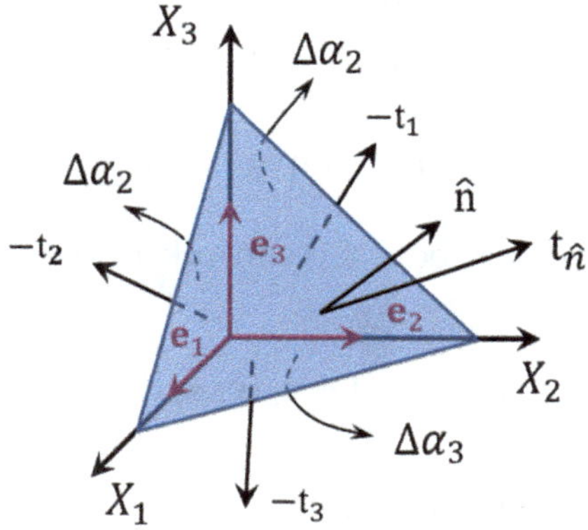

Figure 4.2.3 A tetrahedral element with stress vectors on all its faces.

in Cartesian coordinates. The tetrahedron can originate either from an interior point or from a boundary point. Let $-\mathbf{t}_1, -\mathbf{t}_2, -\mathbf{t}_3$, and $\mathbf{t}(\mathbf{n})$ denote the stress vectors in the outward directions on the faces of the infinitesimal tetrahedron whose areas are $\Delta a_1, \Delta a_2, \Delta a_3$, and Δa, respectively, as shown in Figure 4.2.3. We can derive the following relationship using Newton's second law for the mass inside the tetrahedron considering the equilibrium of the tetrahedron element:

$$\mathbf{t}\Delta a - \mathbf{t}_1\Delta a_1 - \mathbf{t}_2\Delta a_2 - \mathbf{t}_3\Delta a_3 + \rho\Delta v\mathbf{f}_{\mathrm{b}} = \rho\Delta v\mathbf{a}, \tag{4.2.2}$$

where Δv is the volume of the tetrahedron, ρ is the density, $\mathbf{f}_b$ is the body force per unit mass, and $\mathbf{a}$ is the acceleration. Because the total vector area of a closed surface is zero, we have

$$\Delta a\mathbf{n} - \Delta a_1\mathbf{e}_1 - \Delta a_2\mathbf{e}_2 - \Delta a_3\mathbf{e}_3 = 0. \tag{4.2.3}$$

And it follows that

$$\Delta a_1 = (\mathbf{e}_1 \cdot \mathbf{n})\Delta a, \Delta a_2 = (\mathbf{e}_2 \cdot \mathbf{n})\boldsymbol{\Delta}\mathbf{a}, \boldsymbol{\Delta}\mathbf{a_3} = (\mathbf{e_3} \cdot \mathbf{n})\boldsymbol{\Delta}\mathrm{a}. \tag{4.2.4}$$

The volume of the element Δv can be expressed as

$$\Delta v = \frac{\Delta h}{3}\Delta a, \tag{4.2.5}$$

where Δh is the perpendicular distance from the origin to the slant face of tetrahedron. Substitution of Equations (4.2.4) and (4.2.5) into Equation (4.2.2) and dividing throughout by Δa yields

$$\mathbf{t} = \mathbf{t}_1(\mathbf{e}_1 \cdot \mathbf{n}) + \mathbf{t}_2(\mathbf{e}_2 \cdot \mathbf{n}) + \mathbf{t}_3(\mathbf{e}_3 \cdot \mathbf{n}) + \frac{\Delta h}{3}\rho(\mathbf{a} - \mathbf{f}_{\mathrm{b}}). \tag{4.2.6}$$

If the limit as the tetrahedron is shrunk to a point, $\Delta h \to 0$, we obtain

$$\mathbf{t} = \mathbf{t}_1(\mathbf{e}_1 \cdot \mathbf{n}) + \mathbf{t}_2(\mathbf{e}_2 \cdot \mathbf{n}) + \mathbf{t}_3(\mathbf{e}_3 \cdot \mathbf{n}) = \mathbf{t}_{\mathrm{i}}(\mathbf{e}_{\mathrm{i}} \cdot \mathbf{n}). \tag{4.2.7}$$

4.2.3 *Cauchy Stress Tensor*

From Equation (4.2.7), we have

$$\mathbf{t} = (\mathbf{t}_1\mathbf{e}_1 + \mathbf{t}_2\mathbf{e}_2 + \mathbf{t}_3\mathbf{e}_3) \cdot \mathbf{n}. \tag{4.2.8}$$

The terms in the parentheses should be treated as a dyadic, called a stress dyadic or stress tensor (a second-order tensor), denoted by $\boldsymbol{\sigma}$:

$$\boldsymbol{\sigma} \equiv (\mathbf{t}_1\mathbf{e}_1 + \mathbf{t}_2\mathbf{e}_2 + \mathbf{t}_3\mathbf{e}_3) = \mathbf{t}_{\mathbf{j}}\mathbf{e}_{\mathbf{j}}. \tag{4.2.9}$$

From the above definition, it can be found that the stress tensor is a property of the medium that is independent of the unit outward normal vector $\mathbf{n}$. Thus, from Equations (4.2.8) and (4.2.9), we have

$$\mathbf{t}(\mathbf{n}) = \boldsymbol{\sigma} \cdot \mathbf{n} \equiv \mathbf{n} \cdot \boldsymbol{\sigma}^T, t_i = \boldsymbol{\sigma}_{ij}n_j. \tag{4.2.10}$$

Equation (4.2.10) is known as the Cauchy stress formula, and $\boldsymbol{\sigma}$ is termed the Cauchy stress tensor. Thus, the Cauchy stress tensor $\boldsymbol{\sigma}$

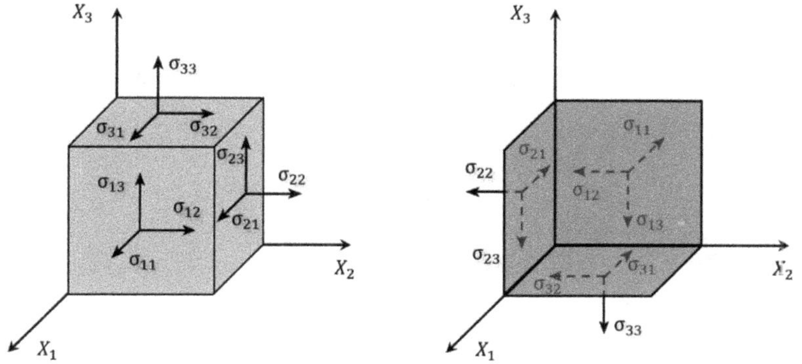

Figure 4.2.4 Definition of the components of the stress components in stress matrix.

is defined to be the current force per unit deformed area, $\mathrm{d}\mathbf{f} = \Delta\mathbf{f} = \mathbf{t}(\mathbf{n})\Delta a = \mathbf{t}(\mathbf{n})\mathrm{d}a = \boldsymbol{\sigma} \cdot \mathrm{d}\mathbf{a}$, where Cauchy's formula, $\mathbf{t}(\mathbf{n}) = \boldsymbol{\sigma} \cdot \mathbf{n}$, and $\mathrm{d}\mathbf{a} = \mathbf{n}\mathrm{d}a$ are used.

In the Cartesian component form, the Cauchy formula in Equation (4.2.10) can be expressed in matrix form as

$$\begin{pmatrix} t_1 \\ t_2 \\ t_3 \end{pmatrix} = \begin{bmatrix} \sigma_{11} & \sigma_{12} & \sigma_{13} \\ \sigma_{21} & \sigma_{22} & \sigma_{23} \\ \sigma_{31} & \sigma_{32} & \sigma_{33} \end{bmatrix} \begin{pmatrix} n_1 \\ n_2 \\ n_3 \end{pmatrix}. \tag{4.2.11}$$

It is useful to resolve the stress vectors into their orthogonal components in a rectangular Cartesian system:

$$\mathbf{t}_j = \mathbf{e}_1\sigma_{1j} + \mathbf{e}_2\sigma_{2j} + \mathbf{e}_3\sigma_{3j} = \mathbf{e}_i\sigma_{ij}, \quad j = 1, 2, 3. \tag{4.2.12}$$

Hence, the stress tensor can be expressed on the Cartesian basis as

$$\boldsymbol{\sigma} = \mathbf{t}_{\mathrm{j}}\mathbf{e}_{\mathrm{j}} = \sigma_{ij}\mathbf{e}_{\mathrm{i}}\mathbf{e}_{\mathrm{j}} = \sigma_{ij}(\mathbf{e}_{\mathrm{i}} \otimes \mathbf{e}_{\mathrm{j}}). \tag{4.2.13}$$

The component σ_{ij} represents the stress in the x_i coordinate direction and on a plane perpendicular to the x_j coordinate, as shown in Figure 4.2.4 on the faces of a point cube (i.e., the faces of the cube can be imagined as the planes passing through a point). We note that the symmetry of $\boldsymbol{\sigma}$ is not assumed. However, it should be noted that the Cauchy stress tensor is a symmetric tensor. Therefore, it holds that $\boldsymbol{\sigma} = \boldsymbol{\sigma}^T$. A proof of this using the basic law of mechanics is provided in Chapter 5.

Example 4.2.1

The state of stress at a point is given in the matrix form

$$[\sigma] = \begin{bmatrix} 2 & 1 & 3 \\ 1 & 2 & -2 \\ 3 & -2 & 1 \end{bmatrix}.$$

Determine:

(a) the traction vector acting on a plane through the point whose unit normal is $\mathbf{n} = (1/3)\mathbf{e}_1 + (2/3)\mathbf{e}_2 - (2/3)\mathbf{e}_3$.
(b) the component of this traction acting perpendicular to the plane,
(c) the shear component of traction.

Solution:

(a) The traction is

$$\begin{pmatrix} t_1 \\ t_2 \\ t_3 \end{pmatrix} = \begin{bmatrix} \sigma_{11} & \sigma_{12} & \sigma_{13} \\ \sigma_{21} & \sigma_{22} & \sigma_{23} \\ \sigma_{31} & \sigma_{32} & \sigma_{33} \end{bmatrix} \begin{pmatrix} n_1 \\ n_2 \\ n_3 \end{pmatrix} = \frac{1}{3} \begin{bmatrix} 2 & 1 & 3 \\ 1 & 2 & -2 \\ 3 & -2 & 1 \end{bmatrix}$$

$$\times \begin{pmatrix} 1 \\ 2 \\ -2 \end{pmatrix} = \frac{1}{3} \begin{pmatrix} -2 \\ 9 \\ -3 \end{pmatrix} \quad \text{or} \quad \mathbf{t} = (-2/3)\mathbf{e}_1 + 3\mathbf{e}_2 - \mathbf{e}_3.$$

(b) The component normal to the plane is the projection of $\mathbf{t}$ in the direction of $\mathbf{n}$, i.e.,

$$\sigma_n = \mathbf{t} \cdot \mathbf{n} = (-2/3)(1/3) + 3(2/3) + (2/3) = 22/9 = 2.4.$$

(c) The shearing component of traction is

$$\sigma_s = \mathbf{t} - (22/9)\mathbf{n} = (-40/27)\mathbf{e}_1 + (37/27)\mathbf{e}_2 + (17/27)\mathbf{e}_3.$$

The magnitude can be obtained as 2.1.

4.3 Other Stress Measures

The Cauchy stress tensor is the most natural and physically meaningful measure of the state of stress at a point in the deformed configuration. It is measured per unit area of the deformed configuration and is the quantity commonly used in spatial descriptions of problems in fluid mechanics or solid mechanics. In order to utilize the Lagrangian description, which is common in solid mechanics, the equations of motion or equilibrium of a material body derived in the deformed configuration must be expressed in terms of the known reference configuration. To achieve this, it is necessary to introduce various other measures of stress.

4.3.1 *First Piola–Kirchhoff Stress Tensor*

Consider a continuum body undergoing a deformation mapping $\mathbf{F}$ that leads to the deformed configuration as illustrated in Figure 4.3.1. Let the force vector acting on an elemental area $\mathrm{d}a$ with a normal vector $\mathbf{n}$ in the deformed configuration be denoted as $\mathrm{d}\mathbf{f}$. The force $\mathrm{d}\mathbf{f}$ can be expressed in terms of the stress vector $\mathbf{t}$ multiplied by the deformed area $\mathrm{d}a$ as follows:

$$\mathrm{D}\mathbf{f} = \mathbf{t}(\mathbf{n})\mathrm{d}a = \boldsymbol{\sigma} \cdot \mathbf{n}\mathrm{d}a = \boldsymbol{\sigma} \cdot \mathrm{d}\mathbf{a}, \tag{4.3.1}$$

where $\boldsymbol{\sigma}$ is the Cauchy stress tensor.

Now, let's consider the area element in the undeformed configuration that corresponds to dA, as shown in Figure 4.3.1. We define a stress vector $\mathbf{T}(\mathbf{N})$ over the area element $\mathrm{d}A$ with a normal vector $\mathbf{N}$ in the undeformed configuration. This stress vector $\mathbf{T}(\mathbf{N})$ is chosen such that it results in the same total force as in the deformed configuration. It is assumed to be the force parallel transport of $\mathrm{d}\mathbf{f}$ from the deformed to undeformed configuration (see Figure 4.3.2):

$$\mathrm{D}\mathbf{f} = \mathbf{t}(\mathbf{n})\mathrm{d}a = \mathbf{T}(\mathbf{N})\mathrm{d}A. \tag{4.3.2}$$

It is clear that both stress vectors have the same direction. The stress vector $\mathbf{T}(\mathbf{N})$ is measured per unit undeformed area, while the stress vector $\mathbf{t}(\mathbf{n})$ is measured per unit deformed area. Similar to Cauchy's formula that relates the Cauchy stress tensor $\boldsymbol{\sigma}$ to the

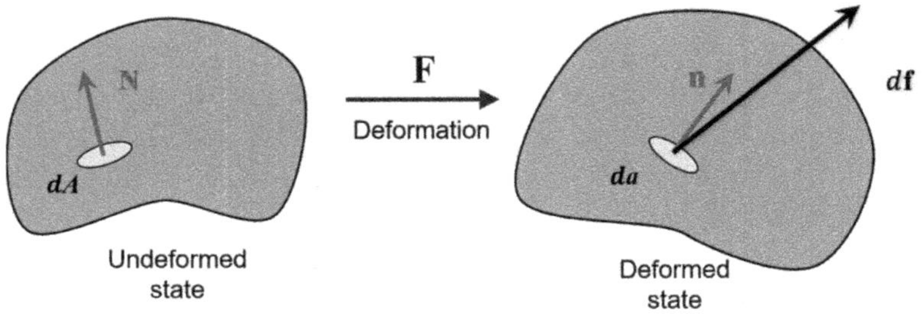

Figure 4.3.1 Deformed and undeformed states of body.

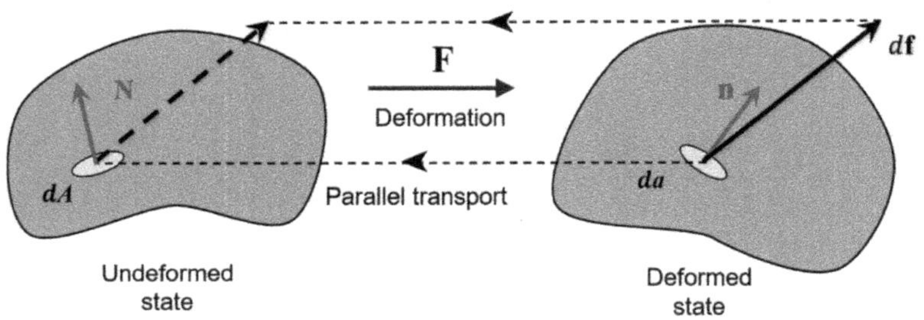

Figure 4.3.2 Definition of the first Piola–Kirchhoff stress tensor in undeformed states.

stress vector $\mathbf{t}$, we can introduce a stress tensor $\mathbf{P}$, known as the first Piola–Kirchhoff stress tensor, to relate the stress vector $\mathbf{T}(\mathbf{N})$. However, they have different magnitudes due to the difference in areas. This can be expressed as follows:

$$\mathbf{t}(\mathbf{n}) = \boldsymbol{\sigma} \cdot \mathbf{n}, \quad \mathbf{T}(\mathbf{N}) = \mathbf{P} \cdot \mathbf{N}. \tag{4.3.3}$$

Therefore, we have

$$\mathrm{d}\mathbf{f} = \boldsymbol{\sigma} \cdot \mathrm{d}\mathbf{a} = \mathbf{P} \cdot \mathrm{d}\mathbf{A}, \quad \mathrm{d}\mathbf{a} = (\mathrm{d}a)\mathbf{n}, \quad \mathrm{d}\mathbf{A} = (\mathrm{d}A)\mathbf{N}. \tag{4.3.4}$$

The first Piola–Kirchhoff stress tensor, also referred to as the nominal stress tensor or Lagrangian stress tensor, gives the current force per unit undeformed area.

The stress vector $\mathbf{T}(\mathbf{N})$ is known as the pseudo-stress vector associated with the first Piola–Kirchhoff stress tensor. The Cartesian component representation of tensor $\mathbf{P}$ is given by

$$\mathbf{P} = P_{ij}\mathbf{e}_{\mathrm{i}}\mathbf{E}_{\mathrm{j}} = P_{ij}\mathbf{e}_{\mathrm{i}} \otimes \mathbf{E}_{\mathrm{j}}, \tag{4.3.5}$$

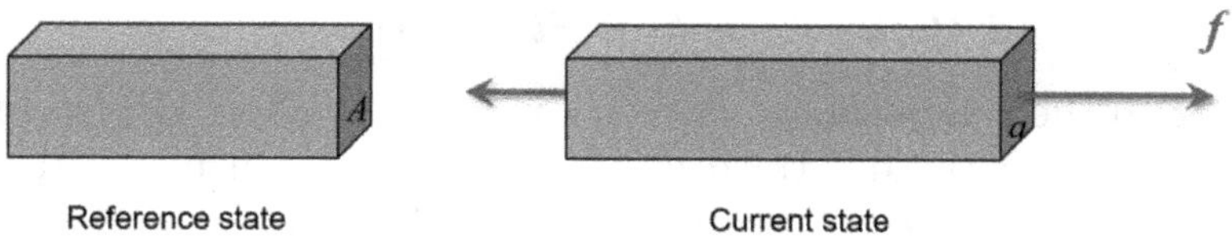

Figure 4.3.3 Nominal stress definition in a rod.

where $\mathbf{e}_\mathrm{i}$ refers to coordinate system for the current configuration and $\mathbf{E}_\mathrm{j}$ refers to the coordinate system for the reference configuration.

The first Piola–Kirchhoff stress tensor is a two-point tensor, similar to the deformation gradient tensor $\mathbf{F}$, as it relates a point in the undeformed body to the corresponding point in the deformed body.

In order to express the first Piola–Kirchhoff stress tensor $\mathbf{P}$ in terms of the Cauchy stress tensor $\boldsymbol{\sigma}$, we need to establish a relationship between the differential area da and the area dA. This relation can be derived from Nanson's formula, which was discussed in Chapter 3, and is given by

$$\mathrm{d}\mathbf{a} = J\mathbf{F}^{-T} \cdot \mathrm{d}\mathbf{A} = J \cdot \mathrm{d}\mathbf{A} \cdot \mathbf{F}^{-1}, \tag{4.3.6}$$

where J is the Jacobian, $J = |\mathbf{F}|$. Substituting this relation into Equation (4.3.4), we obtain

$$\mathbf{P} \cdot \mathrm{d}\mathbf{A} = \boldsymbol{\sigma} \cdot \mathrm{d}\mathbf{a} = J\boldsymbol{\sigma} \cdot \mathbf{F}^{-T} \cdot \mathrm{d}\mathbf{A}. \tag{4.3.7}$$

Thus,

$$\mathbf{P} = J\boldsymbol{\sigma} \cdot \mathbf{F}^{-T}, \quad \boldsymbol{\sigma} = \frac{1}{J}\mathbf{P} \cdot \mathbf{F}^{T}. \tag{4.3.8}$$

In general, the first Piola–Kirchhoff stress tensor $\mathbf{P}$ is unsymmetric, even when the Cauchy stress tensor $\boldsymbol{\sigma}$ is symmetric.

As an example, let us revisit the definition of nominal stress for a rod (see Figure 4.3.3). When subjected to an axial force, the rod undergoes changes in length and cross-sectional area. Let A be the cross-sectional area of the rod in the reference state, in which no force is applied. Let $\mathbf{f}$ represent the axial force in the current state. The nominal stress is defined as

$$\text{nominal stress} = \frac{\text{force in current state}}{\text{area in reference state}}, \quad \mathbf{P} = \frac{\mathbf{f}}{A}. \tag{4.3.9}$$

4.3.2 *Second Piola–Kirchhoff Stress Tensor*

Similar to the relationship between $\mathrm{d}\mathbf{x}$ and $\mathrm{d}\mathbf{X}, \mathrm{d}\mathbf{X} = (\mathbf{F}^{-1}) \cdot (\mathrm{d}\mathbf{x})$, the force $\mathrm{d}\mathbf{f}$ on the deformed elemental area $\mathrm{d}a$ can be related by analogy to the relation between $\mathrm{d}\mathbf{x}$ and $\mathrm{d}\mathbf{X}$, to a force $\mathrm{d}\hat{\mathbf{f}}$ on the undeformed elemental area $\mathrm{d}A$ by

$$\mathrm{d}\hat{\mathbf{f}} = \mathbf{F}^{-1} \cdot \mathrm{d}\mathbf{f}. \tag{4.3.10}$$

This is a modified version of the forces in the deformed body, as shown in Figure 4.3.4.

Then, we can think of the existence of a stress tensor $\mathbf{S}$, in the same way as in Equation (4.4.1), such that

$$\mathrm{d}\hat{\mathbf{f}} = \mathbf{S} \cdot \mathrm{d}\mathbf{A}, \quad \mathrm{d}\mathbf{a} = \mathrm{d}a\mathbf{n}, \quad \mathrm{d}\mathbf{A} = \mathrm{d}A\mathbf{N}. \tag{4.3.11}$$

The quantity $\mathbf{S}$ in the equation is known as the second Piola–Kirchhoff stress tensor. It represents the transformed current force

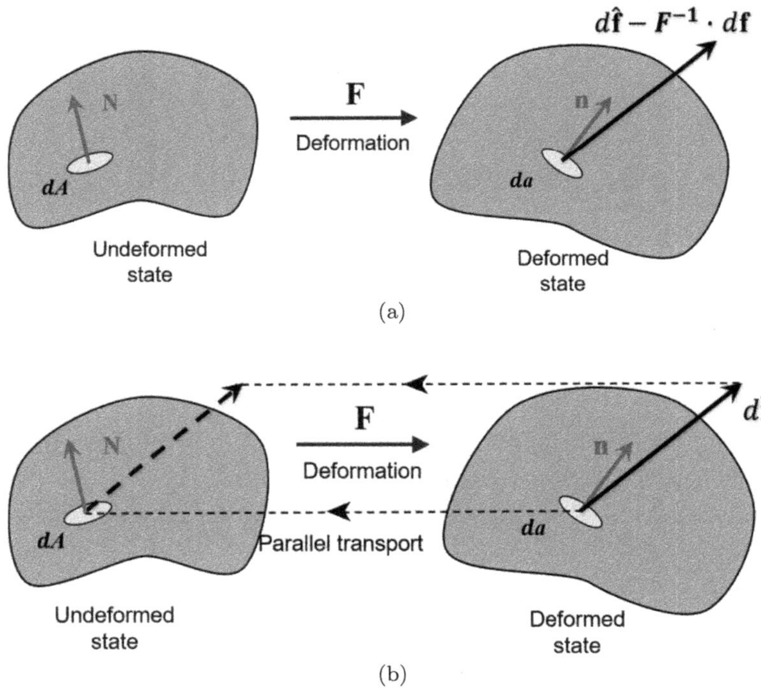

Figure 4.3.4 Second Piola–Kirchhoff stress measure determined in the undeformed state: (a) imaging to create a new force vector, and (b) parallel transport of new force vector from deformed state to undeformed state on area image.

per unit undeformed area or the modified version of the forces in the deformed body per unit undeformed area.

The stress measure $\mathbf{S}$ is similar to the first Piola–Kirchhoff stress measure, except that a new force vector $\mathrm{d}\hat{\mathbf{f}} = \mathbf{F}^{-1} \cdot \mathrm{d}\mathbf{f}$. is created based on $\mathrm{d}\mathbf{f}$ before subjecting the force to parallel transport from the deformed state to the undeformed state. The second Piola–Kirchhoff stress tensor $\mathbf{S}$ can be related to the first Piola–Kirchhoff stress tensor $\mathbf{P}$ using Equations (4.3.4), (4.3.8), and (4.3.10) as follows:

$$\mathbf{S} = \mathbf{F}^{-1} \cdot \mathbf{P}. \tag{4.3.12}$$

The relation between $\mathbf{S}$ and $\boldsymbol{\sigma}$ can also be established using the above equations:

$$\mathbf{S} \cdot \mathrm{d}\mathbf{A} = \mathbf{F}^{-1} \cdot \boldsymbol{\sigma} \cdot \mathrm{d}\mathbf{a} = J\mathbf{F}^{-1} \cdot \boldsymbol{\sigma} \cdot \mathbf{F}^{-T} \cdot \mathrm{d}\mathbf{A} \tag{4.3.13}$$

and

$$\mathbf{S} = J\mathbf{F}^{-1} \cdot \boldsymbol{\sigma} \cdot \mathbf{F}^{-T}, \quad \text{or} \quad \boldsymbol{\sigma} = \frac{1}{J}\mathbf{F} \cdot \mathbf{S} \cdot \mathbf{F}^{T}. \tag{4.3.14}$$

As the Cauchy stress is symmetric, the second Piola–Kirchhoff stress tensor will now be a symmetric tensor (i.e., $\mathbf{S} = \mathbf{S}^T$,) while the first Piola–Kirchhoff stress tensor is nonsymmetric.

The Cartesian component representation of the tensor $\mathbf{S} = \mathbf{S}^T$ is

$$\mathbf{S} = S_{ij}\mathbf{E}_\mathrm{i}\mathbf{E}_\mathrm{j} = S_{ij}\mathbf{E}_\mathrm{i} \otimes \mathbf{E}_\mathrm{j}. \tag{4.3.15}$$

According to definition, we can introduce the pseudo-stress vector $\tilde{\mathbf{T}}(\mathbf{N})$ associated with the second Piola–Kirchhoff stress tensor by

$$\mathrm{d}\hat{\mathbf{f}} = \tilde{\mathbf{T}}\mathrm{d}A = \mathbf{S} \cdot \mathbf{N}\mathrm{d}A = \mathbf{S} \cdot \mathrm{d}\mathbf{A}, \quad \tilde{\mathbf{T}} = \mathbf{S} \cdot \mathbf{N}. \tag{4.3.16}$$

Actually, there is no physical meaning for the second Piola–Kirchhoff stress. However, an interpretation of the second Piola–Kirchhoff stress tensor is possible in the case of rigid-body motion, in which the polar decomposition theorem gives $\mathbf{F} = \mathbf{R}$ and $J = 1$. Hence, we have

$$\mathbf{S} = J\mathbf{F}^{-1} \cdot \boldsymbol{\sigma} \cdot \mathbf{F}^{-T} = \mathbf{R}^T \cdot \boldsymbol{\sigma} \cdot \mathbf{R}. \tag{4.3.17}$$

That is, the second Piola–Kirchhoff stress components are the same as the components of the Cauchy stress tensor expressed in the local set of orthogonal axes that are obtained from rotating the global Cartesian coordinates by the rotation matrix.

4.3.3 *Other Stress Tensors*

Similar to previous definitions for the stress measure, we can define other stress tensors.

We define the Kirchhoff stress tensor $\boldsymbol{\tau}$, which is related to the traction vector $\tilde{\mathbf{t}}(\mathbf{n})$ (current configuration), as

$$\tilde{\mathbf{t}}(\mathbf{n}) = J\mathbf{t} = J\boldsymbol{\sigma}\cdot\mathbf{n} = \boldsymbol{\tau}\cdot\mathbf{n}, \quad \boldsymbol{\tau} = J\boldsymbol{\sigma}. \tag{4.3.18}$$

As we can verify, the Kirchhoff stress tensor is a symmetric second-order tensor and is related to the Cauchy stress tensor and to the first Piola–Kirchhoff stress tensor by means of the following relationships:

$$\boldsymbol{\tau} = J\boldsymbol{\sigma}, \quad \boldsymbol{\tau} = \mathbf{P}\cdot\mathbf{F}^T, \quad \mathbf{P} = \mathbf{F}^{-1}\cdot\boldsymbol{\tau}. \tag{4.3.19}$$

We can also introduce the Biot stress tensor, $\tilde{\mathbf{B}}$, which in general is nonsymmetric:

$$\tilde{\mathbf{B}} = \mathbf{R}^T\cdot\mathbf{P} = J\mathbf{R}^T\cdot\boldsymbol{\sigma}\cdot\mathbf{F}^{-T}. \tag{4.3.20}$$

In different applications, it is possible to define additional stress tensors based on specific requirements. It is important to note that these stress tensors should correspond to a conjugate pair of stress measures. The relationship between these stress measures and their associated tensors is discussed in the following section.

4.4 Stress State and Principal Stresses

4.4.1 *Stress State of a Point*

If a continuum body is subjected to external forces, such as surface forces or gravity, it will also experience internal forces. These internal forces can be represented by the traction vector field or stress, which is the force per unit area. This traction vector field serves as the basis for establishing the stress state at each material point within the continuum body. Various stress measures can be employed to characterize the stress state in the continuous medium. It is important to note that the stress state at a material point in the continuum is not influenced by the choice of coordinate system.

The stress state at a point P can be fully described by determining the traction vector for any arbitrary plane passing through

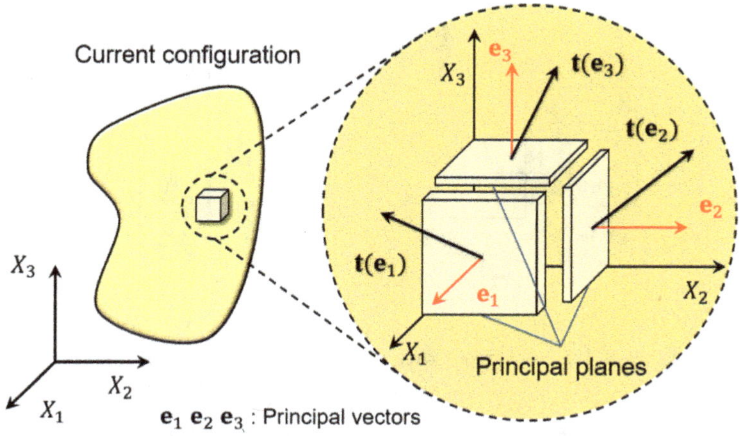

Figure 4.4.1 The stress state at the point P.

that point. Consequently, the stress state is defined regardless of the stress measurement techniques employed.

As defined in the preceding section, the Cauchy stress tensor, denoted by $\boldsymbol{\sigma}$, is a second-order tensor possessing all the properties discussed in Chapter 2. These properties include the definition of principal invariants I_1, I_2, I_3, transformation laws for the components of the tensor, and the eigenvalues (principal values) and eigenvectors (principal planes) of the Cauchy stress tensor (refer to Figure 4.4.1).

4.4.1.1 *Invariants of stress tensor*

For a given stress state, the stress tensor $\boldsymbol{\sigma}$ can be expressed matrix form, as shown in Figure 4.4.2.

The matrix form of stress is

$$[\sigma] = \begin{bmatrix} \sigma_{11} & \sigma_{12} & \sigma_{13} \\ \sigma_{21} & \sigma_{22} & \sigma_{23} \\ \sigma_{31} & \sigma_{32} & \sigma_{33} \end{bmatrix}. \tag{4.4.1}$$

Therefore, the invariants of the stress tensor $\boldsymbol{\sigma}$ are defined by

$$I_1 = \mathrm{tr}[\boldsymbol{\sigma}], \quad I_2 = \frac{1}{2}[(\mathrm{tr}[\boldsymbol{\sigma}])^2 - \mathrm{tr}([\boldsymbol{\sigma}]^2), \quad I_3 = |\boldsymbol{\sigma}| \tag{4.4.2}$$

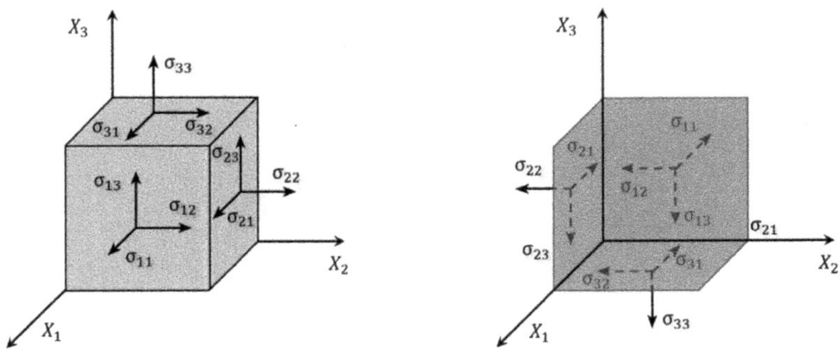

Figure 4.4.2 A stress state of a point as the stress matrix.

and, in terms of the rectangular Cartesian components, by

$$I_1 = \sigma_{ii}, \quad I_2 = \frac{1}{2}(\sigma_{ii}\sigma_{jj} - \sigma_{ij}\sigma_{ji}), \quad I_3 = |\boldsymbol{\sigma}|. \tag{4.4.3}$$

4.4.1.2 *Transformation equations of stress tensor*

The components of the Cauchy stress tensor, denoted as $\boldsymbol{\sigma}$, in one rectangular Cartesian coordinate system, denoted as $(\hat{\mathbf{e}}_1, \hat{\mathbf{e}}_2, \hat{\mathbf{e}}_3)$, are related to the components in another rectangular Cartesian system, denoted as $(\mathbf{e}_1, \mathbf{e}_2, \mathbf{e}_3)$, according to the transformation law discussed in Chapter 2 for second-order tensors:

$$\hat{\sigma}_{ii} = l_{ik}l_{jl}\sigma_{kl}, \quad \text{or} \quad [\hat{\boldsymbol{\sigma}}] = [\mathbf{L}][\hat{\boldsymbol{\sigma}}][\mathbf{L}]^T, \tag{4.4.4}$$

where l_{ij} are the direction cosines

$$l_{ij} = \hat{\mathbf{e}}_i\mathbf{e}_j. \tag{4.4.5}$$

Note that Equation (4.4.4) is valid for the rectangular components of any second-order tensor and for a general coordinate transformation.

4.4.2 *Principal Stresses and Principal Planes for Stress State of a Point*

In the design of structures, it is crucial to determine the maximum normal and shear stresses at a given point for a specific state of stress. Failures often occur when the magnitudes of these stresses surpass the allowable stress values, known as the strengths of the material.

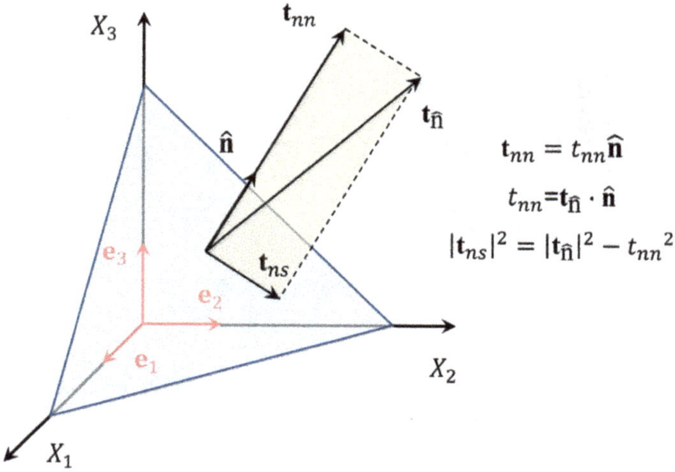

Figure 4.4.3 A tetrahedral element with stress vectors on its $\hat{\mathbf{n}}$ plan.

The determination of these maximum stresses depends on the chosen strength criteria. Consequently, it becomes important to identify both the values and the planes on which these stresses are maximized. To accomplish this, it is necessary to determine the eigenvalues and eigenvectors associated with the stress tensor.

Based on Figure 4.4.3, it is evident that the normal component of a stress vector reaches its maximum when the direction of alignment is parallel to the unit outward normal vector $\hat{\mathbf{n}}$, denoted as $\mathbf{t} = \mathbf{t}_{\hat{\mathbf{n}}} = |\mathbf{t}|\hat{\mathbf{n}}$. In other words, we need to identify the plane (represented by $\hat{\mathbf{n}}$) where the normal stress $\mathbf{t}_{\hat{\mathbf{n}}}$ is maximized. It is worth noting that there exist three planes in which the normal stress reaches its maximum value, while the projected shear stress is zero.

If we denote this value of the normal stress by λ, then we can write $\mathbf{t} = \lambda\hat{\mathbf{n}}$, and by Cauchy's formula, $\mathbf{t} = \boldsymbol{\sigma} \cdot \hat{\mathbf{n}}$. Thus, we have

$$\mathbf{t} = \boldsymbol{\sigma} \cdot \hat{\mathbf{n}} = \lambda\hat{\mathbf{n}} \quad \text{or} \quad (\boldsymbol{\sigma} - \lambda\mathbf{I}) \cdot \hat{\mathbf{n}} = 0. \tag{4.4.6}$$

This is a set of equations for the components of vector $\hat{\mathbf{n}}$; hence, a nontrivial solution will not exist unless the determinant of the matrix satisfies $|(\boldsymbol{\sigma} - \lambda\mathbf{I})| = 0$. The vanishing of this determinant yields a cubic equation for λ, called the characteristic equation

$$\text{Det}(\boldsymbol{\sigma} - \lambda\mathbf{I}) = -\lambda^3 + I_1(\boldsymbol{\sigma})\lambda^2 - I_2(\boldsymbol{\sigma})\lambda + I_3(\boldsymbol{\sigma}) = 0. \tag{4.4.7}$$

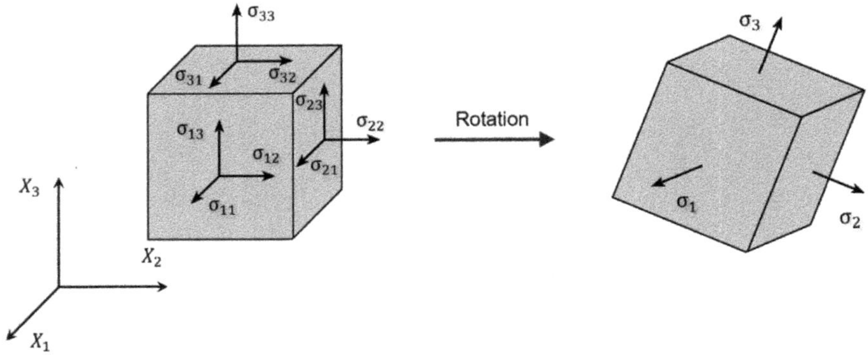

Figure 4.4.4 For a state of stress in one point, a state of principal stresses can be obtained through rotation of unit element.

Solving this cubic equation provides three values of λ known as the principal stresses. The corresponding eigenvectors are referred to as the principal planes. Consequently, for a given state of stress at a specific point P within the body B, a set of planes $\hat{\mathbf{n}}$ exists where the stress vector is perpendicular to the planes, implying the absence of shear components on those planes. For a state of stress in one point, a state of principal stresses can be obtained through rotation of unit element, as shown in Figure 4.4.4.

4.4.3 *Deviatoric Stress Tensor*

In stress analysis, it is sometimes convenient to introduce a deviatoric stress tensor. This is particularly useful when computing the eigenvalues of the stress tensor, as finding the eigenvalues of the deviatoric stress tensor can simplify the process. The deviatoric stress tensor, denoted as $\boldsymbol{\sigma}'$, can be defined as follows:

$$\boldsymbol{\sigma}' = \boldsymbol{\sigma} - \frac{1}{3}\text{tr}(\boldsymbol{\sigma})\mathbf{I} \quad \text{or} \quad \left(\sigma'_{ij} = \sigma_{ij} - \frac{1}{3}\sigma_{kk}\delta\lambda_{ij}\right). \tag{4.4.8}$$

Let σ_m denote the mean normal stress:

$$\sigma_m = \frac{1}{3}\text{tr}(\boldsymbol{\sigma}) = \frac{1}{3}I_1 \quad \text{or} \quad \left(\sigma_m = \frac{1}{3}\sigma_{kk}\right). \tag{4.4.9}$$

Then, any stress tensor can be expressed as the sum of the spherical or hydrostatic part and the deviatoric part of the stress

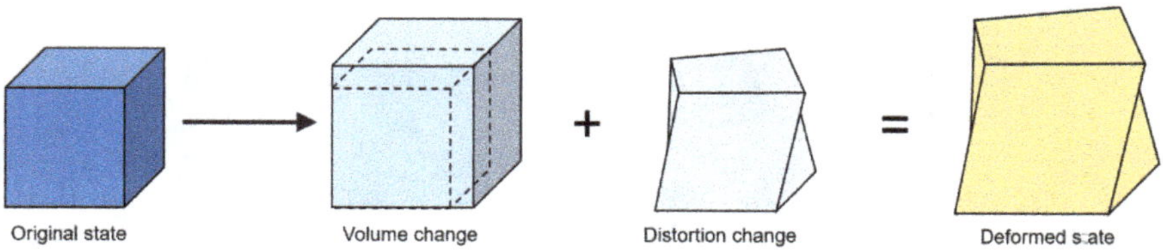

Figure 4.4.5 The deformation can be decomposed volume change and distortion change.

tensor:

$$\boldsymbol{\sigma} = \boldsymbol{\sigma}_{\mathrm{m}}\mathbf{I} + \boldsymbol{\sigma}', \tag{4.4.10}$$

$$\begin{bmatrix} \sigma_{11} & \sigma_{12} & \sigma_{13} \\ \sigma_{21} & \sigma_{22} & \sigma_{23} \\ \sigma_{31} & \sigma_{32} & \sigma_{33} \end{bmatrix} = \begin{bmatrix} \sigma_m & 0 & 0 \\ 0 & \sigma_m & 0 \\ 0 & 0 & \sigma_m \end{bmatrix} + \begin{bmatrix} \sigma'_{11} & \sigma'_{12} & \sigma'_{13} \\ \sigma'_{21} & \sigma'_{22} & \sigma'_{23} \\ \sigma'_{31} & \sigma'_{32} & \sigma'_{33} \end{bmatrix}. \tag{4.4.11}$$

Similarly, the invariants of the deviatoric stress tensor I'_1, I'_2, I'_3 are

$$I'_1 = 0, \quad I'_2 = \frac{1}{2}\sigma'_{ij}\sigma'_{ij}, \quad I'_3 = \frac{1}{3}\sigma'_{ij}\sigma'_{jk}\sigma'_{ki}. \tag{4.4.12}$$

The deviatoric stress invariants are particularly important in the determination of the principal stresses.

For isotropic materials, the deformation of a body can be understood as a combination of volume change and distortion change, as illustrated in Figure 4.4.5. The volume change is influenced by the mean normal stress, while the distortion change is influenced by the deviatoric stress.

4.4.4 *Graphical Representation of a Symmetric Stress Tensor (Mohr's Circle)*

In the preceding section, we explored the process of determining the maximum normal stresses at a given point. The eigenvalues of the stress tensor at that point represent the maximum normal stresses on three mutually perpendicular planes, with their corresponding eigenvectors as the plane normals. The highest of these three stresses is considered the true maximum normal stress. It is important to note

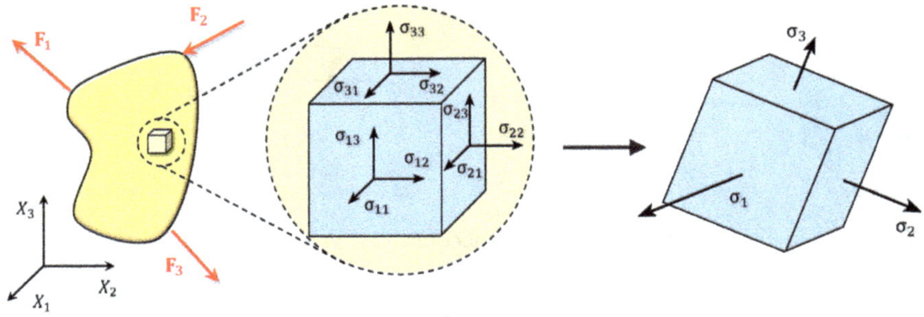

Figure 4.4.6 Principal stresses $\sigma_1 > \sigma_2 > \sigma_3$ of a stress state.

that the principal planes have zero shear stresses (see Figure 4.4.6). However, how do we determine the maximum shear stresses and the planes associated with them? To achieve this, we employ the graphical representation of a symmetric second-order stress tensor, known as Mohr's circle.

Once again, we work in the principal space, and we assume that the eigenvalues λ are ordered such that $\sigma_1 > \sigma_2 > \sigma_3$.

From Figure 4.4.3, it can be found that

$$t_{nn}^2 + t_{ns}^2 = \mathbf{t}_n \cdot \mathbf{t}_n = |\mathbf{t}_n|. \tag{4.4.13}$$

Then, the components of $\mathbf{t}_n$ in the principal space can be given as

$$t_1 = \sigma_1 n_1, \quad \mathrm{t}_2 = \sigma_2 n_2, \quad \mathrm{t}_3 = \sigma_3 n_3, \tag{4.4.14}$$

where n_1, n_2, n_3 are components of $\mathbf{n}$ in the principal space. Next, the dot product $\mathbf{t}_n \cdot \mathbf{t}_n$ is evaluated as follows:

$$\begin{aligned}\mathbf{t}_n \cdot \mathbf{t}_n &= t_i \mathbf{e}_\mathrm{i} \cdot t_j \mathbf{e}_\mathrm{j} = t_i t_j \delta_{ij} = t_i t_i = \mathrm{t}_1 t_1 + t_2 t_2 + t_3 t_3 \\ &= \sigma_1^2 n_1^2 + \sigma_2^2 n_2^2 + \sigma_3^2 n_3^2, \end{aligned} \tag{4.4.15}$$

and by combining the above equations, we obtain

$$t_{nn}^2 + t_{ns}^2 = \sigma_1^2 n_1^2 + \sigma_2^2 n_2^2 + \sigma_3^2 n_3^2. \tag{4.4.16}$$

Then, the normal component t_{nn}, in the principal space, can be expressed as

$$t_{nn} = \mathbf{t}_n \cdot \mathbf{n} = \sigma_{ij} n_j n_i = \sigma_1 n_1^2 + \sigma_2 n_2^2 + \sigma_3 n_3^2. \tag{4.4.17}$$

Let us consider the constraint $n_i n_i = 1 \Rightarrow n_1^2 = 1 - n_2^2 - n_3^2$, which if we substitute into above equation give us the value of n_2^2:

$$t_{nn} = \sigma_1(1 - n_2^2 - n_3^2) + \sigma_2 n_2^2 + \sigma_3 n_3^2 \Rightarrow \mathrm{n}_2^2$$
$$= \frac{t_{nn} - \sigma_3 n_3^2 + \sigma_1 n_3^2 - \sigma_1}{(\sigma_2 - \sigma_1)}. \tag{4.4.18}$$

Then, substituting $n_1^2 = 1 - n_2^2 - n_3^2$ into the equation

$$t_{nn}^2 + t_{ns}^2 = \sigma_1^2 n_1^2 + \sigma_2^2 n_2^2 + \sigma_3^2 n_3^2 = \sigma_1^2(1 - n_2^2 - n_3^2) + \sigma_2^2 n_2^2 + \sigma_3^2 n_3^2, \tag{4.4.19}$$

and substituting n_2^2, obtained from Equation (4.4.18), into the above equation results in

$$t_{nn}^2 + t_{ns}^2 = [(\sigma_3 - \sigma_1)(\sigma_3 - \sigma_2)]n_3^2 + \sigma_2 t_{nn} + \sigma_1 t_{nn} - \sigma_2\sigma_3. \tag{4.4.20}$$

Next, if we evaluate the term n_3^2, we obtain

$$n_3^2 = \frac{(t_{nn} - \sigma_1)(t_{nn} - \sigma_2) + t_{ns}^2}{(\sigma_3 - \sigma_1)(\sigma_3 - \sigma_2)}. \tag{4.4.21}$$

Then, we find n_1^2, n_2^2 in a similar fashion. Finally, we can summarize the results as follows:

$$\begin{cases} n_1^2 = \dfrac{(t_{nn} - \sigma_2)(t_{nn} - \sigma_3) + t_{ns}^2}{(\sigma_1 - \sigma_2)(\sigma_1 - \sigma_3)} \geq 0, \\ n_2^2 = \dfrac{(t_{nn} - \sigma_3)(t_{nn} - \sigma_1) + t_{ns}^2}{(\sigma_2 - \sigma_3)(\sigma_2 - \sigma_1)} \geq 0, \\ n_3^2 = \dfrac{(t_{nn} - \sigma_1)(t_{nn} - \sigma_2) + t_{ns}^2}{(\sigma_3 - \sigma_1)(\sigma_3 - \sigma_2)} \geq 0. \end{cases} \tag{4.4.22}$$

If we consider the equation $\sigma_1 > \sigma_2 > \sigma_3$ and examine its components, we can verify that the first and third equations have positive denominators. Therefore, their numerators must also be positive. However, the second equation in the sequence has negative denominators, indicating that its numerator must be negative. In other words, we can summarize the relationship as follows:

$$\begin{cases} (t_{nn} - \sigma_2)(t_{nn} - \sigma_3) + t_{ns}^2 \geq 0, \\ (t_{nn} - \sigma_3)(t_{nn} - \sigma_1) + t_{ns}^2 \leq 0, \\ (t_{nn} - \sigma_1)(t_{nn} - \sigma_2) + t_{ns}^2 \geq 0. \end{cases} \tag{4.4.23}$$

Then, after some algebraic manipulations, the previous inequalities (4.4.23) become

$$\begin{cases} t_{ns}^2 + \left[t_{nn} - \frac{1}{2}(\sigma_2 + \sigma_3)\right]^2 \geq \left[\frac{1}{2}(\sigma_2 - \sigma_3)\right]^2, \\ t_{ns}^2 + \left[t_{nn} - \frac{1}{2}(\sigma_1 + \sigma_3)\right]^2 \leq \left[\frac{1}{2}(\sigma_1 - \sigma_3)\right]^2, \\ t_{ns}^2 + \left[t_{nn} - \frac{1}{2}(\sigma_1 + \sigma_2)\right]^2 \leq \left[\frac{1}{2}(\sigma_1 - \sigma_2)\right]^2. \end{cases} \tag{4.4.24}$$

The above are equations of circles. The first circle with the center at $\frac{1}{2}(\sigma_2 + \sigma_3)$ and a radius of $\frac{1}{2}(\sigma_2 - \sigma_3)$ indicates that the feasible points for the pair (t_{nn}, t_{ns}) are outside the circle C_1, including the circumference.

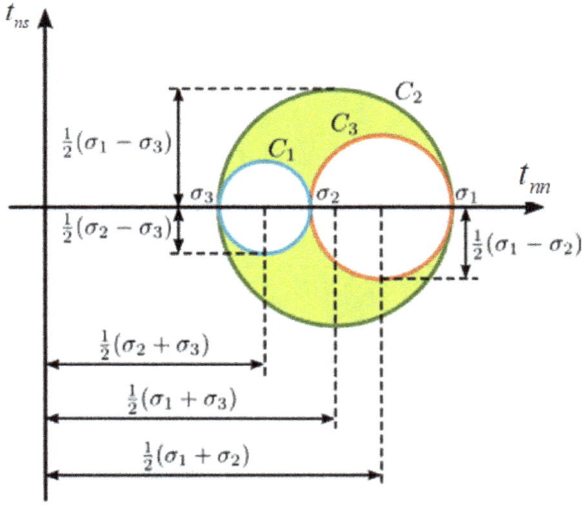

Figure 4.4.7 Mohr's circle: feasible region.

The second circle with the center at $\frac{1}{2}(\sigma_1 + \sigma_3)$ and a radius of $\frac{1}{2}(\sigma_1 - \sigma_3)$ indicates that the feasible values for the pair (t_{nn}, t_{ns}) are inside the circle C_2, including the circumference.

The third inequality indicates that the feasible values for the pair (t_{nn}, t_{ns}) are outside the circle C_3, which is defined by a radius of $\frac{1}{2}(\sigma_1 - \sigma_2)$ and the center at $\frac{1}{2}(\sigma_1 + \sigma_2)$.

Then, taking the three equations into account simultaneously, the feasible region is formed by the pair (t_{nn}, t_{ns}), defined in the light-green area, which includes the circumferences C_1, C_2, and C_3 (see Figure 4.4.7).

In Mohr's circle, we can identify the maximum values of shear stress t_{ns}, which is $\frac{1}{2}(\sigma_1 - \sigma_3)$.

4.5 Objectivity of Stress Tensors

Let κ represent a reference frame with the origin at O, where $\mathbf{x}$ denotes the current position of a specific particle at time t. Let κ^* denote another reference frame with the origin at O^* and time denoted as t^*. In the case of second-order tensor fields, the tensors are referred to as frame-indifferent or objective if they undergo transformations as described by the following equations:

$$\mathbf{S}^*(\mathrm{x}^*, t^*) = \mathbf{Q}(t) \cdot \mathbf{S}(\mathrm{x}, t) \cdot \mathbf{Q}^T(t), \tag{4.5.1}$$

where $\mathbf{x}^* = \mathbf{c}(t) + \mathbf{Q}(t) \cdot \mathbf{x}, t^* = t - a$ and $\mathbf{Q}$ is a proper orthogonal tensor that rotates frame κ^* into frame κ, $\mathbf{c}(t)$ is a vector from O to O^* that depends only on time t, and a is a constant.

Thus, a change in observer simply alters the description of an event. In essence, objectivity ensures that the direction(s) and magnitude are independent of the coordinate frame used to describe them. As discussed in the previous chapter, under the general rigid-body mapping between observer O and observer O^*, if the reference configuration is independent of the observer, the right Cauchy–Green deformation tensor $\mathbf{C}$ and the Green–Lagrange strain tensor $\mathbb{E}$ remain unchanged under the observer transformation, making them objective. What about stress tensors? We address this in the following section.

4.5.1 *Cauchy Stress Tensor*

The Cauchy stress tensor is objective if we can show that $\boldsymbol{\sigma}* = \mathbf{Q} \cdot \boldsymbol{\sigma} \cdot \mathbf{Q}^T$ according to the definition of the objectivity of various order tensors. We begin with the relations

$$\mathbf{t} = \boldsymbol{\sigma}\mathbf{n}, \quad \mathbf{t}^* = \boldsymbol{\sigma}^*\mathbf{n}^*; \quad \mathbf{t}^* = \mathbf{Q} \cdot \mathbf{t}, \quad \mathbf{n}^* = \mathbf{Q} \cdot \mathbf{n}. \tag{4.5.2}$$

Then, we have

$$\mathbf{t}^* = \boldsymbol{\sigma}^*\mathbf{n}^* = \boldsymbol{\sigma}^* \cdot (\mathbf{Q} \cdot \mathbf{n}), \quad \mathbf{t}^* = \mathbf{Q} \cdot \mathbf{t} = \mathbf{Q} \cdot \boldsymbol{\sigma} \cdot \mathbf{n}. \tag{4.5.3}$$

Therefore,

$$\boldsymbol{\sigma}^* \cdot \mathbf{Q} = \mathbf{Q} \cdot \boldsymbol{\sigma} \quad \text{and} \quad \boldsymbol{\sigma}^* = \mathbf{Q} \cdot \boldsymbol{\sigma} \cdot \mathbf{Q}^T. \tag{4.5.4}$$

Thus, the Cauchy stress tensor is objective.

4.5.2 *First Piola–Kirchhoff Stress Tensor*

The first Piola–Kirchhoff stress tensor $\mathbf{P}$ is a two-point tensor that undergoes transformations similar to those of other two-point tensors, such as $\mathbf{F}$. To establish this, we begin by examining the relation between $\mathbf{P}$ and $\boldsymbol{\sigma}$ following the superposed rigid-body motion. In doing so, we utilize the following relationships:

$$\begin{cases} \mathbf{F}^* = \mathbf{Q} \cdot \mathbf{F}, \quad J = J^*, \\ \mathbf{P} = J\boldsymbol{\sigma} \cdot \mathbf{F}^{-T}, \quad \boldsymbol{\sigma} = \frac{1}{J}\mathbf{P} \cdot \mathbf{F}^T. \end{cases} \tag{4.5.5}$$

Then, we have

$$\begin{aligned} \mathbf{P}^* &= J^*\boldsymbol{\sigma}^* \cdot (\mathbf{F}^*)^{-T} = J(\mathbf{Q} \cdot \boldsymbol{\sigma} \cdot \mathbf{Q}^T) \cdot (\mathbf{Q} \cdot \mathbf{F})^{-T} \\ &= J\mathbf{Q} \cdot \boldsymbol{\sigma} \cdot (\mathbf{Q}^T \cdot \mathbf{Q}^{-T}) \cdot \mathbf{F}^{-T} = J\mathbf{Q} \cdot \boldsymbol{\sigma} \cdot \mathbf{F}^{-T} = \mathbf{Q} \cdot \mathbf{P}. \end{aligned} \tag{4.5.6}$$

Hence, based on Equation (4.5.6), $\mathbf{P}$, being a two-point tensor, undergoes transformations similar to a vector during superposed rigid-body motion, establishing its objectivity. This tensor serves the purpose of connecting a point in the undeformed body to its corresponding point in the deformed body.

4.5.3 *Second Piola–Kirchhoff Stress Tensor*

The second Piola–Kirchhoff stress tensor $\mathbf{S}$ is a widely used stress tensor in the field of solid mechanics. Since it is defined with respect to the reference configuration, rigid-body motion should not affect it. This can be shown using the following relationships: $\mathbf{F}^* = \mathbf{Q} \cdot \mathbf{F}$, $J = J^*$ and $\boldsymbol{\sigma}^* = \mathbf{Q} \cdot \boldsymbol{\sigma} \cdot \mathbf{Q}^T$. Hence,

$$\begin{aligned} \mathbf{S}^* &= J^*(\mathbf{F}^*)^{-1} \cdot \boldsymbol{\sigma}^* \cdot (\mathbf{F}^*)^{-T} \\ &= J(\mathbf{F}^{-1} \cdot \mathbf{Q}^{-1}) \cdot (\mathbf{Q} \cdot \boldsymbol{\sigma} \cdot \mathbf{Q}^T) \cdot (\mathbf{Q}^{-T} \cdot \mathbf{F}^{-T}) \\ &= J\mathbf{F}^{-1} \cdot \boldsymbol{\sigma} \cdot \mathbf{F}^{-T} = \mathbf{S}. \end{aligned} \tag{4.5.7}$$

Thus, the second Piola–Kirchhoff stress tensor $\mathbf{S}$ is not affected by the superposed rigid-body motion; therefore, it is objective.

4.6 Conjugate Pair for Stress Tensors

When establishing constitutive equations, it is necessary to understand the relationship between stress tensors and strain tensors. Formulating a constitutive relation for a material involves finding a formula that connects the stress measure to the strain measure. Therefore, when using a specific stress measure, the corresponding strain measure must be selected appropriately. The key question is: Given a stress tensor, such as those discussed earlier, how do we determine or select the correct strain tensor to be used in conjunction with it?

To discuss this in a more general context, the stress tensor is denoted as $\tilde{\mathbf{T}}$ and its conjugate pair, the strain tensor, as $\tilde{\mathbf{E}}$. The stress measure $\tilde{\mathbf{T}}$ can be any of the stress measures mentioned earlier, such as the Cauchy stress tensor or the second Piola–Kirchhoff stress tensor. The appropriate strain tensor is determined accordingly. Regardless of the stress and strain measures chosen (or the rate of strain), their combination provides a measure of the work done or power expended. Therefore, it is crucial for the stress and strain tensors to be conjugate. Hence, we need to consider the conjugate pair, denoted as $(\tilde{\mathbf{T}}, \tilde{\mathbf{E}})$.

Let W denote the current amount of energy stored per unit volume due to the deformation of the body. The rate at which this

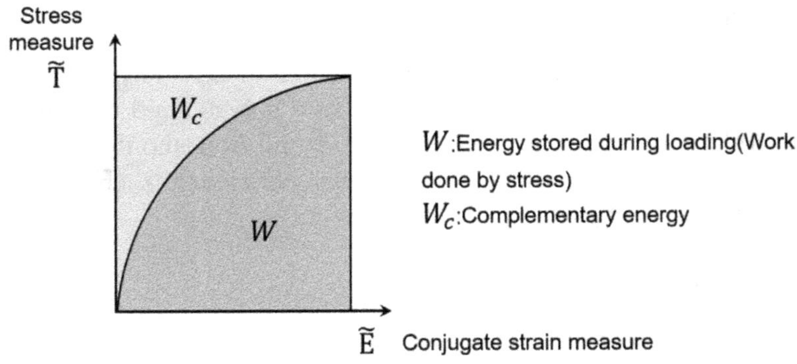

Figure 4.6.1 Stress and conjugate strain relationship and their work density.

energy changes over time is equal to the stress multiplied by the strain rate. Therefore, we have the following relation:

$$\dot{W} = \tilde{\mathbf{T}} : \frac{\partial \tilde{\mathbf{E}}}{\partial t}. \tag{4.6.1}$$

For example, a stress–strain diagram of hyperelastic materials under large deformation is shown in Figure 4.6.1.

The strain measure $\tilde{\mathbf{E}}$ (the conjugate pair for the stress measure $\tilde{\mathbf{T}}$) must satisfy the relation

$$\begin{cases} \dfrac{\partial W}{\partial t} = \dfrac{\partial W}{\partial \tilde{\mathbf{E}}} : \dfrac{\partial \tilde{\mathbf{E}}}{\partial t}, \\ \dot{W} = \tilde{\mathbf{T}} : \dfrac{\partial \tilde{\mathbf{E}}}{\partial t} = \tilde{\mathbf{T}} : \dot{\tilde{\mathbf{E}}}. \end{cases} \tag{4.6.2}$$

Therefore, for each stress/strain conjugate pair, the terms $\frac{\partial W}{\partial t}, \frac{\partial \tilde{\mathbf{E}}}{\partial t}, \tilde{\mathbf{E}}$ will be derived.

4.6.1 *Conjugate Pair for Cauchy Stress Tensor*

In the deformed state, the true stress tensor is the Cauchy stress tensor denoted as $\boldsymbol{\sigma}$, and the corresponding strain rate in this state is known to be

$$\frac{1}{2}(\tilde{\mathbf{e}} + \tilde{\mathbf{e}}^T) = \mathbf{D} = \frac{1}{2}(\mathbf{L} + \mathbf{L}^T), \tag{4.6.3}$$

where $\tilde{\mathbf{e}}$ or $\mathbf{L}$ is the velocity gradient tensor. It is shown in the following:

$$\tilde{\mathbf{e}} = \dot{\mathbf{F}} \cdot \mathbf{F}^{-1} = \mathbf{L}. \tag{4.6.4}$$

Hence, in the deformed state,

$$\dot{W} = \boldsymbol{\sigma} : \mathbf{D} = \boldsymbol{\sigma} : \frac{1}{2}(\dot{\mathbf{F}} \cdot \mathbf{F}^{-1} + \mathbf{F}^{-T} \cdot \dot{\mathbf{F}}^{T}). \tag{4.6.5}$$

In other words, the conjugate strain for the Cauchy stress tensor is given by $\tilde{\mathbf{E}}$ such that

$$\frac{\partial \tilde{\mathbf{E}}}{\partial t} = \mathbf{D} = \frac{1}{2}(\dot{\mathbf{F}} \cdot \mathbf{F}^{-1} + \mathbf{F}^{-T} \cdot \dot{\mathbf{F}}^{T}). \tag{4.6.6}$$

From the previous chapter, we can find that $\tilde{\mathbf{E}}$ should come out to be the Almansi strain tensor, which is

$$\tilde{\mathbf{E}} = \mathbf{e} = \frac{1}{2}[(\mathbf{I} - \mathbf{F}^{-T} \cdot \mathbf{F}^{-1})] = \frac{1}{2}[(\mathbf{I} - (\mathbf{F} \cdot \mathbf{F}^{T})^{-1})]. \tag{4.6.7}$$

The strain tensor $\mathbf{e}$, referred to as the Almansi–Hamel (Eulerian) strain tensor, Almansi strain tensor, or Euler strain tensor, is defined in Equation (3.5.19) in Chapter 3. Therefore, for the Cauchy or true stress tensor, the corresponding energy conjugate pair strain is the Almansi strain tensor.

4.6.2 *Conjugate Pair for Second Piola–Kirchhoff Stress Tensor*

Now, we consider Equation (4.6.1) and introduce unit tensors $\mathbf{I} = (\mathbf{F} \cdot \mathbf{F}^{-1}) = (\mathbf{F}^{-T} \cdot \mathbf{F}^{T})$

$$\dot{W} = \tilde{\mathbf{T}} : \frac{\partial \tilde{\mathbf{E}}}{\partial t} = \boldsymbol{\sigma} : \dot{\mathbf{e}}. \tag{4.6.8}$$

Through pre-dot multiplying $\dot{\mathbf{e}}$ by $\mathbf{I} = (\mathbf{F}^{-T} \cdot \mathbf{F}^{T})$ and post-dot multiplying it with $\mathbf{I} = (\mathbf{F} \cdot \mathbf{F}^{-1})$, we have

$$\dot{W} = \boldsymbol{\sigma} : \dot{\mathbf{e}} = \boldsymbol{\sigma} : (\mathbf{F}^{-T} \cdot \mathbf{F}^{-1}) \cdot \dot{\mathbf{e}} \cdot (\mathbf{F} \cdot \mathbf{F}^{-1}). \tag{4.6.9}$$

It makes no change in the value and results in

$$\dot{W} = \boldsymbol{\sigma} : \dot{\mathbf{e}} = (\mathbf{F}^{-1} \cdot \boldsymbol{\sigma} \mathbf{F}^{-T}) : (\mathbf{F}^{T} \cdot \dot{\mathbf{e}} \cdot \mathbf{F}). \tag{4.6.10}$$

By utilizing the relationship between the second Piola–Kirchhoff stress tensor and the Cauchy stress tensor $\mathbf{S} = J\mathbf{F}^{-1} \cdot \boldsymbol{\sigma} \cdot \mathbf{F}^{-T}$, or

$\boldsymbol{\sigma} = \mathbf{F} \cdot \mathbf{S} \cdot \mathbf{F}^T/J$, the above equation is written as

$$\dot{W} = \frac{\mathbf{S}}{J} : (\mathbf{F}^T \cdot \dot{\mathbf{e}} \cdot \mathbf{F}). \tag{4.6.11}$$

Using $\dot{\mathbf{e}} = \dot{\mathbf{F}} \cdot \mathbf{F}^{-1}$,

$$\dot{W} = \frac{\mathbf{S}}{J} : (\mathbf{F}^T \cdot \dot{\mathbf{F}} \cdot \mathbf{F}^{-1} \cdot \mathbf{F}) = \mathbf{S} : \frac{1}{J}(\mathbf{F}^T \cdot \dot{\mathbf{F}} \cdot \mathbf{F}^{-1} \cdot \mathbf{F}). \tag{4.6.12}$$

Therefore,

$$\frac{\partial \tilde{E}}{\partial t} = \frac{1}{J}(\mathbf{F}^T \cdot \dot{\mathbf{F}} \cdot \mathbf{F}^{-1} \cdot \mathbf{F}). \tag{4.6.13}$$

This shows that

$$\tilde{\mathbf{E}} = \mathbf{E} = \frac{1}{2}(\mathbf{F}^{\mathbf{T}} \cdot \mathbf{F} - \mathbf{I}) \tag{4.6.14}$$

or

$$\tilde{\mathbf{E}} = \frac{1}{2J}(\mathbf{F}^T \cdot \mathbf{F} - \mathbf{I}). \tag{4.6.15}$$

Therefore, the conjugate strain for the second Piola–Kirchhoff stress tensor is the Green–Lagrange strain tensor, $\tilde{\mathbf{E}} = \frac{1}{2}(\mathbf{F}^T \cdot \mathbf{F} - \mathbf{I})$.

The advantage of using the second Piola–Kirchhoff stress tensor instead of the Cauchy or the first Piola–Kirchhoff stress tensor is that calculations are performed in the reference configuration (undeformed state). In the undeformed state, the state measurements are known, whereas in the deformed configuration, the state measurements are unknown.

Considering the concept of conjugate pairs, we understand that the mechanical work produced by combining the second Piola–Kirchhoff stress with the Green–Lagrange strain must match that obtained by combining the Cauchy stress with the Almansi strain. In the weak form, we have the following equation:

$$\begin{aligned}\int_v \sigma_{ij} e_{ij} \mathrm{d}v &= \int_V J\left(\frac{1}{J} F_{ij} S_{jk} F_{jk}\right) e_{ij} \mathrm{d}V \\ &= \int_V S_{jk}(F_{ij} e_{ij} F_{jk}) \mathrm{d}V = \int_V S_{jk} E_{jk} \mathrm{d}V\end{aligned} \tag{4.6.16}$$

or

$$\int_v \boldsymbol{\sigma} : \mathbf{e}\mathrm{d}v = \int_V J\left(\frac{1}{J}\mathbf{F}\mathbf{S}\mathbf{F}^T\right) : \mathbf{e}\mathrm{d}V$$
$$= \int_V \mathbf{S} : (\mathbf{F}^T\mathbf{e}\mathbf{F})\mathrm{d}V = \int_V \mathbf{S} : \mathbf{E}\mathrm{d}V, \qquad (4.6.17)$$

which demonstrates that $\mathbf{S} : \mathbf{E}$ and $\boldsymbol{\sigma} : \mathbf{e}$ form corresponding work conjugates.

Similarly, for the spatial rate-of-deformation tensor and considering work power, we have

$$\int_v \sigma_{ij}\mathrm{d}_{ij}\mathrm{d}v = \int_V J\left(\frac{1}{J}F_{ij}S_{jk}F_{jk}\right)\mathrm{d}_{ij}\mathrm{d}V = \int_V S_{jk}\left(F_{ij}\mathrm{d}_{ij}F_{jk}\right)\mathrm{d}V$$
$$= \frac{1}{2}\int_V S_{jk}\dot{C}_{jk}\mathrm{d}V = \int_V S_{jk}\dot{E}_{jk}\mathrm{d}V \qquad (4.6.18)$$

or

$$\int_v \boldsymbol{\sigma} : \mathbf{d}\mathrm{d}v = \int_V J\left(\frac{1}{J}\mathbf{F}\mathbf{S}\mathbf{F}^T\right) : \mathbf{d}\mathrm{d}V = \int_V \mathbf{S} : (\mathbf{F}^T\mathbf{d}\mathbf{F})\mathrm{d}V$$
$$= \frac{1}{2}\int_V \mathbf{S} : \dot{\mathbf{C}}\mathrm{d}V = \int_V \mathbf{S} : \dot{\mathbf{E}}\mathrm{d}V. \qquad (4.6.19)$$

This equation demonstrates that $\mathbf{S} : \mathbf{E}$ and $\boldsymbol{\sigma} : \dot{\mathbf{e}}$ form corresponding power conjugates. Conjugation in power is valuable in the development of weak forms, as measures of stress and rate that are power conjugates can be utilized to establish principles of virtual work or power. These principles, known as weak forms of the momentum equation, can be constructed using variables that are conjugate in power. Furthermore, variables that are conjugate in power are also conjugate in work.

4.6.3 *Conjugate Pair for First Piola–Kirchhoff Stress Tensor*

Similar to the previous discussion and using $\dot{\mathbf{e}} = \dot{\mathbf{F}} \cdot \mathbf{F}^{-1}$, we have

$$\dot{W} = \tilde{\mathbf{T}} : \frac{\partial \tilde{\mathbf{E}}}{\partial t} = \boldsymbol{\sigma} : \dot{\mathrm{e}} = \boldsymbol{\sigma} : \dot{\mathbf{F}} \cdot \mathbf{F}^{-1}. \qquad (4.6.20)$$

Using the property that $\mathbf{A}:\mathbf{B}\cdot\mathbf{C}$ equals $\mathbf{A}\cdot\mathbf{C}^T\!:\mathbf{B}$, the above expression can be written as

$$\dot{W} = \boldsymbol{\sigma} : \dot{\mathbf{e}} = \boldsymbol{\sigma}\cdot\mathbf{F}^{-T} : \dot{\mathbf{F}}. \tag{4.6.21}$$

Applying the property $\mathbf{A}\cdot\mathbf{C}^T : \mathbf{B} = \mathbf{C}\cdot\mathbf{A} : \mathbf{B}^T$ to the above equation, we have

$$\dot{W} = \mathbf{F}^{-1}\cdot\boldsymbol{\sigma} : \dot{\mathbf{F}}^T. \tag{4.6.22}$$

According to definition of First Piola–Kirchhoff stress tensor

$$\mathbf{P} = J\boldsymbol{\sigma}\cdot\mathbf{F}^{-T}, \quad \boldsymbol{\sigma} = \frac{1}{J}\mathbf{P}\cdot\mathbf{F}^T. \tag{4.6.23}$$

Substituting Equation (4.6.23) into Equation (4.6.22), we have

$$\dot{W} = \frac{1}{J}\mathbf{P} : \dot{\mathbf{F}}^T. \tag{4.6.24}$$

This shows that $\frac{\partial\tilde{\mathbf{E}}}{\partial t} = \frac{1}{J}\dot{\mathbf{F}}^T$; therefore,

$$\tilde{\mathbf{E}} = \frac{1}{J}\mathbf{F}^T. \tag{4.6.25}$$

4.6.4 *Conjugate Pair for other Stress Tensors*

Similar to the previous discussion, we can also determine the conjugate pairs for other strain tensors. For instance, for the Kirchhoff stress tensor $\boldsymbol{\tau} = J\boldsymbol{\sigma}$, the corresponding conjugate strain tensor rate and the conjugate strain tensor are as follows:

$$\frac{\partial\tilde{\mathbf{E}}}{\partial t} = \frac{1}{2}(\dot{\mathbf{F}}\cdot\mathbf{F}^{-1} + (\dot{\mathbf{F}}\cdot\mathbf{F}^{-1})^T), \tag{4.6.26}$$

$$\tilde{\mathbf{E}} = \frac{1}{2}(\mathbf{F}^{-\mathrm{T}}\cdot\mathbf{F}^{-\mathbf{1}} - \mathbf{I}). \tag{4.6.27}$$

For the Biot stress tensor $\tilde{\mathbf{B}} = \mathbf{R}^T\cdot\mathbf{P} = J\mathbf{R}^T\cdot\boldsymbol{\sigma}\cdot\mathbf{F}^{-T}$, the conjugate strain tensor rate and the conjugate strain tensor are, respectively,

$$\frac{\partial\tilde{\mathbf{E}}}{\partial t} = \frac{1}{J}\dot{\mathbf{U}}, \tag{4.6.28}$$

$$\tilde{\mathbf{E}} = \frac{1}{J}\mathbf{U}, \tag{4.6.29}$$

where $\mathbf{U}$ is the right Cauchy stretch tensor.

4.7 Summary

In this chapter, we introduced the concept of stress on a continuum and defined the stress vector at a point. We demonstrated that the stress vector **t** at a point depends on the orientation of the plane on which it acts. We established a relation between the stress vector **t** acting on a plane with unit normal **n** and the stress vectors $(\boldsymbol{t}_1, \boldsymbol{t}_2, \boldsymbol{t}_3)$ acting on three mutually perpendicular planes. It is at this point that we introduced the Cauchy stress tensor $\boldsymbol{\sigma}$ as a dyadic with respect to the Cartesian basis, along with Cauchy's formula.

We established the transformation relations for the components of the stress tensor in one coordinate system to its components in another coordinate system, and we provided detailed procedures for determining the principal values and principal planes of a stress tensor. We then delved into the first and second Piola–Kirchhoff stress tensors, **P** and **S**, respectively, providing a more in-depth understanding. While the Cauchy stress tensor $\boldsymbol{\sigma}$ is measured as the current force per unit deformed area, the first Piola–Kirchhoff stress tensor **P** is measured as the current force per unit undeformed area, and the second Piola–Kirchhoff stress tensor **S** is measured as the transformed current force per unit undeformed area. We established the relationships between the Cauchy stress tensor and the first and second Piola–Kirchhoff stress tensors.

We also demonstrated that under superposed rigid-body transformations, the three stress tensors introduced in this chapter are objective, which are characterized by the proper orthogonal tensor $\mathbf{Q}(t)$ representing the rigid-body rotation. Finally, we discussed the concept of conjugate pairs for stress tensors and provided the energy conjugate pair strain tensors for different stress measures.

General References

Oden, J.T. (2011). *An Introduction to Mathematical Modeling: A Course in Mechanics* (John Wiley & Sons Inc., New Jersey, USA).

Reddy, J.N. (2013). *An Introduction to Continuum Mechanics* (Cambridge University Press, New York, USA).

Reddy, J.N. (2017). *Principles of Continuum Mechanics: Conservation and Balance Laws with Applications* (Cambridge University Press, New York, USA).

Problems

4.1. The components of a stress tensor at a point, with respect to the position (x_1, x_2, x_3) system, are (in MPa)

$$\text{(i)}\quad [\boldsymbol{\sigma}] = \begin{bmatrix} 25 & 0 & 0 \\ 0 & -30 & -60 \\ 0 & -60 & 5 \end{bmatrix}, \qquad \text{(ii)}\quad [\boldsymbol{\sigma}] = \begin{bmatrix} 9 & 0 & 12 \\ 0 & -25 & 0 \\ 12 & 0 & 16 \end{bmatrix}.$$

Determine the following:

(a) The stress vector acting on a plane perpendicular to the vector $\mathbf{2e_1} - 2\mathbf{e_2} + \mathbf{e_3}$.
(b) The magnitude of the stress vector and the angle between the stress vector and the normal to the plane.
(c) The magnitudes of the normal and tangential components of the stress vector.

4.2. The three-dimensional state of stress at a point $(1, 1, -2)$ within a body relative to the coordinate system (x_1, x_2, x_3) is (in MPa)

$$[\boldsymbol{\sigma}] = \begin{bmatrix} 2.0 & 3.5 & 2.5 \\ 3.5 & -30 & -1.5 \\ 2.5 & -1.5 & 1.0 \end{bmatrix}.$$

Determine the normal and shear stresses at the point and on the surface of an internal sphere whose equation is $(X_1)^2 + (X_2 - 2)^2 + (X_3)^2 = 6$.

4.3. The Cauchy stress tensor components at a point P in the deformed body with respect to the coordinate system (x_1, x_2, x_3) are given by (in MPa)

$$[\boldsymbol{\sigma}] = \begin{bmatrix} 1 & 4 & -2 \\ 4 & 0 & 0 \\ -2 & 0 & 3 \end{bmatrix}.$$

(a) Determine the Cauchy stress vector $\mathbf{t}_n$ at the point P on a plane passing through the point and parallel to the plane $2X_1 + 3X_2 + X_3 = 4$.

(b) Determine the components of the Cauchy stress tensor in a rectangular coordinate system $(\hat{\mathbf{x}}_1, \hat{\mathbf{x}}_2, \hat{\mathbf{x}}_3)$ whose orthonormal base vectors $(\hat{\mathbf{e}}_1, \hat{\mathbf{e}}_2, \hat{\mathbf{e}}_3)$ are given in terms of the base vectors $(\mathbf{e}_1, \mathbf{e}_2, \mathbf{e}_3)$ of the coordinate system (x_1, x_2, x_3):

$$\hat{\mathbf{e}}_2 = \frac{1}{\sqrt{2}}(\mathbf{e}_1 - \mathbf{e}_3), \quad \hat{\mathbf{e}}_3 = \frac{1}{3}(2\mathbf{e}_1 - \mathbf{e}_2 + 2\mathbf{e}_3).$$

4.4. Find the maximum principal stress, maximum shear stress, and their orientations for the given states of stress:

$$\text{(i)} \quad [\boldsymbol{\sigma}] = \begin{bmatrix} 12 & 9 & 0 \\ 9 & -12 & 0 \\ 0 & 0 & 6 \end{bmatrix}, \quad \text{(ii)} \quad [\boldsymbol{\sigma}] = \begin{bmatrix} 3 & 5 & 8 \\ 5 & 1 & 0 \\ 8 & 0 & 2 \end{bmatrix}.$$

Chapter 5

The Fundamental Laws of Continuum Mechanics

Table of Contents

5.1 Introduction

Almost every natural phenomenon can be described using mathematical relationships among specific quantities that govern the phenomenon. Mathematical models of physical phenomena are typically based on fundamental scientific laws of physics, which have been developed through centuries of observation and research on the behavior of mechanical systems under the influence of natural forces. These laws, also known as "principles of mechanics," have a fascinating aspect in their ability to govern mechanical systems through the transport of mass and energy. However, when it comes to biological systems, additional laws from biology and chemistry may be required to comprehensively describe them, such as those related to cellular processes.

This chapter focuses on the study of the fundamental laws of physics and the mathematical models applied to mechanical systems. These laws are expressed analytically using the concepts and quantities introduced in previous chapters, including stress, strain, temperature, and velocity. The principles of mechanics are as follows: (1) the principle of conservation of mass, (2) the principle of balance of linear momentum, (3) the principle of balance of angular momentum, (4) the principle of balance of energy, and (5) the principle of irreversibility. These principles allow us to establish mathematical relationships, whether algebraic, differential, or integral, among quantities such as displacements, velocities, temperatures, stresses, and strains that arise in mechanical systems.

Solving these equations, in conjunction with constitutive relations and boundary and initial conditions, provides the response of the system. The equations developed in this chapter not only serve as the foundation for subsequent chapters in this book but are also valuable in other engineering and applied science courses as well as in your future research endeavors. Moreover, the equations presented here form the basis of most mathematical models used to study a wide range of phenomena. Therefore, it can be said that this chapter is the heart and soul of a course on continuum mechanics.

The fundamental equations of continuum mechanics are derived from the principles of conservation for various physical quantities. In this chapter, we focus on five of these principles to establish the basic equations that govern the initial boundary-value problem. These principles are as follows:

- the principle of conservation of mass or balance of mass;
- the principle of conservation of linear momentum or balance of linear momentum;
- the principle of conservation of angular momentum or balance of angular momentum;
- the principle of conservation of energy or balance of energy;
- the principle of irreversibility or entropy inequality, specifically related to thermodynamic irreversibility.

As discussed in the previous two chapters, we address these fundamental principles of mechanics in both the reference and current configurations. Depending on the specific problem, it may be more convenient to describe the problem using one of these configurations. Toward the end of this chapter, we discover that these principles alone are insufficient to establish a complete set of partial differential equations for the initial boundary-value problem. Therefore, it becomes necessary to incorporate additional equations, known as constitutive equations, to fully resolve the problem. The topic of constitutive equations will be discussed in the following chapter.

5.2 Basic Concepts and Preliminary Discussions

5.2.1 *Mass Density*

Density is a scalar function that quantifies the amount of a particular property per unit volume at a given material point $P(\mathbf{x})$ and time t. Examples of density include mass density and energy density. One crucial density function is mass density, denoted as $\rho(\mathbf{x}, t)$, which measures the amount of mass per unit volume.

In any continuous medium or continuum body, mass is a positive scalar quantity assumed to be distributed throughout the continuum. To understand this concept, let's consider an infinitesimally small sphere centered at point P in the reference configuration (refer to Figure 5.2.1). The material enclosed within this sphere is represented

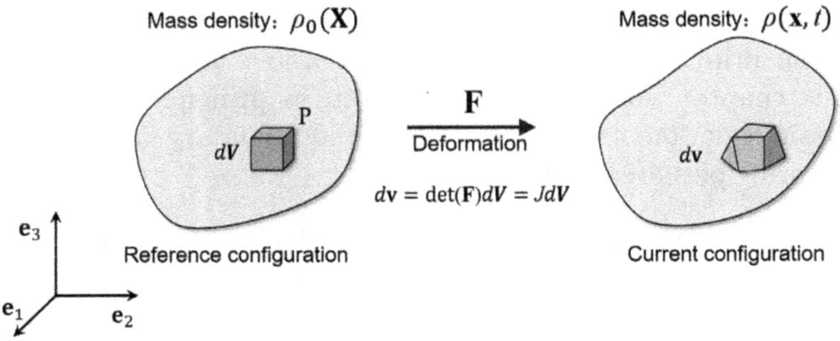

Figure 5.2.1 Mass density in the reference and current configurations.

as Δm, and the volume of the sphere is denoted as ΔV_0 or $\mathrm{d}V = \mathrm{d}X_1\mathrm{d}X_2\mathrm{d}X_3$. The mass density ρ_0, in the reference configuration, is defined as the limit of the ratio:

$$\rho(\mathbf{x}, t = 0) = \rho_0(\mathbf{X}) = \lim_{\Delta V_0 \to 0} \frac{\Delta m}{\Delta V_0} = \frac{\mathrm{d}m}{\mathrm{d}V}. \tag{5.2.1}$$

We assume that the infinitesimal volume in the current configuration is $\mathrm{d}v = \mathrm{d}x_1\mathrm{d}x_2\mathrm{d}x_3$, Likewise, mass density in the current configuration is given by

$$\rho = \rho(\mathbf{x}, t) = \lim_{\Delta V_0 \to 0} \frac{\Delta m}{\Delta V} = \frac{\mathrm{d}m}{\mathrm{d}v}. \tag{5.2.2}$$

Then, the functions $\rho_0(\mathbf{X})$ and $\rho(\mathbf{x}, t)$ are continuous density functions and are interrelated to each other by

$$\rho_0(\mathbf{X}) = J\rho(\mathbf{x}, t). \tag{5.2.3}$$

5.2.2 *Flux*

The properties associated with density, such as mass, energy, and entropy, are mobile. The rate of change and direction of these quantities are determined by the flux vector, typically denoted as $\mathbf{q}$. Using this information, we can define the amount of a property that passes through a differential area element $\mathrm{d}a$ per unit time (refer to Figure 5.2.2) as

$$\mathbf{q} \cdot \mathbf{n}\mathrm{d}a = |\mathbf{q}| \cos(\alpha)\mathrm{d}a = \mathrm{q}_n\mathrm{d}a, \tag{5.2.4}$$

where $\mathbf{n}$ is the unit normal vector of a differential area element $\mathrm{d}a$ and α is the angle formed between $\mathbf{q}$ and $\mathbf{q}_n$. Note that only the normal

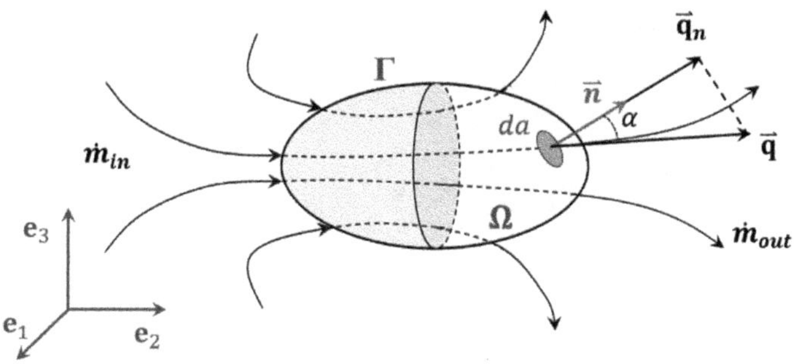

Figure 5.2.2 Flux vector in current configuration, control surface, and control volume.

vector $\mathbf{q}_n = q_n\mathbf{n}$ crosses the surface since the tangential vector $\mathbf{q}_s$ remains on the surface of da.

5.2.3 *Control Volume*

Let Ω represent an arbitrary region in a continuous medium B, and let Γ denote the bounding closed surface of this region, which is continuous. Consider an arbitrary fixed volume Ω in space with fluid flux across its boundaries Γ. The outer surface of Γ is denoted as the control surface (C.S.), and the volume Ω itself is referred to as the control volume. The system contains mass within the control volume at a particular instant in time t, as illustrated in Figure 5.2.2.

5.2.4 *Material Time Derivative*

As discussed in Section 3.2.3 in Chapter 3, it is important to distinguish between the partial time derivative with the material coordinates $\mathbf{X}$ held constant and the partial time derivative with the spatial coordinate $\mathbf{x}$ held constant due to the difference in the descriptions of motion. The material time derivative, denoted here as $\mathrm{D}/\mathrm{D}t$, represents the time derivative with the material coordinates held constant. Therefore, the time derivative of a function φ in the material description (i.e., $\phi = \phi(\mathbf{X}, t)$) with $\mathbf{X}$ held constant is simply the partial derivative with respect to time (refer to Figure 5.2.3):

$$\frac{\mathrm{D}\phi}{\mathrm{D}t} \equiv \left(\frac{\partial \phi}{\partial t}\right)_{\mathbf{X}=\mathrm{const}} = \frac{\partial \phi}{\partial t}. \tag{5.2.5}$$

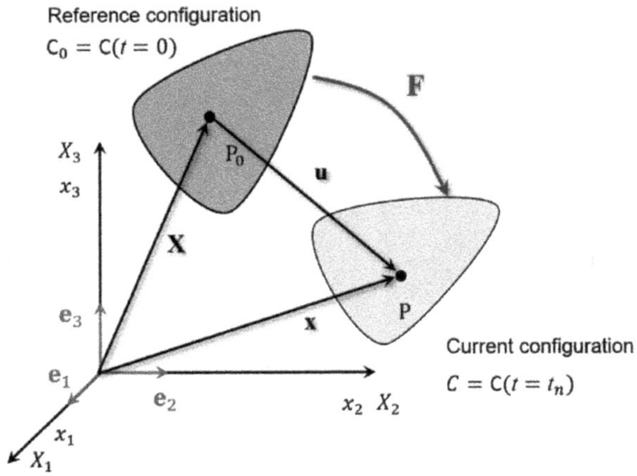

Figure 5.2.3 A body B in reference and current configurations.

For the current position, we have

$$\frac{\mathrm{D}\mathbf{x}}{\mathrm{D}t} \equiv \left(\frac{\partial \mathbf{x}}{\partial t}\right)_{\mathbf{X}=\text{const}} = \frac{\partial \mathbf{x}}{\partial t} \equiv \mathbf{v}, \tag{5.2.6}$$

where $\mathbf{v}$ is the velocity vector. Similarly, the time derivative of $\mathbf{v}$ is

$$\mathbf{a} = \frac{\mathrm{D}\mathbf{v}}{\mathrm{D}t} = \frac{\partial \mathbf{v}}{\partial t} + \mathbf{v}\cdot\nabla\mathbf{v}, \quad \left(a_i = \frac{\partial v_i}{\partial t} + v_j\frac{\partial v_i}{\partial x_j}\right), \tag{5.2.7}$$

where $\mathbf{a}$ is the acceleration vector.

However, if we have $\phi = \phi(\mathbf{x}, t)$, which is in the spatial description, the partial time derivative $(\frac{\partial \phi}{\partial t})_{\mathbf{X}=\text{const}}$ and $(\frac{\partial \phi}{\partial t})_{\mathbf{x}=\text{const}}$ are different. $(\frac{\partial \phi}{\partial t})_{\mathbf{X}=\text{const}}$ is the local rate of change of ϕ:

$$\frac{\mathrm{D}\phi}{\mathrm{D}t} \equiv \left(\frac{\partial \phi}{\partial t}\right)_{\mathbf{X}=\text{const}} = \left(\frac{\partial \phi}{\partial t}\right)_{\mathbf{x}=\text{const}} + \mathbf{v}\cdot\nabla\phi. \tag{5.2.8}$$

5.2.5 *The Reynolds' Transport Theorem*

Let $\Phi = \Phi(\mathbf{x}, t)$ be an Eulerian scalar field that describes a certain physical quantity per unit volume. If $\Phi = \Phi(\mathbf{x}, t)$ is continuous and differentiable, the material derivative operator $\mathrm{D}/\mathrm{D}t$, known as Reynolds' transport theorem (also called Leibniz's rule), can be expressed as follows:

$$\begin{aligned}\frac{\mathrm{D}}{\mathrm{D}t}\int_{\Omega}\Phi(\mathbf{x},t)\mathrm{d}v &= \int_{\Omega}\left[\frac{\partial\Phi(\mathbf{x},t)}{\partial t}+\nabla\cdot(\Phi(\mathbf{x},t)\mathbf{v})\right]\mathrm{d}v\\ &= \int_{\Omega}\left[\frac{\partial\Phi(\mathbf{x},t)}{\partial t}\right]\mathrm{d}v+\int_{\Gamma}[\Phi(\mathbf{x},t)\mathbf{v}\cdot\mathbf{n}]\mathrm{d}s,\end{aligned} \tag{5.2.9}$$

where Ω is the control volume, Γ is the control surface, and $\mathbf{n}$ is the outward unit normal to the boundary, as shown in Figure 5.2.2.

5.3 Conservation of Mass

The law of conservation of mass states that the total mass of a continuum does not change. This implies that the total mass in the reference configuration is equal to the total mass in the current configuration if there is no mass entering and exiting the control volume:

$$m = \int_{\Omega_0}\rho_0\,\mathrm{d}V = \int_{\Omega}\rho\,\mathrm{d}v. \tag{5.3.1}$$

As a result of conservation of mass, the material time derivative of the total mass is zero, $\frac{\mathrm{D}m}{\mathrm{D}t}=0$, and using the relationship $\frac{\mathrm{D}*}{\mathrm{D}t}=\frac{\partial *}{\partial t}+\frac{\partial *}{\partial x_k}v_k$,

$$\begin{aligned}\frac{\mathrm{D}}{\mathrm{D}t}m &= \frac{\mathrm{D}}{\mathrm{D}t}\int_{\Omega}\rho(\mathbf{x},t)\mathrm{d}v = \int_{\Omega}\frac{\mathrm{D}}{\mathrm{D}t}[\rho(\mathbf{x},t)\mathrm{d}v]\\ &= \int_{\Omega}\left[\mathrm{d}v\frac{\mathrm{D}}{\mathrm{D}t}[\rho(\mathbf{x},t)]+\rho(\mathbf{x},t)\frac{\mathrm{D}}{\mathrm{D}t}[\mathrm{d}v]\right]\\ &= \int_{\Omega}\left[\frac{\mathrm{D}}{\mathrm{D}t}[\rho(\mathbf{x},t)]+\rho(\mathbf{x},t)\nabla\cdot\mathbf{v}\right]\mathrm{d}v=0.\end{aligned} \tag{5.3.2}$$

If the above equation is valid for the entire domain, then it must also be satisfied locally:

$$\begin{aligned}\frac{\mathrm{D}\rho}{\mathrm{D}t}+\rho(\mathbf{x},t)v_{k,k}&=0,\\ \frac{\mathrm{D}\rho}{\mathrm{D}t}+\rho(\mathbf{x},t)(\nabla\cdot\boldsymbol{v})&=0,\end{aligned} \tag{5.3.3}$$

which is the mass continuity equation in Eulerian description and is expressed in tensorial notation.

Then, by applying the material time derivative operator $\frac{\mathrm{D}*}{\mathrm{D}t} = \frac{\partial *}{\partial t} + \frac{\partial *}{\partial x_k} v_k$, the mass continuity equation becomes

$$\begin{aligned} \frac{\mathrm{D}\rho}{\mathrm{D}t} + \rho v_{k,k} &= \frac{\partial \rho}{\partial t} + v_j \frac{\partial \rho}{\partial x_j} + \rho \frac{\partial v_k}{\partial x_k} \\ &= \frac{\partial \rho}{\partial t} + \frac{\partial}{\partial x_k}(\rho v_k) = \frac{\partial \rho}{\partial t} + (\rho v_k)_{,k} = 0. \end{aligned} \tag{5.3.4}$$

Hence, we have two ways to express the mass continuity equation:

$$\begin{aligned} &\frac{\mathrm{D}\rho}{\mathrm{D}t} + \rho(\nabla \cdot \mathbf{v}) = 0, \\ &\frac{\partial \rho}{\partial t} + \nabla \cdot (\rho \mathbf{v}) = 0. \end{aligned} \tag{5.3.5}$$

These equations represent the mass continuity equations in the Eulerian description. It is worth noting that we could have obtained the same equation using Reynolds' transport theorem:

$$\frac{\mathrm{D}}{\mathrm{D}t} \int_\Omega \rho(\mathbf{x}, t) \mathrm{d}v = \int_\Omega \left[\frac{\partial \rho(\mathbf{x}, t)}{\partial t} + \nabla \cdot (\rho(\mathbf{x}, t)\mathbf{v}) \right] \mathrm{d}v = 0. \tag{5.3.6}$$

Therefore,

$$\Rightarrow \frac{\partial \rho(\mathbf{x}, t)}{\partial t} + \nabla \cdot (\rho(\mathbf{x}, t)\mathbf{v}) = 0. \tag{5.3.7}$$

Example 5.3.1

As an example, we study the mass continuity equation by means of the principle of conservation of mass in a differential volume element $\mathrm{d}v = \mathrm{d}x_1 \mathrm{d}x_2 \mathrm{d}x_3$ (see Figure 5.3.1).

In this case, the mass accumulation should equal the inward mass flux minus the outward mass flux in the differential volume element $\mathrm{d}v = \mathrm{d}x_1 \mathrm{d}x_2 \mathrm{d}x_3$.

From Figure 5.3.1, it can be seen that the rate of mass entering through face A is represented by the mass flux $(\rho v_2)_{x_2} \mathrm{d}x_1 \mathrm{d}x_3$,

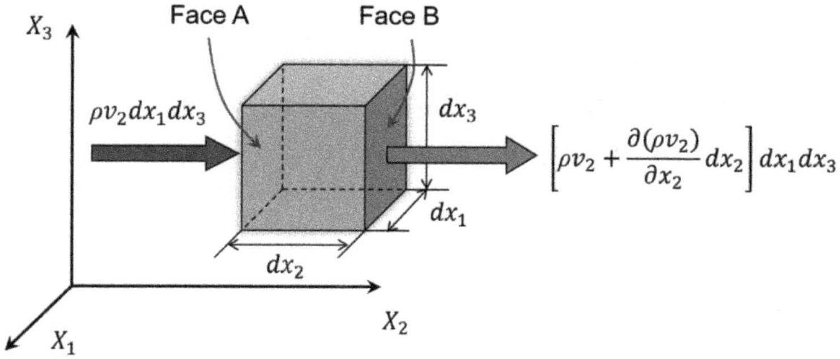

Figure 5.3.1 Conservation of mass in a differential volume element.

while the rate of mass that goes through face B is given by $[\rho v_2 + \frac{\partial(\rho v_2)}{\partial x_2} \mathrm{d}x_2]\mathrm{d}x_1\mathrm{d}x_3$.

By applying the conservation of mass for the differential volume element, we obtain

$$\frac{\partial \rho}{\partial t}\mathrm{d}x_1\mathrm{d}x_2\mathrm{d}x_3 = \rho v_2 \mathrm{d}x_1\mathrm{d}x_3 - \left[\rho v_2 + \frac{\partial(\rho v_2)}{\partial x_2}\mathrm{d}x_2\right]\mathrm{d}x_1\mathrm{d}x_3. \quad (5.3.8)$$

From the above equation, we can get

$$\frac{\partial \rho}{\partial t} = -\frac{\partial(\rho v_2)}{\partial x_2}. \quad (5.3.9)$$

The mass continuity equation can also be expressed in Lagrangian description (material). To do this, we can start from the conservation of mass $\rho_0(\mathbf{X}) = J\rho(\mathbf{x}, t)$, which establishes

$$\int_{\Omega_0} \rho_0(\mathbf{X})\mathrm{d}V = \int_{\Omega} \rho(\mathbf{x}, t)\mathrm{d}v = \int_{\Omega_0} (J\rho(\mathbf{x}, t))\mathrm{d}V. \quad (5.3.10)$$

Since the above equation is valid for any volume, it means that it will be valid locally too.

Note that $\rho_0(\mathbf{X})$ is independent of time and so is $J\rho(\mathbf{x}, t)$, i.e., $\rho_0(\mathbf{X}) = J\rho(\mathbf{x}, t)$, which results in the Lagrangian description of the mass continuity equation:

$$\rho_0(\mathbf{X}) = J\rho(\mathbf{x}, t), \quad \frac{\mathrm{D}(J\rho)}{\mathrm{D}t} = 0. \quad (5.3.11)$$

This is the mass continuity equation in the Lagrangian description.

5.3.1 *Special Case: Incompressibility*

Compressibility refers to the ability of a continuous medium to change its volume. It is well known that gases are more compressible than liquids. However, for practical purposes, in many cases, liquids such as water or other fluids can be considered incompressible.

An incompressible medium is characterized by isochoric motion, meaning that the volume remains constant (i.e., $J = 1$). Consequently, the mass density field is independent of time. In this scenario, the mass continuity equations in (5.3.5) and (5.3.11) can be simplified to

$$\frac{\mathrm{D}\rho}{\mathrm{D}t} + \rho(\nabla \cdot \mathbf{v}) = 0 \to \frac{\mathrm{D}\rho}{\mathrm{D}t} = -\rho(\nabla \cdot \mathbf{v}) = -\rho v_{k,k} = 0. \tag{5.3.12}$$

This equation is the mass continuity equation for an incompressible medium.

Therefore, an incompressible medium can be characterized by

$$\frac{\mathrm{D}\rho}{\mathrm{D}t} = \dot{\rho} = 0, \quad \frac{\mathrm{D}}{\mathrm{D}t}[\det(\mathbf{F})] = \dot{J} = 0, \quad J = 1, \quad \rho = \rho_0, \tag{5.3.13}$$

or

$$v_{k,k} = 0, \to \frac{\partial v_1}{\partial x_1} + \frac{\partial v_2}{\partial x_2} + \frac{\partial v_3}{\partial x_3} = \mathrm{tr}(\mathbf{D}) = 0, \tag{5.3.14}$$

where $\mathbf{D}$ is the rate-of-deformation tensor, which is equal to the symmetrical part of the spatial velocity gradient.

5.4 Balance of Linear and Angular Momentum and the Equations of Motion

Let us consider a body, denoted by $\mathfrak{B}$, in motion, which is subjected to both body forces $\mathbf{b}$ (per unit mass) and surface forces $\mathbf{t}$, acting on its surface (see Figure 5.4.1). Let $\mathbf{v}$ be the Eulerian velocity field. In this context, we can define the linear momentum $\mathbf{I}(\mathfrak{B}, t)$ and the angular momentum $\mathbf{H}(\mathfrak{B}, t)$ of the mass system $\mathfrak{B}$ as follows:

$$\mathbf{I}(\mathfrak{B}, t) = \int_{\Omega} \rho \mathbf{v} \, \mathrm{d}v, \tag{5.4.1}$$

$$\mathbf{H}(\mathfrak{B}, t) = \int_{\Omega} \mathbf{x} \times \rho \mathbf{v} \, \mathrm{d}v. \tag{5.4.2}$$

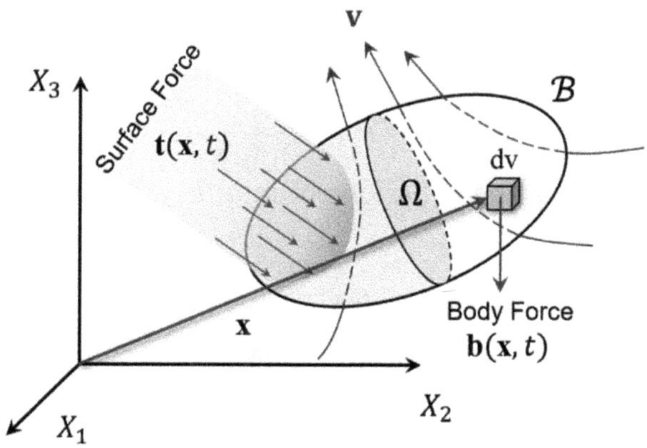

Figure 5.4.1 Continuum in motion of mass body.

5.4.1 *Conservation of Linear Momentum*

The principle of conservation of linear momentum, based on Newton's second law, states that the rate of change of linear momentum of an arbitrary part of a continuous medium is equal to the resultant force (body and surface forces) $\vec{\mathbf{F}}$ acting on that part. In other words, the time rate of change of the linear momentum of a collection of particles is equal to the net force exerted on the collection. Mathematically, this can be expressed as

$$\frac{\mathrm{d}(\mathbf{I}(\mathfrak{B}, t))}{\mathrm{d}t} = \vec{\mathbf{F}}, \tag{5.4.3}$$

$$\vec{F} = \int_\Omega \mathbf{b}\rho \,\mathrm{d}v + \int_\Gamma \mathbf{t}\mathrm{d}A. \tag{5.4.4}$$

According to Equation (5.4.1), we have

$$\frac{\mathrm{d}(\mathbf{I}(\mathfrak{B}, t))}{\mathrm{d}t} = \int_\Omega \rho \frac{\mathrm{d}\mathbf{v}}{\mathrm{d}t}\mathrm{d}v. \tag{5.4.5}$$

Therefore,

$$\frac{\mathrm{D}}{\mathrm{D}t}\int_\Omega \rho\mathbf{v}\,\mathrm{d}v = \int_\Omega \rho\frac{\mathrm{d}\mathbf{v}}{\mathrm{d}t}\mathrm{d}v = \vec{\mathbf{F}} = \int_\Omega \mathbf{b}\rho\,\mathrm{d}v + \int_\Gamma \mathbf{t}\mathrm{d}A. \tag{5.4.6}$$

Using Cauchy's formula, $\mathbf{t} = \boldsymbol{\sigma}\cdot\mathbf{n} \equiv \mathbf{n}\cdot\boldsymbol{\sigma}^{\boldsymbol{T}}, t_i = \sigma_{ij}n_j$ and then the divergence theorem, we have

$$\int_\Omega (\sigma_{ij,j} + \rho b_i - \rho\dot{v}_i)\mathrm{d}v = 0. \tag{5.4.7}$$

If the above equation is valid for the entire volume, it is also valid locally, i.e.,

$$\sigma_{ij,j} + \rho b_i - \rho \dot{v}_i = 0, \tag{5.4.8}$$

which are known as the equations of motion or Cauchy's first equation of motion:

$$\nabla \cdot \boldsymbol{\sigma} + \rho \mathbf{b} = \rho \dot{\mathbf{v}} = \rho \mathbf{a}. \tag{5.4.9}$$

This is the equation of motion in the Eulerian description.

Sometimes, it is useful to express the equations of motion in the reference configuration. To do this, we can rewrite the equation above in the undeformed configuration. Mathematically, it can be expressed as follows:

$$\int_{\Gamma_0} \mathbf{P} \cdot \mathbf{N} \mathrm{d}S + \int_{\Omega_0} \rho_0 \mathbf{b}_0 \mathrm{d}V = \frac{\mathrm{D}}{\mathrm{D}t} \int_{\Omega_0} \rho_0 \mathbf{v}_0 \mathrm{d}V = \int_{\Omega_0} \rho_0 \mathbf{a}_0 \mathrm{d}V, \tag{5.4.10}$$

where $\mathbf{v}_0 = \mathbf{v}(\mathbf{X}, t)$ is the Lagrangian velocity and $\mathbf{a}_0 = \mathbf{a}(\mathbf{X}, t)$ is the Lagrangian acceleration field, $\mathbf{P}$ is the first Piola–Kirchhoff stress tensor.

Then, by applying the divergence theorem to the surface integral, we obtain

$$\int_{\Omega_0} (\nabla \cdot \mathbf{P} + \rho_0 \mathbf{b}_0 - \rho_0 \mathbf{a}_0) dV = 0. \tag{5.4.11}$$

Then, the local form of the equations of motion in material description (Lagrangian) can be expressed as

$$\nabla \cdot \mathbf{P} + \rho_0 \mathbf{b}_0 - \rho_0 \mathbf{a}_0 = 0. \tag{5.4.12}$$

Since $\mathbf{P}$ is a nonsymmetric tensor, it is not widely used in computational approaches, especially for the finite element method. By using the relationship of $\mathbf{P} = \mathbf{F} \cdot \mathbf{S}$,

$$\nabla \cdot (\mathbf{F} \cdot \mathbf{S}) + \rho_0 \mathbf{b}_0 - \rho_0 \mathbf{a}_0 = 0, \tag{5.4.13}$$

where $\mathbf{S}$ is the second Piola–Kirchhoff stress tensor and $\mathbf{S}$ is the symmetric tensor. Equations (5.4.12) and (5.4.13) are the equations of motion in the Lagrangian description.

Expressing the deformation tensor $\mathbf{F}$ in terms of the displacement vector $\mathbf{u}$, we can obtain:

$$\nabla \cdot [\mathbf{S}^T \cdot (\mathbf{I} + \nabla \mathbf{u})] + \rho_0 b_0 = \rho_0 \frac{\partial^2 \mathbf{u}}{\partial t^2}. \tag{5.4.14}$$

In rectangular Cartesian component form, we have

$$\frac{\partial}{\partial X_j}\left[S_{kj}\left(\delta_{ki} + \frac{\partial u_i}{\partial X_k}\right)\right] + \rho_0 (b_0)_i = \rho_0 \frac{\partial^2 u_i}{\partial t^2}, \quad i = 1, 2, 3. \tag{5.4.15}$$

Clearly, the equations of motion expressed in terms of the second Piola–Kirchhoff stress tensor are nonlinear due to the presence of the term $S_{kj}\frac{\partial u_i}{\partial X_k}$. This nonlinearity is in addition to the nonlinearity already present in the strain–displacement relations and constitutive relations.

In the exceptional cases when we have a static or quasi-static equilibrium, the acceleration components are zero; thus, we obtain the equilibrium equations as

$$\nabla \cdot \boldsymbol{\sigma} + \rho \mathbf{b} = 0. \tag{5.4.16}$$

And explicitly, the equations $\sigma_{ij,j} + \rho b_i = 0$ can expressed as

$$\begin{cases} \dfrac{\partial \sigma_{11}}{\partial x_1} + \dfrac{\partial \sigma_{12}}{\partial x_2} + \dfrac{\partial \sigma_{13}}{\partial x_3} + \rho b_1 = 0 \\ \dfrac{\partial \sigma_{21}}{\partial x_1} + \dfrac{\partial \sigma_{22}}{\partial x_2} + \dfrac{\partial \sigma_{23}}{\partial x_3} + \rho b_2 = 0 \\ \dfrac{\partial \sigma_{31}}{\partial x_1} + \dfrac{\partial \sigma_{32}}{\partial x_2} + \dfrac{\partial \sigma_{33}}{\partial x_3} + \rho b_3 = 0 \end{cases}. \tag{5.4.17}$$

The above equations are widely used in solid mechanics or elasticity.

Example 5.4.1

The Cauchy stress tensor field $\boldsymbol{\sigma}$ is represented by its components in the Cartesian coordinate basis as

$$\sigma_{11} = x_1^2; \quad \sigma_{22} = x_2^2; \quad \sigma_{33} = x_1^2 + x_2^2;$$

$$\sigma_{12} = \sigma_{21} = 2x_1x_2; \quad \sigma_{23} = \sigma_{32} = \sigma_{13} = \sigma_{31} = 0.$$

Considering that the body is in equilibrium, find the body forces acting on the continuum.

Solution:
By applying the equilibrium equations, $\nabla\cdot\boldsymbol{\sigma}+\rho\mathbf{b}=0$, we can obtain

$$\sigma_{ij,j}+\rho b_i=0 \Longrightarrow \begin{cases} \dfrac{\partial\sigma_{11}}{\partial x_1}+\dfrac{\partial\sigma_{12}}{\partial x_2}+\dfrac{\partial\sigma_{13}}{\partial x_3}+\rho b_1=0 \\ \dfrac{\partial\sigma_{21}}{\partial x_1}+\dfrac{\partial\sigma_{22}}{\partial x_2}+\dfrac{\partial\sigma_{23}}{\partial x_3}+\rho b_2=0 \\ \dfrac{\partial\sigma_{31}}{\partial x_1}+\dfrac{\partial\sigma_{32}}{\partial x_2}+\dfrac{\partial\sigma_{33}}{\partial x_3}+\rho b_3=0 \end{cases}$$

$$\Longrightarrow \begin{cases} 2x_1+2x_1+\rho b_1=0 \\ 2x_2+2x_2+\rho b_2=0 \\ \rho b_3=0 \end{cases}.$$

Thus, to satisfy the equilibrium equations, the following conditions must be met:

$$\rho b_1=-4x_1;\quad \rho b_2=-4x_2;\quad \rho b_3=0$$

or

$$\rho\mathbf{b}=-4(x_1\mathbf{e}_1+x_2\mathbf{e}_2).$$

5.4.2 *Conservation of Angular Momentum*

The principle of conservation of angular momentum states that the rate of change of angular momentum with respect to a point is equal to the resultant moment (with respect to this point) produced by all forces acting on the body under consideration. By obtaining the resultant moment with respect to the origin and applying the principle of angular momentum, we can derive the following equations:

$$\frac{\mathrm{d}(\mathbf{H}(\mathfrak{B},t))}{\mathrm{d}t}=\mathfrak{M}=\overrightarrow{\mathbf{M}}, \tag{5.4.18}$$

$$\mathfrak{M}=\overrightarrow{\mathbf{M}}=\mathbf{x}\times\vec{\mathbf{F}}=\textstyle\int_{\Omega_t}\mathbf{x}\times\mathbf{b}\rho\,\mathrm{d}v+\int_{\partial\Omega_t}\mathbf{x}\times t\mathrm{d}A, \tag{5.4.19}$$

$$\frac{\mathrm{d}(\mathbf{H}(\mathfrak{B},t))}{\mathrm{d}t}=\textstyle\int_{\Omega_t}\mathbf{x}\times\rho\frac{\mathrm{d}\mathbf{v}}{\mathrm{d}t}\mathrm{d}v. \tag{5.4.20}$$

Thus, from previous equations, we can infer that the Cauchy stress tensor is symmetrical. It is also called Cauchy's second law of motion, also known as the Boltzmann postulate:

$$\sigma_{ij}=\sigma_{ji},\quad \sigma=\sigma^T. \tag{5.4.21}$$

Then, bearing in mind the relationship $\boldsymbol{\sigma} = J^{-1}\mathbf{P}\cdot\mathbf{F}^T$, the Boltzmann postulate in the reference configuration becomes

$$\left.\begin{aligned} \boldsymbol{\sigma} &= \boldsymbol{\sigma}^T \\ J^{-1}\mathbf{P}\cdot\mathbf{F}^{\mathrm{T}} &= (J^{-1}\mathbf{P}\cdot\mathbf{F}^T)^T \end{aligned}\right\}, \tag{5.4.22}$$

and considering that $\mathbf{P} = \mathbf{F}\cdot\mathbf{S}$, where $\mathbf{S}$ is the second Piola–Kirchhoff stress tensor, we obtain that this stress tensor is symmetrical:

$$\mathbf{S} = \mathbf{S}^T. \tag{5.4.23}$$

5.5 Thermodynamic Principles

The principle of conservation of energy states that the rate of change of kinetic energy plus the rate of change of internal energy is equal to the sum of the rate of work done by the system and the rate of any other energy supplied to or removed from the system. The energy supplied to or removed from the system per unit time can take various forms, such as thermal, chemical, or electromagnetic energy. In this subject, we specifically focus on thermal energy as the energy added to the system. For discussions on chemical and electromagnetic energy, readers are encouraged to refer to specialized topics in mechanics. Consequently, in these circumstances, the principle of conservation of energy is known as the first law of thermodynamics.

As previously stated, mathematically, the principle of conservation of energy in continuum thermodynamics can be expressed as follows:

$$\frac{\mathrm{D}\kappa}{\mathrm{D}t} + \frac{\mathrm{D}U}{\mathrm{D}t} = \frac{\mathrm{D}W}{\mathrm{D}t} + \frac{\mathrm{D}Q}{\mathrm{D}t}, \tag{5.5.1}$$

where κ is the kinetic energy, U is the internal energy, W is the work done by the system, and Q is the energy added to the system. In the following, we discuss these concepts in detail.

5.5.1 *Kinetic Energy*

The kinetic energy of the system represented is given by

$$\kappa(t) = \frac{1}{2}\int_\Omega \rho(\mathbf{v}\cdot\mathbf{v})\mathrm{d}v = \frac{1}{2}\int_\Omega \rho(v_i v_i)\mathrm{d}v. \tag{5.5.2}$$

Then, the rate of change of the kinetic energy becomes

$$\frac{\mathrm{D}}{\mathrm{D}t}\kappa(t) \equiv \dot{\kappa} = \frac{\mathrm{D}}{\mathrm{D}t}\left[\frac{1}{2}\int_\Omega \rho(v_i v_i)\mathrm{d}v\right] = \frac{1}{2}\int_\Omega \rho\frac{\mathrm{D}}{\mathrm{D}t}(v_i v_i)\mathrm{d}v$$
$$= \frac{1}{2}\int_\Omega \rho(\dot{v}_i v_i + v_i\dot{v}_i)\mathrm{d}v. \tag{5.5.3}$$

Therefore,

$$\frac{\mathrm{D}}{\mathrm{D}t}\kappa(t) \equiv \dot{\kappa} = \int_\Omega \rho(\dot{v}_i v_i)\mathrm{d}v. \tag{5.5.4}$$

5.5.2 *External and Internal Mechanical Power*

Let us consider the equations of motion $\sigma_{ij,j} + \rho b_i - \rho\dot{v}_i = 0$, and if we substitute them into that of the rate of kinetic energy given in (5.5.4), we obtain

$$\dot{\kappa} = \int_\Omega v_i(\sigma_{ij,j} + \rho b_i)\mathrm{d}v. \tag{5.5.5}$$

We also know that

$$v_i\sigma_{ij,j} = (v_i\sigma_{ij})_{,j} - v_{i,j}\sigma_{ij}. \tag{5.5.6}$$

We recall the velocity gradient tensor $\mathbf{L}$ (discussed in Chapter 3) as the sum of symmetric $\mathbf{D}$ and skew-symmetric $\mathbf{W}$ tensors:

$$\mathbf{L} \equiv (\nabla\mathbf{v})^T = \frac{1}{2}[(\nabla\mathbf{v})^T + (\nabla\mathbf{v})] + \frac{1}{2}[(\nabla\mathbf{v})^T - (\nabla\mathbf{v})] = \mathbf{D} + \mathbf{W}, \tag{5.5.7}$$

where $\mathbf{D}$ is called the rate-of-deformation tensor (or rate of strain tensor) and $\mathbf{W}$ is called the vorticity tensor or spin tensor.

Thus, the rate of change of kinetic energy becomes

$$\dot{\kappa} = \int_\Omega [(v_i\sigma_{ij})_{,j} - v_{i,j}\sigma_{ij} + v_i\rho b_i]\mathrm{d}v$$
$$= \int_\Omega [(v_i\sigma_{ij})_{,j} - \sigma_{ij}(D_{ij} + W_{ij}) + \rho b_i v_i]\mathrm{d}v$$
$$= \int_\Omega [\rho b_i v_i]\mathrm{d}v + \int_\Omega [(v_i\sigma_{ij})_{,j}]\mathrm{d}v - \int_\Omega [\sigma_{ij}D_{ij}]\mathrm{d}v. \tag{5.5.8}$$

Here, we have taken into account that the double scalar product of a symmetric and antisymmetric tensor is equal to zero, i.e., $\sigma_{ij}W_{ij} = 0$, or $\boldsymbol{\sigma}:\mathbf{W} = 0$. Then, by applying the divergence theorem to the second integral on the right-hand side of the equation, we find that

$$\int_{\Omega} [(v_i \sigma_{ij})_{,j}] \mathrm{d}v = \int_{\Gamma} v_i \sigma_{ij} n_j \mathrm{d}S = \int_{\Gamma} v_i t_i \mathrm{d}S. \tag{5.5.9}$$

Thus,

$$\dot{\kappa} = \int_{\Omega} \rho b_i v_i \mathrm{d}v + \int_{\Gamma} v_i t_i \mathrm{d}S - \int_{\Omega} \sigma_{ij} D_{ij} \mathrm{d}v. \tag{5.5.10}$$

It can be clearly seen that the first two terms in the above equation are external mechanical power and that the third one is internal mechanical power:

$$\frac{\mathrm{D}\kappa}{\mathrm{D}t} = P_{\text{ext}}(t) - P_{\text{int}}(t). \tag{5.5.11}$$

The principle of conservation of energy involves the consideration of two components: the kinetic power, which is the rate of change of kinetic energy, and the internal mechanical power, which represents the rate of change of work done by the internal forces within the system:

$$P_{\text{int}}(t) = \int_{\Omega} \sigma_{ij} D_{ij} \mathrm{d}v = \int_{\Omega} \boldsymbol{\sigma}:\mathbf{D}\, \mathrm{d}v = \int_{\Omega} \mathrm{tr}(\boldsymbol{\sigma}^T \cdot \mathbf{D}) \mathrm{d}v = \int_{\Omega} \mathrm{tr}(\boldsymbol{\sigma} \cdot \mathbf{D}) \mathrm{d}v_{\text{int}}. \tag{5.5.12}$$

It is also called stress power.

We can also define stress power per unit volume:

$$W_{\text{int}}(t) = \boldsymbol{\sigma}:\mathbf{D} = \mathrm{tr}(\boldsymbol{\sigma} \cdot \mathbf{D}). \tag{5.5.13}$$

Then, if we take into account all the equations obtained before, we can summarize the stress power at current volume and reference volume by:

$$\int_{\Omega} \boldsymbol{\sigma}:\mathbf{D} \mathrm{d}v = \int_{\Omega_0} J \boldsymbol{\sigma}:\mathbf{D} \mathrm{d}V = \int_{\Omega_0} \boldsymbol{\tau}:\mathbf{D} \mathrm{d}V, \tag{5.5.14}$$

where we use the Kirchhoff stress tensor $\boldsymbol{\tau} = J\boldsymbol{\sigma}$.

Bearing in mind that the Kirchhoff stress tensor components exhibit the relationships $\tau_{ij} = P_{ik}F_{jk}$ and $\mathbf{P} \cdot \mathbf{F}^T = \mathbf{F} \cdot \mathbf{P}^T$, as well as $D_{ij} = F_{pi}^{-1}\dot{E}_{pl}F_{lj}^{-1}$, we can further obtain

$$\begin{aligned}
\int_{\Omega_0} \boldsymbol{\tau} : \mathbf{D}\,\mathrm{d}V &= \int_{\Omega_0} P_{ik}F_{jk}F_{pi}^{-1}\dot{E}_{pl}F_{lj}^{-1}dV = \int_{\Omega_0} P_{ik}F_{jk}D_{ij}\mathrm{d}V \\
&= \int_{\Omega_0} P_{ik}F_{pi}^{-1}\dot{E}_{pl}F_{lj}^{-1}F_{jk}\mathrm{d}V = \int_{\Omega_0} P_{ik}F_{jk}(L_{ij} - W_{ij})\mathrm{d}V \\
&= \int_{\Omega_0} P_{ik}F_{pi}^{-1}\dot{E}_{pk}\mathrm{d}V = \int_{\Omega_0} F_{pi}^{-1}P_{ik}\dot{E}_{pk}\mathrm{d}V = \int_{\Omega_0} P_{ik}L_{ij}F_{jk}\mathrm{d}V \\
&= \int_{\Omega_0} S_{pk}\dot{E}_{pk}\mathrm{d}V = \int_{\Omega_0} P_{ik}\dot{F}_{ik}\mathrm{d}V = \int_{\Omega_0} \mathbf{P} : \dot{\mathbf{F}}\mathrm{d}V \\
&= \int_{\Omega_0} \mathbf{S} : \dot{\mathbf{E}}dV = \frac{1}{2}\int_{\Omega_0} \mathbf{S} : \dot{\mathbf{C}}\mathrm{d}V \\
&= \int_{\Omega_0} \frac{1}{J}\mathbf{P} : \dot{\mathbf{F}}dv = \int_{\Omega_0} \frac{\rho}{\rho_0}\mathbf{P} : \dot{\mathbf{F}}\mathrm{d}v. \qquad (5.5.15)
\end{aligned}$$

Therefore, we have the stress power per unit current volume and the stress power per unit reference volume:

$$W_{\text{int}}(t) = \boldsymbol{\sigma} : \mathbf{D} = \frac{\rho}{\rho_0}\mathbf{P} : \dot{\mathbf{F}} = \frac{1}{J}\mathbf{P} : \dot{\mathbf{F}}. \qquad (5.5.16)$$

Equation (5.5.16) gives the stress power per unit current volume. Similarly, for reference configuration, we have

$$W_{\text{int}}(t) = \boldsymbol{\tau} : \mathbf{D} = \mathbf{S} : \dot{\mathbf{E}} = \frac{1}{2}\mathbf{S} : \dot{\mathbf{C}}. \qquad (5.5.17)$$

Equation (5.5.17) gives the stress power per unit reference volume.

From the above derivations, we can also observe that the rate of change of the deformation gradient and the first Piola–Kirchhoff stress tensor form a conjugate pair, denoted as $\mathbf{P} : \dot{\mathbf{F}}$. Similarly, we can identify other conjugate pairs as follows: The second Piola–Kirchhoff stress tensor and the rate of change of the Green–Lagrange strain tensor ($\mathbf{S} : \dot{\mathbf{E}}$) form a conjugate pair, and the Kirchhoff stress tensor and the rate-of-deformation tensor ($\boldsymbol{\tau} : \mathbf{D}$) form a conjugate pair. Additionally, it is possible to establish other conjugate pairs through further analysis.

5.5.3 *Internal Energy*

If we consider a collection of atoms as a material point and calculate the average of all forms of energy within it, we obtain the internal energy. In continuum thermodynamics, the rate of change of internal energy is commonly represented as

$$\frac{\mathrm{D}U}{\mathrm{D}t} = \frac{\mathrm{D}}{\mathrm{D}t}\int_{\Omega} \rho u \, \mathrm{d}v = \int_{\Omega} \rho \dot{u} \, \mathrm{d}v, \tag{5.5.18}$$

where u is the specific internal energy, i.e., energy per unit mass.

5.5.4 *Thermal Power*

We define thermal power as the rate of increase of total heat in the continuum, denoted by $\frac{\mathrm{D}Q}{\mathrm{D}t}$. The contribution to thermal power considered here arises from the following two cases: (i) the Cauchy heat flux (non-convective, without mass transport), and (ii) heat sources. By considering the heat flux (incoming) and the heat source, we can define the thermal power as the rate of thermal work:

$$\frac{\mathrm{D}Q}{\mathrm{D}t} = \int_{\Omega} \rho r \mathrm{d}v - \int_{\Gamma} \mathbf{q} \cdot \mathbf{n} \mathrm{d}S. \tag{5.5.19}$$

Here, $r = r(\mathbf{x}, t)$ represents the radiant heat constant (also known as the heat source) per unit mass per unit time, which is a scalar function. Assuming the presence of a temperature gradient in the continuum, there is scientific evidence of energy transfer (heat) from the hottest region to the colder region. This transferred energy per unit area per unit time can be represented by the thermal flux vector $\mathbf{q}(\mathbf{x}, t)$, also referred to as the Cauchy heat flux or true heat flux.

5.5.5 *The First Law of Thermodynamics*

When considering only mechanical and thermal energy, the principle of conservation of energy gives rise to what is commonly known as the first law of thermodynamics, or the energy equation. This principle asserts the interchangeability of mechanical and thermal energy:

$$\frac{\mathrm{D}\kappa}{\mathrm{D}t} + \frac{\mathrm{D}U}{\mathrm{D}t} = \frac{\mathrm{D}W}{\mathrm{D}t} + \frac{\mathrm{D}Q}{\mathrm{D}t}. \tag{5.5.20}$$

It is important to note that while mechanical power and thermal power are not exact differentials individually, experimental evidence suggests that their sum forms an exact differential.

By considering Equations (5.5.4), (5.5.11), (5.5.18), and (5.5.19) and substituting them into Equation (5.5.20), we can use the divergence theorem to convert the surface integral into a volume integral, resulting in the following expression:

$$\frac{\mathrm{D}}{\mathrm{D}t}\int_{\Omega} \rho \frac{v_i v_i}{2} \mathrm{d}v + \int_{\Omega} \rho \dot{u} \mathrm{d}v = \int_{\Omega} (\sigma_{ij} v_i)_j \mathrm{d}v + \int_{\Omega} \rho v_i b_i \mathrm{d}v + \int_{\Omega} \rho r \mathrm{d}v - \int_{\Omega} q_{i,i} \mathrm{d}v. \tag{5.5.21}$$

Additionally, by rearranging the above equation, we obtain

$$\int_{\Omega} \rho \dot{u}\, \mathrm{d}v = \int_{\Omega} [v_i(\sigma_{ij,j} + \rho b_i - \rho \dot{v}_i) + \sigma_{ij} v_{i,j} + \rho r - q_{i,i}] \mathrm{d}v. \tag{5.5.22}$$

And using equations of motion $\sigma_{ij,j} + \rho b_i - \rho \dot{v}_i = 0$ and $v_{i,j} = D_{ij} + W_{ij}$, we obtain

$$\int_{\Omega} \rho \dot{u}\, \mathrm{d}v = \int_{\Omega} (\sigma_{ij} D_{ij} + \rho r - q_{i,i}) \mathrm{d}v. \tag{5.5.23}$$

The local form of the above equation is known as the energy equation, whose index form and tensorial notation are:

$$\rho \dot{u} = \sigma_{ij} D_{ij} + \rho r - q_{i,i}, \tag{5.5.24}$$

$$\rho \dot{u} = \boldsymbol{\sigma} : \mathbf{D} + \rho r - \nabla \cdot \mathbf{q}. \tag{5.5.25}$$

The above equations are energy equations in the current configuration.

Similarly, the energy equation can also be established in the Lagrangian description (material description) as

$$\int_{\Omega_0} \rho_0 \dot{u}(\mathbf{X}, t) \mathrm{d}V = \int_{\Omega_0} (\mathbf{S} : \dot{\mathbf{E}} + \rho_0 r(\mathbf{X}, t) - \nabla \cdot \mathbf{q}_0) \mathrm{d}V. \tag{5.5.26}$$

Additionally, the local form of the above equation is

$$\rho_0 \dot{u}(\mathbf{X}, t) = \mathbf{S} : \dot{\mathbf{E}} + \rho_0 r(\mathbf{X}, t) - \nabla \cdot \mathbf{q}_0. \tag{5.5.27}$$

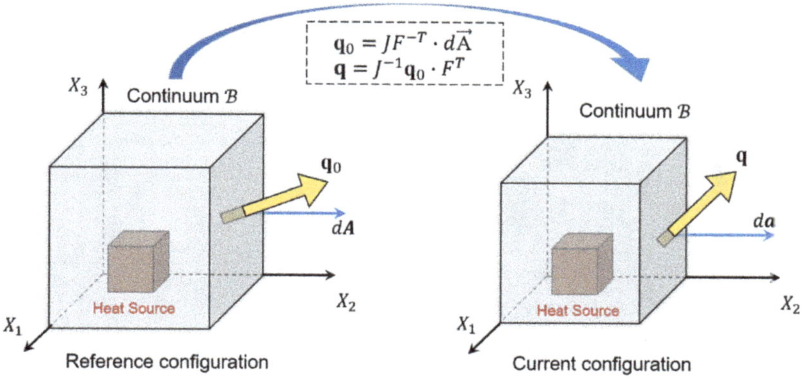

Figure 5.5.1 Heat flux in the reference and current configurations.

Please note that the amount of heat that passes through the area element $\mathbf{da}$ in the current configuration must be the same as that which passes through the area element $\mathrm{d}\mathbf{A}$ in the reference configuration (see Figure 5.5.1). Then the following relationship must be met: $\mathbf{q}_0 \cdot \mathrm{d}\mathbf{A} = \mathbf{q} \cdot \mathrm{d}\mathbf{a}$.

5.5.6 *The Second Law of Thermodynamics*

Before applying the second law of thermodynamics, it is important to define the concept of entropy, which is a state function. In thermodynamics, entropy is a physical quantity that measures the amount of energy that cannot be utilized to perform work. It can also be understood as a measure of the disorder or randomness within a system. The unit of entropy is J/K (joules per Kelvin), and a process characterized by constant entropy is referred to as an isentropic process.

The second law of thermodynamics introduces restrictions on the possible directions of thermodynamic processes. While the first law of thermodynamics does not establish the direction of heat flow, the second law states that the change in the total entropy, denoted as ΔS, is always equal to or greater than the sum of the entropy flow entering through the surface of the continuum and the entropy created inside the continuum. It is also stated that "the total entropy S is never less than the sum of the entropy flow that enters through the surface of the continuum plus the entropy created inside the continuum."

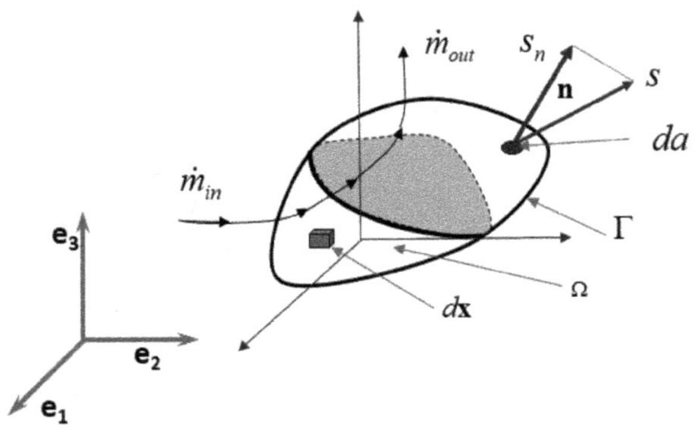

Figure 5.5.2 Continuum in motion of a massive body.

For a given system, as shown in Figure 5.5.2, the total entropy of the system $\mathcal{S}$ is given by

$$\mathcal{S} = \int_{\Omega} (\rho\eta(\mathbf{x}, t)\mathrm{d}v = \int_{\Omega_0} \rho\eta_0(\mathbf{X}, t)\mathrm{d}V, \tag{5.5.28}$$

where $\eta(\mathbf{x}, t)$ is the specific entropy (per unit mass).

The change rate of entropy supplied to the system $\mathfrak{B}$ is given by

$$\mathfrak{B} = \int_{\Omega} (\rho\tilde{b}(\mathbf{x}, t)\mathrm{d}v = \int_{\Omega_0} \rho\tilde{b}_0(\mathbf{X}, t)\mathrm{d}V, \tag{5.5.29}$$

where $\tilde{b}$ is the source of local entropy per unit mass per unit time.

Then, the entropy flux that enters the system through the material surface is defined by

$$-\int_{\Gamma} \tilde{\mathbf{s}} \cdot \mathbf{n}\mathrm{d}S. \tag{5.5.30}$$

Thus, we can set the entropy inequality as

$$\begin{aligned} \tilde{\Gamma}(t) = \dot{\mathcal{S}} &= \frac{\mathrm{D}}{\mathrm{D}t}\int_{\Omega} (\rho\eta(\mathbf{x}, t)\mathrm{d}v \geq \int_{\Omega} (\rho\tilde{b}(\mathbf{x}, t)\mathrm{d}v - \int_{\Gamma} \tilde{\mathbf{s}} \cdot \mathbf{n}\mathrm{d}S, \\ \text{or}\quad \tilde{\Gamma}(t) = \dot{\mathcal{S}} &= \int_{\Omega} (\rho\dot{\eta}(\mathbf{x}, t)\mathrm{d}v \geq \int_{\Omega} (\rho\tilde{b}(\mathbf{x}, t)\mathrm{d}v - \int_{\Gamma} \tilde{\mathbf{s}} \cdot \mathbf{n}\mathrm{d}S. \end{aligned} \tag{5.5.31}$$

Then, by applying the divergence theorem to the surface integral, we obtain

$$\tilde{\Gamma}(t) = \dot{\mathcal{S}} = \int_{\Omega} (\rho\dot{\eta}(\mathbf{x}, t)\mathrm{d}v \geq \int_{\Omega} (\rho\tilde{b}(\mathbf{x}, t)\mathrm{d}v - \int_{\Omega} \nabla \cdot \tilde{\mathbf{s}}\mathrm{d}v. \quad (5.5.32)$$

This is the second law of thermodynamics, also called the "entropy inequality."

The global form of the entropy inequality implies that if entropy occurs, it indicates an irreversible process. In other words, once a system undergoes a change in entropy, it is not possible to return to the original state without adding work to the system. On the other hand, if the equality in the above equation holds, it represents a reversible process.

The local form of the equation in (5.5.32) is given by

$$\rho\dot{\eta}(\mathbf{x}, t) \geq \rho\tilde{b}(\mathbf{x}, t) - \nabla \cdot \tilde{\mathbf{s}}. \quad (5.5.33)$$

Normally, we consider

$$\tilde{\mathbf{s}} = \frac{\mathbf{q}}{\theta} + \tilde{\mathbf{s}}^{(1)}, \quad \tilde{b} = \frac{r}{\theta} + \tilde{b}^{(1)}, \quad (5.5.34)$$

where θ is the absolute temperature, and normally, assuming that $\tilde{\mathbf{s}}^{(1)}, \tilde{b}^{(1)}$ are equal to zero, this means the entropy is only related to the internal part and entropy flux. Thus, the entropy inequality becomes

$$\rho\dot{\eta}(\mathbf{x}, t) \geq \rho\frac{r}{\theta} - \nabla \cdot \left(\frac{\mathbf{q}}{\theta}\right) = \rho\frac{r}{\theta} - \frac{1}{\theta}\nabla \cdot \mathbf{q} + \frac{1}{\theta^2}\mathbf{q} \cdot \nabla\theta. \quad (5.5.35)$$

Thus, the entropy inequality in the current configuration is

$$\rho\dot{\eta}(\mathbf{x}, t) - \rho\frac{r}{\theta} + \nabla \cdot \left(\frac{\mathbf{q}}{\theta}\right) \geq 0, \quad \text{or}$$

$$\rho\dot{\eta}(\mathbf{x}, t) - \rho\frac{r}{\theta} + \frac{1}{\theta}\nabla \cdot \mathbf{q} - \frac{1}{\theta^2}\mathbf{q} \cdot \nabla\theta \geq 0. \quad (5.5.36)$$

Similarly, we can express the entropy inequality given in the reference configuration as

$$\rho_0\dot{\eta}(\mathbf{X}, t) - \rho_0\frac{r(\mathbf{X}, t)}{\theta} + \nabla \cdot \left(\frac{\mathbf{q}_0}{\theta}\right) \geq 0, \quad \text{or}$$

$$\rho_0\dot{\eta}(\mathbf{X}, t) - \rho_0\frac{r(\mathbf{X}, t)}{\theta} + \frac{1}{\theta}\nabla \cdot \mathbf{q}_0 - \frac{1}{\theta^2}\mathbf{q}_0 \cdot \nabla\theta \geq 0, \quad (5.5.37)$$

where $\mathbf{q}_0 = J\mathbf{q} \cdot \mathbf{F}^{-\mathrm{T}}$, or, in indicial notation, $q_{0_i} = Jq_k F_{ik}^{-1}$.

If we combine the entropy inequality with the energy equation given above, we can further obtain the new form of the entropy inequality, which is called the Clausius–Duhem inequality. In the current configuration, the Clausius–Duhem inequality can be expressed as

$$\rho\dot{\eta}(\mathbf{x},t) + \frac{1}{\theta}\boldsymbol{\sigma} : \mathbf{D} - \frac{1}{\theta}\rho\dot{u} - \frac{1}{\theta^2}\mathbf{q}\cdot\nabla\theta \geq 0. \tag{5.5.38}$$

We can also express the Clausius–Duhem inequality in the reference configuration as follows:

$$\rho_0\dot{\eta}(\mathbf{X},t) + \frac{1}{\theta}\mathbf{S} : \dot{\mathbf{E}} - \frac{1}{\theta}\rho_0\dot{u} - \frac{1}{\theta^2}\mathbf{q}_0\cdot\nabla\theta \geq 0, \quad \text{or}$$
$$\rho_0\dot{\eta}(\mathbf{X},t) + \frac{1}{\theta}\mathbf{P} : \dot{\mathbf{F}} - \frac{1}{\theta}\rho_0\dot{u} - \frac{1}{\theta^2}\mathbf{q}_0\cdot\nabla\theta \geq 0. \tag{5.5.39}$$

We now examine the term $\mathbf{q}\cdot\nabla\theta$. It is important to note that the inequality $\mathbf{q}\cdot\nabla\theta \leq 0$ is always valid because the heat flux vector is oriented opposite to the temperature gradient. Consequently, we can express the heat conduction inequality in both the current and reference configurations, as illustrated in Figure 5.5.3.

Then, we can formulate the heat conduction inequality for the current and reference configurations:

$$\begin{aligned} -\mathbf{q}\cdot\nabla\theta &\geq 0, \\ -\mathbf{q}_0\cdot\nabla\theta &\geq 0. \end{aligned} \tag{5.5.40}$$

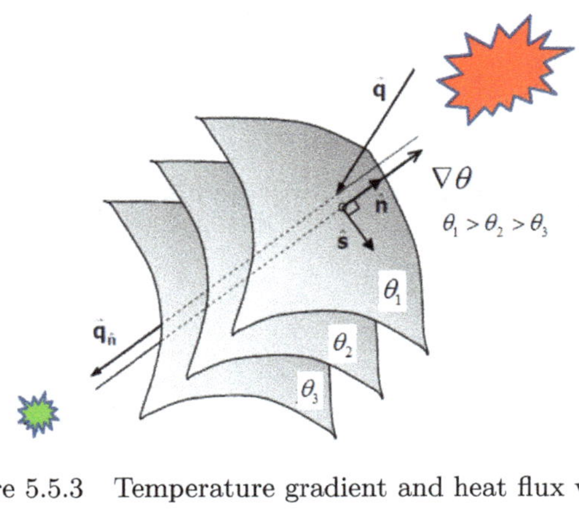

Figure 5.5.3 Temperature gradient and heat flux vector.

Now, if we incorporate the restrictions from the above equations into the Clausius–Duhem inequality, we obtain a less restrictive inequality known as the Clausius–Planck inequality in both the current configuration and reference configurations:

$$\rho\dot{\eta}(\mathbf{x},t) + \frac{1}{\theta}\boldsymbol{\sigma} : \mathbf{D} - \frac{1}{\theta}\rho\dot{u} \geq 0; \tag{5.5.41}$$

$$\begin{aligned} \rho_0\dot{\eta}(\mathbf{X},t) + \frac{1}{\theta}\mathbf{S} : \dot{\mathbf{E}} - \frac{1}{\theta}\rho_0\dot{u} \geq 0, \\ \rho_0\dot{\eta}(\mathbf{X},t) + \frac{1}{\theta}\mathbf{P} : \dot{\mathbf{F}} - \frac{1}{\theta}\rho_0\dot{u} \geq 0. \end{aligned} \tag{5.5.42}$$

The left-hand parts of the above equations are the internal energy dissipations, which require positiveness at any time.

5.5.7 *The Helmholtz Free Energy Form of the Clausius–Duhem Inequality*

An alternative form of the entropy inequality is expressed in terms of the Helmholtz free energy, denoted as ψ, which is a thermodynamic potential per unit mass and is given by the Eulerian description. A thermodynamic potential represents the amount of energy available in the system. The Helmholtz free energy, ψ, can be defined as follows:

$$\psi = u - \theta\eta. \tag{5.5.43}$$

If we calculate the change rate of the Helmholtz free energy, we obtain

$$\dot{\psi} = \dot{u} - \theta\dot{\eta} - \dot{\theta}\eta. \tag{5.5.44}$$

Thus, we can obtain the Clausius–Duhem inequality in the current configuration in terms of the Helmholtz free energy:

$$\boldsymbol{\sigma} : \mathbf{D} - \rho[\eta\dot{\theta} + \dot{\psi}] - \frac{1}{\theta}\mathbf{q} \cdot \nabla\theta \geq 0. \tag{5.5.45}$$

The Clausius–Duhem inequality in the reference configuration can also be written in terms of the Helmholtz free energy:

$$\begin{aligned} \mathbf{S} : \dot{\mathbf{E}} - \rho_0[\dot{\psi} + \dot{\theta}\eta] - \frac{1}{\theta}\mathbf{q}_0 \cdot \nabla\theta \geq 0 \\ \mathbf{P} : \dot{\mathbf{F}} - \rho_0[\dot{\psi} + \dot{\theta}\eta] - \frac{1}{\theta}\mathbf{q}_0 \cdot \nabla\theta \geq 0. \end{aligned} \tag{5.5.46}$$

The Helmholtz free energy per unit reference volume is denoted by $\Psi = \rho_0 \psi$, and it holds that $\dot{\Psi} = \rho_0 \dot{\psi}$.

The Clausius–Planck inequality can also be expressed in terms of Helmholtz free energy. Then, if we consider the heat conduction inequalities of $-\mathbf{q} \cdot \nabla\theta \geq 0$ and $-\mathbf{q}_0 \cdot \nabla\theta \geq 0$, the alternative form of the Clausius–Planck inequality in the current and reference configurations becomes

$$\boldsymbol{\sigma} : \mathbf{D} - \rho[\eta\dot{\theta} + \dot{\psi}] \geq 0 \tag{5.5.47}$$

and

$$\begin{aligned} \mathbf{S} : \dot{\mathbf{E}} - \rho_0[\dot{\psi} + \dot{\theta}\eta] &\geq 0 \\ \mathbf{P} : \dot{F} - \rho_0[\dot{\psi} + \dot{\theta}\eta] &\geq 0. \end{aligned} \tag{5.5.48}$$

A thermodynamic process is considered reversible if there is no dissipation of energy. A reversible process is characterized by the following two key aspects: (1) the work done by forces between two points is independent of the path taken, and (2) the work done in a closed cycle is zero. By acknowledging that the dissipation of energy is zero in a reversible process, we can obtain the following equations:

$$\boldsymbol{\sigma} : \mathbf{D} - \rho\dot{\psi} = 0 \tag{5.5.49}$$

and

$$\begin{aligned} \mathbf{S} : \dot{\mathbf{E}} &= \frac{1}{2}\mathbf{S} : \dot{\mathbf{C}} = \rho_0\dot{\psi} \\ \mathbf{P} : \dot{\mathbf{F}} &= \rho_0\dot{\psi}. \end{aligned} \tag{5.5.50}$$

Note that the Helmholtz free energy form has been widely used in solid mechanics.

5.6 Summary

This chapter has been dedicated to deriving the field equations that govern a continuous medium using the principles of conservation of mass, balance of momenta, and energy. These equations constitute the essence of this book and have been derived in an invariant form involving vectors and tensors. The conservation of mass leads to the continuity equation, while the balance of linear momentum, which is equivalent to Newton's second law of motion, results in the equations of motion expressed in terms of the Cauchy stress tensor. The balance of angular momentum in the absence of body couples leads to the symmetry of the Cauchy stress tensor. Furthermore, the principles of thermodynamics, specifically the first and second laws, give rise to the energy equation and the Clausius–Duhem inequality.

To summarize, we have derived the fundamental equations of continuum mechanics in the current configuration as follows:

- Mass continuity equation or principle of conservation of mass:

$$\frac{\mathrm{D}\rho}{\mathrm{D}t} + \rho(\nabla \cdot \mathbf{v}) = 0. \tag{5.6.1}$$

- Equation of motion or principle of conservation of linear momentum:

$$\nabla \cdot \boldsymbol{\sigma} + \rho\mathbf{b} = \rho\dot{\mathbf{v}} = \rho\mathbf{a}. \tag{5.6.2}$$

- Principle of conservation of angular momentum or symmetry of the Cauchy stress tensor:

$$\boldsymbol{\sigma} = \boldsymbol{\sigma}^T. \tag{5.6.3}$$

- Energy equation or principle of conservation of energy:

$$\rho\dot{u} = \boldsymbol{\sigma} : \mathbf{D} + \rho r - \nabla \cdot \mathbf{q}. \tag{5.6.4}$$

- Entropy inequality or principle of irreversibility:

$$\rho\dot{\eta}(\mathbf{x}, t) + \frac{1}{\theta}\boldsymbol{\sigma} : \mathbf{D} - \frac{1}{\theta}\rho\dot{u} - \frac{1}{\theta^2}\mathbf{q} \cdot \nabla\theta \geq 0. \tag{5.6.5}$$

To fully describe the behavior of a continuous medium mathematically, the conservation equations derived in this chapter need to be supplemented with constitutive equations. The constitutive relations that will be developed are required to be consistent with the second law of thermodynamics, ensuring the satisfaction of the entropy inequality. The principle of entropy states that constitutive relations should be formulated in such a way that the entropy inequality is identically satisfied for any thermodynamic process. Therefore, the following chapter will be dedicated to the discussion of material constitutive relations.

General References

Oden, J.T. (2011). *An Introduction to Mathematical Modeling: A Course in Mechanics* (John Wiley & Sons Inc., New Jersey, USA).

Reddy, J.N. (2013). *An Introduction to Continuum Mechanics* (Cambridge University Press, New York, USA).

Reddy, J.N. (2017). *Principles of Continuum Mechanics: Conservation and Balance Laws with Applications* (Cambridge University Press, New York, USA).

Problems

5.1. The velocity distribution between two parallel plates separated by a distance b is

$$v_x(y) = \mathrm{c}\frac{y}{\mathrm{b}}v_0 - \mathrm{c}\frac{y}{\mathrm{b}}\left(1 - \frac{y}{\mathrm{b}}\right), \quad v_y = v_z = 0, \quad 0 < y < b,$$

where y is measured from and normal to the bottom plate, x is taken along the plates, v_x is the velocity component parallel to the plates, v_0 is the velocity of the top plate in the x direction, and c is a constant.

Determine if the velocity field satisfies the continuity equation, and find the volume rate of flow and the average velocity.

5.2. If the stress field $\boldsymbol{\sigma} = \boldsymbol{\sigma}^T$ in a continuum has the following components in a rectangular Cartesian coordinate system

$$[\sigma] = \begin{bmatrix} x_1x_2 & x_1^2 & -x_2 \\ x_1^2 & 0 & 0 \\ -x_2 & 0 & x_1^2 + x_2^2 \end{bmatrix},$$

determine the body force components necessary for the body to be in equilibrium.

5.3. A two-dimensional state of stress $\boldsymbol{\sigma} = \boldsymbol{\sigma}^T$ exists in a continuum with no body forces. The following components of the stress tensor are given:

$$[\sigma] = \begin{bmatrix} \mathrm{c}_1x_2^3 + \mathrm{c}_2x_2x_1^2 - \mathrm{c}_3x_1 & \mathrm{c}_6x_1x_2^2 + \mathrm{c}_7x_2x_1^2 - \mathrm{c}_8 \\ \mathrm{c}_6x_1x_2^2 + \mathrm{c}_7x_2x_1^2 - \mathrm{c}_8 & \mathrm{c}_4x_2^3 - \mathrm{c}_5 \end{bmatrix},$$

where c_i are constants. Determine the conditions for the constants so that the stress field is in equilibrium.

5.4. Let us consider the following velocity field:

$$v_i = \mathrm{c}\frac{x_i}{1+t}, \qquad 0 \leq t.$$

(i) Find the mass density field.
(ii) Prove that this motion satisfies $\rho x_1 x_2 x_3 = \rho_0 X_1 X_2 X_3$.

Chapter 6

The Constitutive Equations of Continuum

Table of Contents

6.1 Introduction

Mathematically, the purpose of constitutive equations is to establish connections between kinematic, thermal, and mechanical variables. Kinematic variables, such as strains and temperature gradients, and kinetic variables, such as stresses and heat flux, have been introduced independently of each other in previous chapters (Chapters 4 and 5). Constitutive equations are the relations that connect the primary field variables (e.g., $\rho, \theta, \nabla\theta, \mathrm{u}, \nabla u$) to the secondary field variables

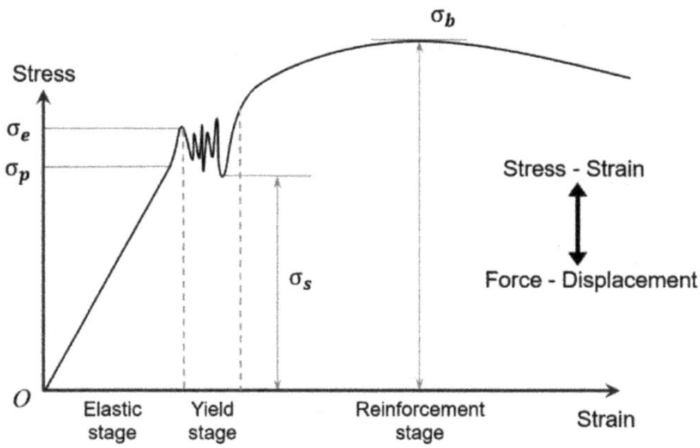

Figure 6.1.1 Constitutive equation for stress and strain (such as steel material).

(e.g., $e, \mathbf{q}, \boldsymbol{\sigma}$), and they involve the intrinsic physical properties of a continuum. It should be noted that constitutive equations are not derived from any physical principles, although they are subject to obeying certain rules and the entropy inequality. In essence, constitutive equations are mathematical models that represent the real behavior of materials and are validated against experimental results. Differences between theoretical predictions and experimental findings are often attributed to an inaccurate mathematical representation of constitutive behavior. Therefore, it is crucial to establish proper constitutive equations for different materials.

As an example, Figure 6.1.1 illustrates the stress–strain relationship for a mechanical problem, representing the constitutive equation for steel material. In this case, constitutive equations should be understood as objective relationships between stress and strain. It is important to note that different constitutive equations can be established for different stages.

Therefore, this chapter provides a framework for the development of constitutive equations for solids by focusing on constitutive laws for linearly and nonlinearly elastic solids. The chapter delves into the specifics of the general stress–deformation relations for each case of symmetry in relation to hyperelastic materials. These materials are characterized by a strain-energy function and may or may not have an internal constraint, such as incompressibility. Detailed explanations are given, along with illustrations of particular prototype models, to elucidate these concepts.

6.2 General Principles of Constitutive Theory and Discussion

6.2.1 *Rules and Physical Requirements for Constitutive Equations*

To establish constitutive relations, it can be beneficial to establish certain principles or restrictions, given the complexity involved in formulating constitutive equations (Gurtin, 1963; Truesdell & Noll, 1965). These principles include:

- *The principle of determinism*: This principle states that the response of a material at any given time is uniquely determined by the values of relevant variables and their rates of change at that particular time.
- *The principle of local action*: According to this principle, the behavior of a material at a specific point depends only on the state variables and their spatial derivatives at that point, without any direct influence from distant points.
- *The principle of equipresence*: This principle implies that the material's response is independent of the path taken to reach the current state, focusing solely on the current state itself.
- *The principle of objectivity*: Objectivity states that the constitutive equations should be independent of the observer's frame of reference or coordinate system. The material's behavior should remain consistent regardless of the chosen frame of reference.
- *The principle of dissipation*: This principle asserts that the constitutive equations should reflect the dissipative nature of real materials. Energy dissipation should occur in accordance with the laws of thermodynamics.

By adhering to these principles, a solid foundation can be established for formulating constitutive equations that accurately describe the behavior of materials.

6.2.1.1 *The principle of determinism*

This principle states that the fields $(\psi, \boldsymbol{\sigma}, \eta, \mathbf{q})$ at a material point $\mathbf{X}$ depend on the entire history of the motion, $\mathbf{x}(\mathbf{X}, t)$, and the

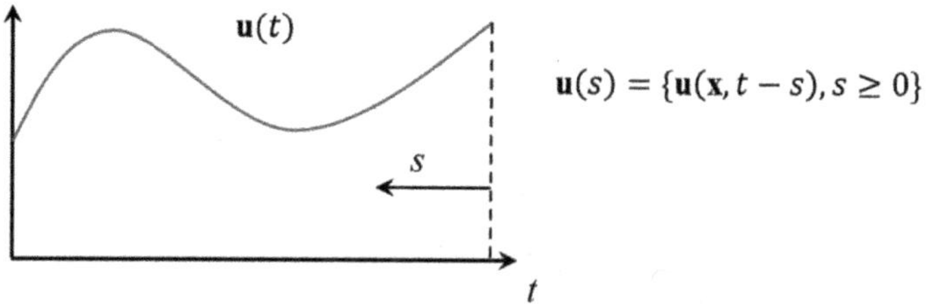

Figure 6.2.1 The time history of a problem.

temperature history, $\theta(\mathbf{X}, t)$, i.e., up until the present time t, but they never depend on the future values of $(\mathbf{x}, \theta)$.

In certain types of thermodynamic processes, it may be unrealistic for the current field values to depend on values that are too distant from the present ones. This leads to the principle of limited memory, where the current fields are not influenced by histories that are far removed from them. Therefore, it is sufficient to consider only the most recent values of the fields, which requires defining the concept of "recent time." In other words, the prevailing conditions at $\mathbf{x}(\mathbf{X}, t)$ at a given time S depend on the past behavior of variables before time S, not the future. In general, the "history" of a function of displacement relies solely on the current time values, as illustrated in Figure 6.2.1 for displacement history.

6.2.1.2 *The principle of local action*

This principle states that the current values of the fields, such as $(\psi, \boldsymbol{\sigma}, \eta, \mathbf{q})$ at a material point, depend on the state of these fields in the vicinity of that point. Local motion information is provided by the deformation gradient $\mathbf{F}(\mathbf{X}, t)$, and local temperature information is conveyed by its gradient $\nabla\theta$. In other words, the dependent (primitive) constitutive variables at $\mathbf{X}$ are not influenced by the actions of independent variables at distant points $\mathbf{X}$.

6.2.1.3 *The principle of equipresence*

This principle states that there is no reason to exclude a state variable (independent variable) *a priori* from the constitutive equations. For instance, in the case of a simple thermoelastic material, it would be illogical if stress were solely a function of the deformation gradient while the heat flux vector were solely a function of temperature.

6.2.1.4 *Principle of objectivity*

This principle states that the constitutive equations must be consistent for all observers. Hence, any constitutive equation must satisfy the principle of objectivity. In other words, if an observer detects a certain stress state in a body $\mathfrak{B}$ undergoing a rigid-body motion, then any other observer must detect the same stress state in that body $\mathfrak{B}^*$.

6.2.1.5 *The principle of physical consistency*

This principle states that constitutive equations must adhere to and not contradict the fundamental physical principles of mechanics, such as the conservation of mass, energy, and momentum balances.

6.2.1.6 *The principle of dissipation*

This principle states that constitutive equations must satisfy the entropy inequality for any admissible thermodynamic process. In other words, constitutive equations cannot violate or contradict the fundamental physical principles of mechanics.

6.2.2 *Principle of Material Frame Indifference*

As discussed in the previous section on the principle of objectivity, this principle states that constitutive equations must be consistent across all observers. Therefore, any constitutive equation must satisfy the principle of objectivity. In other words, if an observer detects a certain stress state in a body $\mathfrak{B}$ undergoing a rigid-body motion, then the same observer must detect the same stress state in the body $\mathfrak{B}^*$ after the rigid-body motion.

For example, where $c(t)$ denotes rigid-body translation and $\mathbf{Q}$ (a orthogonal tensor) represents rigid-body rotation. Frame indifferences is important in calculating/measuring various quantities in the kinematic and kinetic of a continuum. In summary, the following relations are established to show that the displacement vector $\mathbf{u}$, deformation gradient $\mathbf{F}$, the right Cauchy–Green deformation tensor $\mathbf{C}$, the Green–Lagrange strain tensor $\mathbf{E}$, the rate-of-deformation tensor $\mathbf{D}$, the Cauchy stress tensor $\boldsymbol{\sigma}$, the first Piola–Kirchhoff stress tensor $\mathbf{P}$, and the second Piola–Kirchhoff stress tensor $\mathbf{S}$ are all objective:

$$\mathbf{u}^* = \mathbf{Q}\cdot\mathbf{u}, \quad \mathbf{F}^* = \mathbf{Q}\cdot\mathbf{F}, \quad \mathbf{C}^* = \mathbf{C}, \quad \mathbf{E}^* = \mathbf{E}, \quad \mathbf{D}^* = \mathbf{Q}\cdot\mathbf{D}\cdot\mathbf{Q}^T, \tag{6.2.1}$$

$$\boldsymbol{\sigma}^* = \mathbf{Q}\cdot\boldsymbol{\sigma}\cdot\mathbf{Q}^T, \quad \mathbf{P}^* = \mathbf{Q}\cdot\mathbf{P}, \quad \mathbf{S}^* = \mathbf{S}. \tag{6.2.2}$$

The central idea of the material frame indifference is that the constitutive equations relating the quantities introduced in the kinematic description to those appearing in the kinetic description must be independent of the frame of reference (i.e., invariant under observer transformations).

6.2.3 *Consistence with the Entropy Inequality*

To ensure the thermodynamic equilibrium of the processes under consideration, the constitutive equations must be derived using the entropy inequality. If derived through alternative methods, the constitutive equations must still satisfy the conditions that arise from the entropy inequality and adhere to the axioms discussed in Chapter 5.

For example, when analyzing the momentum and energy equations along with the entropy inequality, it can be inferred that the stress tensor $\boldsymbol{\sigma}$, Helmholtz free-energy density Ψ, specific entropy η, and heat flux vector $\mathbf{q}$ must serve as the dependent variables in constitutive models for a homogeneous and isotropic material. The specific form and arguments of these variables depend on the physics of the process. Therefore, we have the following functional forms based on the principle of equipresence:

$$\begin{aligned} \boldsymbol{\sigma} &= \mathfrak{S}(x, t, \Lambda), \\ \mathbf{q} &= Q(x, t, \Lambda), \\ \Psi &= \Psi(x, t, \Lambda), \\ \eta &= \mathfrak{H}(x, t, \Lambda), \end{aligned} \tag{6.2.3}$$

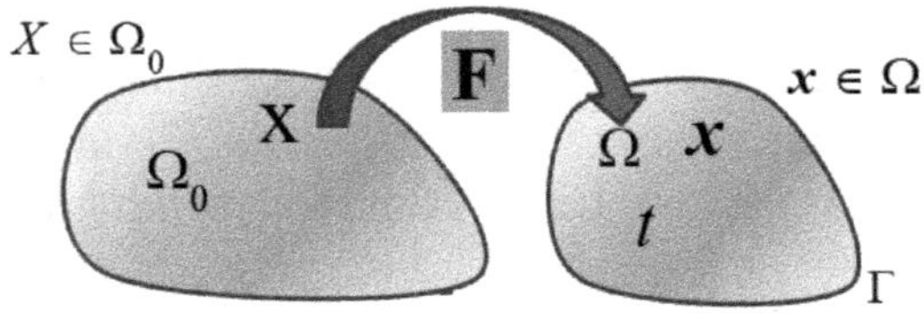

Figure 6.2.2 A body mapping from the reference configuration to the current configuration.

where $\mathfrak{S}, Q, \Psi, \mathfrak{H}$ denote the functional mapping, referred to as the response function, and $\Lambda = (\mathbf{F}, \mathbf{C}, \theta, \nabla\theta, \mathbf{D}, \mathbf{L}, \ldots.)$ denotes everything we might expect to influence the stress, heat flux, etc., at time t. The entropy inequality provides guidelines for the form of the constitutive relations.

For a simple thermoelastic material, the state variables (independent variables) consist of the deformation gradient, temperature, and the temperature gradient $\mathbf{F}, \theta, \nabla\theta$, as depicted in Figure 6.2.2 for a given body. The deformation gradient $\mathbf{F}$ serves as a measure of deformation, the temperature gradient vector $\nabla\theta$ is required due to $\mathbf{q}$, and temperature θ itself is an obvious choice as an argument for thermoelastic solids.

For example, suppose that Ψ is a function of $\mathbf{F}, \theta, \nabla\theta$, i.e., $\psi = \Psi(\mathbf{F}, \theta, \nabla\theta)$. Using the relationship $\sigma_{ij} W_{ij} = 0$ or $\boldsymbol{\sigma} : \mathbf{W} = 0$, the entropy inequality is

$$-\rho\dot{\Psi} + \boldsymbol{\sigma} : \mathbf{L} - \rho\dot{\theta}\eta - \frac{1}{\theta}\mathbf{q} \cdot \nabla\theta \geq 0, \tag{6.2.4}$$

where $\mathbf{L}$ is the velocity gradient tensor, $\mathbf{L} = \mathbf{D} + \mathbf{W}$; $\mathbf{D}$ is the symmetric part, and $\mathbf{W}$ is the skew-symmetric part of the velocity gradient tensor $\mathbf{L}$.

We can also write

$$\dot{\Psi} = \frac{\partial \Psi}{\partial \mathbf{F}} : \dot{\mathbf{F}} + \frac{\partial \Psi}{\partial \theta}\dot{\theta} + \frac{\partial \Psi}{\partial(\nabla\theta)} \cdot \frac{\partial(\nabla\theta)}{\partial t}. \tag{6.2.5}$$

Substituting the above equation in Equation (6.2.4) and noting that $\boldsymbol{\sigma} : \mathbf{L} = \boldsymbol{\sigma} : \mathbf{L}^T$,

$$\begin{aligned} &\left(\boldsymbol{\sigma} - \rho\frac{\partial \Psi}{\partial \mathbf{F}} \cdot \mathbf{F}^T\right) : \mathbf{L}^T - \rho\left(\eta + \frac{\partial \Psi}{\partial \theta}\right)\dot{\theta} \\ &\quad - \frac{\partial \Psi}{\partial(\nabla\theta)} \cdot \frac{\partial(\nabla\theta)}{\partial t} - \frac{1}{\theta}\mathbf{q} \cdot \nabla\theta \geq 0. \end{aligned} \tag{6.2.6}$$

Since $(\mathbf{L}, \dot{\theta}, \nabla\theta)$ are linearly independent of each other, it follows that

$$\boldsymbol{\sigma} - \rho \frac{\partial \Psi}{\partial \mathbf{F}} \cdot \mathbf{F}^T = 0, \tag{6.2.7}$$

$$\eta + \frac{\partial \Psi}{\partial \theta} = 0, \tag{6.2.8}$$

$$- \frac{\partial \Psi}{\partial (\nabla\theta)} = 0, \tag{6.2.9}$$

$$- \frac{1}{\theta} \mathbf{q} \cdot \nabla\theta \geq 0. \tag{6.2.10}$$

Equation (6.2.9) implies that Ψ is not a function of the temperature gradient $\nabla\theta$. Also, Equation (6.2.10) implies that

$$\mathbf{q} \cdot \nabla\theta \leq 0. \tag{6.2.11}$$

Therefore, $\mathbf{q}$ is proportional to the negative of the gradient of the temperature. We discuss it in the Fourier heat conduction law. Equation (6.2.8) implies that η can be determined from Ψ and, hence, cannot be a dependent variable in the constitutive model. Furthermore, we conclude from Equation (6.2.7) that, because Ψ is a function of only $\mathbf{F}$ and $\theta, \boldsymbol{\sigma}$ can depend only on $\mathbf{F}$ and θ. Thus, we can further modify Equation (6.2.3) as

$$\begin{aligned} \Psi &= \Psi(\mathbf{F}, \theta), \\ \boldsymbol{\sigma} &= \rho \frac{\partial \Psi}{\partial \mathbf{F}} \cdot \mathbf{F}^T, \\ \eta &= - \frac{\partial \Psi}{\partial \theta}, \\ \mathbf{q} &= q(\mathbf{F}, \theta, \nabla\theta). \end{aligned} \tag{6.2.12}$$

This is the general form of the constitutive equations for a body system under deformation and thermal loading in the current configuration. Similarly, we can derive the constitutive equations in the reference configuration. For the reference configuration, we can also assume that $\Psi, \eta, \mathbf{q}_0, \mathbf{P}$ (reference configuration) have been established by the history and current values of $\mathbf{F}, \theta, \nabla\theta$ of the body system.

We are aware that the Clausius–Duhem inequality (entropy inequality) in the reference configuration can be expressed in an alternative form as follows:

$$\mathbf{P} : \dot{\mathbf{F}} - \rho_0[\dot{\Psi} - \dot{\theta}\eta] - \frac{1}{\theta}\mathbf{q}_0 \cdot \nabla\theta \geq 0, \tag{6.2.13}$$

where Ψ, η are the Helmholtz free energy per unit mass and the entropy per unit mass, respectively, and $\mathbf{P}$ is the first Piola–Kirchhoff stress tensor. Note that, although the stress power $\mathbf{P} : \dot{\mathbf{F}}$ is defined in the reference configuration, neither $\mathbf{P}$ nor $\mathbf{F}$ are in the reference configuration.

Then, by combining the equation in (6.2.5) with the entropy inequality in (6.2.13), we obtain

$$\mathbf{P} : \dot{\mathbf{F}} - \rho_0\left[\frac{\partial\Psi}{\partial\mathbf{F}} : \dot{\mathbf{F}} + \frac{\partial\Psi}{\partial\theta}\dot{\theta} + \frac{\partial\Psi}{\partial(\nabla\theta)} \cdot \dot{\nabla\theta} + \dot{\theta}\eta\right] - \frac{1}{\theta}\mathbf{q}_0 \cdot \nabla\theta \geq 0 \tag{6.2.14}$$

and

$$\left[\mathbf{P} - \rho_0\frac{\partial\Psi}{\partial\mathbf{F}}\right] : \dot{\mathbf{F}} - \rho_0\left[\frac{\partial\Psi}{\partial\theta} + \eta\right]\dot{\theta} - \rho_0\frac{\partial\Psi}{\partial(\nabla\theta)} \cdot \dot{\nabla\theta} - \frac{1}{\theta}\mathbf{q}_0 \cdot \nabla\theta \geq 0. \tag{6.2.15}$$

The above inequality must be satisfied for any admissible thermodynamic process.

Now, let us consider the process such that $\dot{\mathbf{F}} = 0$ and a system with uniform temperature; thus, $\nabla\theta = 0, \dot{\nabla\theta} = 0$. In this particular thermodynamic process, the inequality becomes

$$-\rho_0\left[\frac{\partial\Psi}{\partial\theta} + \eta\right]\dot{\theta} \geq 0. \tag{6.2.16}$$

Note that this inequality must also hold true for any thermodynamic process. Therefore, if the condition in (6.2.16) is met during the current process, it is possible to apply another process with $-\dot{\theta}$, and in this case, the entropy inequality is violated. Consequently, the only way to satisfy the inequality is when

$$\frac{\partial\Psi}{\partial\theta} + \eta = 0, \quad \eta = -\frac{\partial\Psi}{\partial\theta}; \tag{6.2.17}$$

thus,

$$\left[\mathbf{P} - \rho_0 \frac{\partial \Psi}{\partial \mathbf{F}}\right] : \dot{\mathbf{F}} - \rho_0 \frac{\partial \Psi}{\partial (\nabla \theta)} \cdot \dot{\nabla \theta} - \frac{1}{\theta} \mathbf{q}_0 \cdot \nabla \theta \geq 0. \tag{6.2.18}$$

Now, let us consider a process where $\dot{\mathbf{F}} = 0$. Then, we find that

$$-\rho_0 \frac{\partial \Psi}{\partial (\nabla \theta)} \cdot \dot{\nabla \theta} - \frac{1}{\theta} \mathbf{q}_0 \cdot \nabla \theta \geq 0, \tag{6.2.19}$$

in which we find that the second term is always true since the heat flux vector is always opposite to the temperature gradient:

$$-\rho_0 \frac{\partial \Psi}{\partial (\nabla \theta)} \cdot \dot{\nabla \theta} \geq 0, \tag{6.2.20}$$

and $\frac{\partial \Psi}{\partial (\nabla \theta)} = 0$; otherwise, it will violate the second law of thermodynamics.

We can conclude that Ψ should not depend on the temperature gradient $\nabla \theta$, i.e., $\Psi = \Psi(\mathbf{F}, \theta)$.

Therefore, we can obtain

$$\mathbf{P} - \rho_0 \frac{\partial \Psi}{\partial \mathbf{F}} = 0, \quad \text{or} \quad \mathbf{P} = \rho_0 \frac{\partial \Psi}{\partial \mathbf{F}}. \tag{6.2.21}$$

Subsequently, we can conclude that the constitutive equations for a simple thermoelastic material in the reference configuration are given by

$$\begin{aligned} \Psi &= \Psi(\mathbf{F}, \theta), \\ \mathbf{P} &= \rho_0 \frac{\partial \Psi}{\partial \mathbf{F}}, \\ \eta &= -\frac{\partial \Psi}{\partial \theta}, \\ \mathbf{q}_0 &= \mathbf{q}_0(\mathbf{F} \theta \nabla_0 \theta). \end{aligned} \tag{6.2.22}$$

As $\mathbf{P}$ is related to the second Piola–Kirchhoff stress tensor $\mathbf{S}$ (in the reference configuration) by means of the equation $\mathbf{S} = \mathbf{F}^{-1} \cdot \mathbf{P}$ and the corresponding conjugate strain is the Green–Lagrange strain, we can conclude that

$$\mathbf{S} = \rho_0 \frac{\partial \Psi(\mathbf{E}, \theta)}{\partial \mathbf{E}} = 2\rho_0 \frac{\partial \Psi(\mathbf{C}, \theta)}{\partial \mathbf{C}}, \tag{6.2.23}$$

where $\mathbf{C}$ is the right Cauchy–Green deformation tensors. Also, we have

$$\begin{aligned} \Psi &= \Psi(\mathbf{E}, \theta), \\ \mathbf{S} &= \rho_0 \frac{\partial \Psi}{\partial \mathbf{E}}, \\ \eta &= -\frac{\partial \Psi}{\partial \theta}, \\ \mathbf{q}_0 &= q_0(\mathbf{E}, \theta, \nabla_0 \theta). \end{aligned} \tag{6.2.24}$$

From the above equations, the component form of the second Piola–Kirchhoff stress, the Cauchy stress, can be expressed as

$$S_{ij} = F_{ik}^{-1} P_{kj} = 2\rho_0 \frac{\partial \Psi(\mathbf{C}, \theta)}{\partial C_{ij}}, \tag{6.2.25}$$

$$\sigma_{ij} = \rho \frac{\partial \Psi(F(\mathbf{C}), \theta)}{\partial F_{ik}} F_{jk} = \rho \frac{\partial \Psi(\mathbf{C}, \theta)}{\partial C_{pq}} \frac{\partial C_{pq}}{\partial F_{ik}} F_{jk} = \rho F_{iq} \frac{\partial \Psi(\mathbf{C}, \theta)}{\partial C_{qp}} F_{jp}, \tag{6.2.26}$$

where we have considered the symmetry of $\mathbf{C}$. In tensorial notation, the constitutive equation for stress becomes

$$\boldsymbol{\sigma} = 2\rho \mathbf{F} \cdot \frac{\partial \Psi(\mathbf{C}, \theta)}{\partial \mathbf{C}} \cdot \mathbf{F}^T. \tag{6.2.27}$$

Thus, until now, we have derived the constitutive equations for thermoelastic materials.

6.3 Elastic Materials

6.3.1 *Cauchy-Elastic Materials*

A material is considered Cauchy-elastic or elastic if the stress field at time t depends solely on the state of deformation and temperature at that specific time without dependence on the history of these variables. The constitutive relation for an elastic body under isothermal conditions (where there is no change in temperature from the reference configuration) establishes a connection between the Cauchy stress tensor $\boldsymbol{\sigma}(\mathbf{x}, t)$ at a point $\mathbf{x} = \chi(\mathbf{X}, t)$ and time t and the deformation gradient $\mathbf{F}(\mathbf{X}, t)$. Therefore, the constitutive relation can be expressed as follows:

$$\boldsymbol{\sigma} = \mathfrak{S}(\mathbf{F}(\mathbf{X}, t), \mathbf{X}), \tag{6.3.1}$$

where $\mathfrak{S}$ is the response function. The requirement or restriction we placed is that the response function $\mathfrak{S}$ should not be affected by superposed rigid-body motions.

Therefore, a general homogeneous elastic material can be characterized by the fact that the stress tensor σ depends solely on the deformation gradient F, regardless of the specific path of deformation taken to reach F. This characteristic is expressed by formulating the constitutive equation using a symmetric tensor-valued function. Thus, Equation (6.3.1) can be utilized to describe a Cauchy-elastic material, which does not necessarily require the existence of a strain-energy function but is sufficient for the establishment of objectivity and material symmetry concepts without the need for introducing a strain-energy function.

6.3.2 *Green-Elastic or Hyperelastic Materials*

A hyperelastic material, also referred to as a Green-elastic material, is characterized by the presence of a Helmholtz free-energy potential Ψ (measured per unit volume). The derivative of this potential with respect to strain yields the corresponding stress, while its derivative with respect to temperature gives the heat flux vector.

When Ψ is solely a function of $\mathbf{F}$, $\mathbf{C}$, or some strain tensor, it is called the strain energy density function and denoted by U_0 (measured per unit mass), and $\Psi = U_0$.

For example, if $U_0 = U_0(\mathbf{F})$, we have

$$\mathbf{P} = \rho_0 \frac{\partial U_0(\mathbf{F})}{\partial \mathbf{F}} \quad \left(P_{ij} = \rho_0 \frac{\partial U_0}{\partial \mathbf{F}_{ij}} \right), \tag{6.3.2}$$

$$\boldsymbol{\sigma} = \frac{1}{J} \mathbf{P} \cdot \mathbf{F}^T = \rho \frac{\partial U_0(\mathbf{F})}{\partial \mathbf{F}} \cdot \mathbf{F}^T, \tag{6.3.3}$$

$$\mathbf{S} = \mathbf{F}^{-1} \cdot \mathbf{P} = \rho_0 \mathbf{F}^{-1} \cdot \frac{\partial U_0(\mathbf{F})}{\partial \mathbf{F}}. \tag{6.3.4}$$

Therefore, if we know $U_0 = U_0(\mathbf{F})$, we can determine the stress tensors from the above equations.

For an incompressible elastic material (i.e., material for which the volume is preserved and hence $J = 1$), we postulate the existence of a strain energy density function in the form of

$$\rho_0 \widehat{U}_0 = \rho_0 U_0(\mathbf{F}) - p(J-1), \tag{6.3.5}$$

where p denotes a hydrostatic pressure and $\widehat{U}_0$ is the strain energy density for the case $J = 1$. Equation (6.3.5) can be viewed as one in which the strain energy density for the case $J = 1$ is constructed from $U_0 = U_0(\mathbf{F})$ by treating $J - 1 = 0$ as a constraint and using the Lagrange multiplier method to include the constraint. It turns out that the Lagrange multiplier is $\lambda = -p$. Then, the constitutive equation for incompressible hyperelastic material is $(J = 1)$:

$$\mathbf{P} = \rho_0 \frac{\partial \widehat{U}_0(\mathbf{F})}{\partial \mathbf{F}} = -p\mathbf{F}^{-T} + \rho_0 \frac{\partial U_0(\mathbf{F})}{\partial \mathbf{F}}, \tag{6.3.6}$$

$$\boldsymbol{\sigma} = \frac{1}{J}\mathbf{P} \cdot \mathbf{F}^T = \mathbf{P} \cdot \mathbf{F}^T = -p\mathbf{I} + \rho_0 \frac{\partial U_0(\mathbf{F})}{\partial \mathbf{F}} \cdot \mathbf{F}^T, \tag{6.3.7}$$

$$\mathbf{S} = \mathbf{F}^{-1} \cdot \mathbf{P} = -p\mathbf{F}^{-1} \cdot \mathbf{F}^{-T} + \rho_0 \mathbf{F}^{-1} \cdot \frac{\partial U_0(\mathbf{F})}{\partial \mathbf{F}}. \tag{6.3.8}$$

Note that in the above equations, we have used the relationship of $\frac{\partial J}{\partial \mathbf{F}} = J\mathbf{F}^{-T}$.

Therefore, determining the Helmholtz free-energy potential or strain-energy density is crucial to establishing constitutive equations for different materials.

6.3.3 *Infinitesimal Strains*

For the case of infinitesimal deformation, denoted as $|\nabla u| \ll 1$, there is no distinction made between different measures of stress and strain. In the material description used in solid mechanics, $\mathbf{S} = \boldsymbol{\sigma}$ is used to represent the stress tensor and $\mathbf{E} = \boldsymbol{\varepsilon}$ is used to represent the strain tensor.

For such materials, the Helmholtz free-energy potential, or free-energy density, is equivalent to the strain energy density Ψ. It is more meaningful to assume that the strain energy density U_0 is a function of the strain, ε, rather than the deformation gradient. Consequently, the material coefficients that govern the constitutive relationship between stress and strain components are assumed to be constant throughout the deformation process.

The constitutive equation for linearized hyperelastic materials can be derived using

$$\boldsymbol{\sigma} = \rho_0 \frac{\partial U_0(\varepsilon)}{\partial \boldsymbol{\varepsilon}}, \quad \sigma_{ij} = \rho_0 \frac{\partial U_0}{\partial \varepsilon_{ij}}. \tag{6.3.9}$$

U_0 is a function of $\boldsymbol{\varepsilon}$, and we can expand it in Taylor's series about the strain $\boldsymbol{\varepsilon} = \mathbf{0}$ in the reference configuration

$$\rho_0 U_0(\boldsymbol{\varepsilon}) = c_0 + R_{ij}\varepsilon_{ij} + \frac{1}{2!}C_{ijkl}\,\varepsilon_{ij}\varepsilon_{kl} + \frac{1}{3!}C_{ijklmn}\,\varepsilon_{ij}\varepsilon_{kl}\varepsilon_{mn} + \cdots, \tag{6.3.10}$$

where $c_0, R_{ij}, C_{ijkl}, \ldots$ are material stiffness coefficients that are independent of the deformation. Please note that $c_0, R_{ij}, C_{ijkl}, \ldots$ are constants, second-order tensors, fourth-order tensors, and so on. For linear elastic materials, U_0 is a quadratic function of the strain tensor, and for nonlinear elastic materials, U_0 is a cubic function of the strain tensor $\boldsymbol{\varepsilon}$. For linear elastic materials, the mechanical pressure is the same as the negative of the mean normal stress.

6.4 Hookean Solids

6.4.1 *Generalized Hooke's Law*

Now, let's consider linear elastic materials. In order to establish the stress–strain relations for a linear elastic solid, we employ a coordinate system in which the material parameters are measured. We utilize the Lagrangian description with coordinates (x, y, z) to describe the kinematics, stress state, and field equations. In contrast, the material coordinate system (x_1, x_2, x_3) is employed to describe the constitutive response. The material coordinate system is aligned with the planes of material symmetry, simplifying the measurement of material parameters. However, in practical applications, the constitutive relations must be transformed into the problem coordinates in order to solve the final boundary-value problem.

When no preferred planes of material symmetry exist, the material is called isotropic, and the material coordinates are taken to be the same as the problem coordinates. All tensor quantities measured in (x_1, x_2, x_3) will have integer subscripts, for example, σ_{ij}, ε_{ij}, and so on, whereas those measured in (x, y, z) will have letter subscripts, for example, σ_{xx}, σ_{xy} and $\varepsilon_{xx}, \varepsilon_{xy}$ and so on.

For linear elastic materials, we begin with the quadratic form of U_0 in the material coordinate system:

$$\rho_0 U_0(\varepsilon) = c_0 + R_{ij}\varepsilon_{ij} + \frac{1}{2}C_{ijkl}\,\varepsilon_{ij}\varepsilon_{kl}. \tag{6.4.1}$$

Therefore, we have

$$\begin{aligned}\sigma_{mn} &= \rho_0\frac{\partial U_0}{\partial \varepsilon_{mn}} = R_{ij}\delta_{mi}\delta_{nj} + \frac{1}{2}C_{ijkl}(\varepsilon_{kl}\delta_{im}\delta_{jn} + \varepsilon_{ij}\delta_{km}\delta_{ln})\\ &= R_{mn} + C_{mnij}\varepsilon_{ij},\end{aligned} \tag{6.4.2}$$

where

$$C_{mnij} = \frac{1}{2}\left(C_{mnij} + C_{ijmn}\right) = \rho_0\frac{\partial^2 U_0}{\partial \varepsilon_{ij}\partial \varepsilon_{mn}} = C_{ijmn}. \tag{6.4.3}$$

R_{ij} represent the residual stress components of a solid. Assume that there is no residual stress in the undeformed body; thus, we have the following constitutive relations:

$$\boldsymbol{\sigma} = \mathbf{C} : \boldsymbol{\varepsilon}, \quad \sigma_{ij} = C_{ijkl}\,\varepsilon_{kl}. \tag{6.4.4}$$

This equation is known as the generalized Hooke's law. The coefficients C_{ijkl} are referred to as elastic stiffness coefficients. In general, the fourth-order tensor C_{ijkl} has 81 scalar components. However, the number of coefficients is significantly reduced due to two reasons. First, the components C_{ijkl} satisfy symmetry conditions, and second, the stress and strain tensors are symmetric. Consequently, the equation remains valid when interchanging the subscripts i and j as well as k and l. Therefore, we have

$$\begin{Bmatrix} \sigma_{11} \\ \sigma_{22} \\ \sigma_{33} \\ \sigma_{23} \\ \sigma_{13} \\ \sigma_{12} \end{Bmatrix} = \begin{bmatrix} C_{1111} & C_{1122} & C_{1133} & C_{1123} & C_{1113} & C_{1112} \\ & C_{2222} & C_{2233} & C_{2223} & C_{2213} & C_{2212} \\ & & C_{3333} & C_{3323} & C_{3313} & C_{3312} \\ & & & C_{2323} & C_{2313} & C_{2312} \\ & & & & C_{1313} & C_{1312} \\ & & & & & C_{1212} \end{bmatrix} \begin{Bmatrix} \varepsilon_{11} \\ \varepsilon_{22} \\ \varepsilon_{33} \\ 2\varepsilon_{23} \\ 2\varepsilon_{13} \\ 2\varepsilon_{12} \end{Bmatrix}. \tag{6.4.5}$$

Thus, the number of independent coefficients C_{ijkl} is 21, where $C_{ijkl} = C_{klij}$, $C_{ijkl} = C_{jikl}$, $C_{ijkl} = C_{ijlk}$, and $C_{ijkl} = C_{jilk}$.

A further reduction in the number of independent stiffness (or compliance) parameters arises from material symmetry. When elastic material parameters have identical values at a point for every pair of coordinate systems that are mirror images of each other in a specific plane, that plane is referred to as a material plane of symmetry. Material symmetry can stem from factors such as internal crystallographic form and the regular arrangement of fibers or molecules. Consequently, a material may exhibit a particular elastic symmetry at each point within its body, with properties that can vary from one point to another. The spatial dependence of material properties is what we refer to as material inhomogeneity.

In the case of monoclinic materials, where the elastic coefficients have the same value for every pair of coordinate systems that are mirror images of each other with respect to a plane, the material is said to be monoclinic at that point. For monoclinic materials, eight out of the 21 coefficients are zero. As a result, the stress–strain relations can be expressed as

$$\begin{Bmatrix} \sigma_{11} \\ \sigma_{22} \\ \sigma_{33} \\ \sigma_{23} \\ \sigma_{13} \\ \sigma_{12} \end{Bmatrix} = \begin{bmatrix} C_{1111} & C_{1122} & C_{1133} & 0 & 0 & C_{1112} \\ C_{1122} & C_{2222} & C_{2233} & 0 & 0 & C_{2212} \\ C_{1133} & C_{2233} & C_{3333} & 0 & 0 & C_{3312} \\ 0 & 0 & 0 & C_{2323} & C_{2313} & 0 \\ 0 & 0 & 0 & C_{2313} & C_{1313} & 0 \\ C_{1112} & C_{2212} & C_{3312} & 0 & 0 & C_{1212} \end{bmatrix} \begin{Bmatrix} \varepsilon_{11} \\ \varepsilon_{22} \\ \varepsilon_{33} \\ 2\varepsilon_{23} \\ 2\varepsilon_{13} \\ 2\varepsilon_{12} \end{Bmatrix}. \tag{6.4.6}$$

In this case, there are only 13 independent parameters. It is important to note that monoclinic materials display shear–extension coupling, which means that a shear strain can generate a normal stress, and conversely, a normal stress can generate a shear strain as well.

6.4.2 *Orthotropic Materials*

When three mutually orthogonal planes of material symmetry are present at a point, the number of elastic coefficients is reduced to nine through similar reasoning as for a single material symmetry plane. Materials that exhibit such behavior are referred to as orthotropic at that point. Therefore, the stress–strain relations for an orthotropic material can be expressed as follows:

$$\begin{Bmatrix} \sigma_{11} \\ \sigma_{22} \\ \sigma_{33} \\ \sigma_{23} \\ \sigma_{13} \\ \sigma_{12} \end{Bmatrix} = \begin{bmatrix} C_{1111} & C_{1122} & C_{1133} & 0 & 0 & 0 \\ C_{1122} & C_{2222} & C_{2233} & 0 & 0 & 0 \\ C_{1133} & C_{2233} & C_{3333} & 0 & 0 & 0 \\ 0 & 0 & 0 & C_{2323} & 0 & 0 \\ 0 & 0 & 0 & 0 & C_{1313} & 0 \\ 0 & 0 & 0 & 0 & 0 & C_{1212} \end{bmatrix} \begin{Bmatrix} \varepsilon_{11} \\ \varepsilon_{22} \\ \varepsilon_{33} \\ 2\varepsilon_{23} \\ 2\varepsilon_{13} \\ 2\varepsilon_{12} \end{Bmatrix}. \tag{6.4.7}$$

Therefore, for orthotropic materials, there are only nine independent parameters that can be determined through experimental tests. Similarly, in practical applications, we can apply stresses and measure the corresponding strains. Consequently, in certain cases, we can express the inverse relations in the following form:

$$\begin{Bmatrix} \varepsilon_{11} \\ \varepsilon_{22} \\ \varepsilon_{33} \\ 2\varepsilon_{23} \\ 2\varepsilon_{13} \\ 2\varepsilon_{12} \end{Bmatrix} = \begin{bmatrix} \mathfrak{R}_{1111} & \mathfrak{R}_{1122} & \mathfrak{R}_{1133} & 0 & 0 & 0 \\ \mathfrak{R}_{1122} & \mathfrak{R}_{2222} & \mathfrak{R}_{2233} & 0 & 0 & 0 \\ \mathfrak{R}_{1133} & \mathfrak{R}_{2233} & \mathfrak{R}_{3333} & 0 & 0 & 0 \\ 0 & 0 & 0 & \mathfrak{R}_{2323} & 0 & 0 \\ 0 & 0 & 0 & 0 & \mathfrak{R}_{1313} & 0 \\ 0 & 0 & 0 & 0 & 0 & \mathfrak{R}_{1212} \end{bmatrix} \begin{Bmatrix} \sigma_{11} \\ \sigma_{22} \\ \sigma_{33} \\ \sigma_{23} \\ \sigma_{13} \\ \sigma_{12} \end{Bmatrix}. \tag{6.4.8}$$

In the equation provided, the coefficients $\mathfrak{R}_{ijkl}$ represent the material compliance coefficients, which can often be determined in a laboratory through engineering material parameters, such as Young's modulus and shear modulus. These constants are typically measured using simple tests, such as uniaxial tension or pure shear tests. Due to their direct and clear physical interpretation, engineering constants are commonly used instead of the abstract compliance coefficients $\mathfrak{R}_{ijkl}$.

6.4.3 *Isotropic Materials*

Isotropic materials are characterized by their material properties being independent of direction. This means that there exists an infinite number of material symmetry planes. An isotropic fourth-order tensor can be further represented as follows:

$$C_{ijkl} = \lambda\delta_{ij}\delta_{kl} + \mu(\delta_{ik}\delta_{jl} + \delta_{il}\delta_{jk}) + \kappa(\delta_{ik}\delta_{jl} - \delta_{il}\delta_{jk}), \qquad (6.4.9)$$

where λ, μ, κ are called the Lamê constants, and summation on repeated indices is implied. In view of the symmetry of C_{ijkl} with respect to the first and last two indices, the coefficient of κ is zero, giving

$$C_{ijkl} = \lambda\delta_{ij}\delta_{kl} + 2\mu\delta_{ik}\delta_{jl}. \qquad (6.4.10)$$

Thus, the relationships of stress and strain are

$$\boldsymbol{\sigma} = 2\mu\boldsymbol{\varepsilon} + \lambda\mathrm{tr}(\boldsymbol{\varepsilon})\mathbf{I}, \quad \sigma_{ij} = 2\mu\varepsilon_{ij} + \lambda\varepsilon_{kk}\delta_{ij}. \qquad (6.4.11)$$

Therefore, only two material parameters, λ, μ, are needed to characterize the mechanical response of an isotropic material. And by using Young's modulus and the Poisson ratio, we have the following relations:

$$\mu = \frac{E}{2(1+\nu)}, \quad \lambda = \frac{\nu E}{(1+\nu)(1-2\nu)}, \quad 2\mu + \lambda = \frac{(1-\nu)E}{(1+\nu)(1-2\nu)}. \qquad (6.4.12)$$

E and ν are Young's modulus and the Poisson ratio, respectively. Then, the stress–strain relation can be expressed as

$$\begin{aligned} \boldsymbol{\sigma} &= \frac{E}{(1+\nu)}\boldsymbol{\varepsilon} + \frac{\nu E}{(1+\nu)(1-2\nu)}\mathrm{tr}(\boldsymbol{\varepsilon})\mathbf{I}, \\ \sigma_{ij} &= \frac{E}{(1+\nu)}\varepsilon_{ij} + \frac{\nu E}{(1+\nu)(1-2\nu)}\varepsilon_{kk}\delta_{ij}, \end{aligned} \qquad (6.4.13)$$

or

$$\begin{Bmatrix} \sigma_{11} \\ \sigma_{22} \\ \sigma_{33} \\ \sigma_{23} \\ \sigma_{13} \\ \sigma_{12} \end{Bmatrix} = \frac{E}{(1+\nu)(1-2\nu)}$$

$$\times \begin{bmatrix} 1-\nu & \nu & \nu & 0 & 0 & 0 \\ \nu & 1-\nu & \nu & 0 & 0 & 0 \\ \nu & \nu & 1-\nu & 0 & 0 & 0 \\ 0 & 0 & 0 & \frac{1-2\nu}{2} & 0 & 0 \\ 0 & 0 & 0 & 0 & \frac{1-2\nu}{2} & 0 \\ 0 & 0 & 0 & 0 & 0 & \frac{1-2\nu}{2} \end{bmatrix} \begin{Bmatrix} \varepsilon_{11} \\ \varepsilon_{22} \\ \varepsilon_{33} \\ 2\varepsilon_{23} \\ 2\varepsilon_{13} \\ 2\varepsilon_{12} \end{Bmatrix}. \tag{6.4.14}$$

Sometimes, stress and strain are expressed as matrices in the following form:

$$\begin{Bmatrix} \sigma_1 \\ \sigma_2 \\ \sigma_3 \\ \sigma_4 \\ \sigma_5 \\ \sigma_6 \end{Bmatrix} = \frac{E}{(1+\nu)(1-2\nu)}$$

$$\times \begin{bmatrix} 1-\nu & \nu & \nu & 0 & 0 & 0 \\ \nu & 1-\nu & \nu & 0 & 0 & 0 \\ \nu & \nu & 1-\nu & 0 & 0 & 0 \\ 0 & 0 & 0 & \frac{1-2\nu}{2} & 0 & 0 \\ 0 & 0 & 0 & 0 & \frac{1-2\nu}{2} & 0 \\ 0 & 0 & 0 & 0 & 0 & \frac{1-2\nu}{2} \end{bmatrix} \begin{Bmatrix} \varepsilon_1 \\ \varepsilon_2 \\ \varepsilon_3 \\ \varepsilon_4 \\ \varepsilon_5 \\ \varepsilon_6 \end{Bmatrix}. \tag{6.4.15}$$

Now, we consider a special case in which the only nonzero normal stress component is $\sigma_{11} = \sigma$ and the only nonzero shear component is $\sigma_{12} = \tau$, and if we denote $\varepsilon_{11} = \varepsilon$ and $2\varepsilon_{12} = \gamma$, then Equation (6.4.13) gives the uniaxial strain–stress relations:

$$\varepsilon = \frac{1}{E}\sigma \quad \text{or} \quad \sigma = E\varepsilon; \quad \gamma = \frac{2(1+\nu)}{E}\tau \quad \text{or} \quad \tau = G\gamma, \qquad (6.4.16)$$

where $G = \frac{E}{2(1+\nu)}$ is called the shear modulus.

6.4.4 *Strain Energy Density of Hookean Solids*

In order to solve the initial boundary-value problem, energy principles are typically employed. Therefore, studying the strain energy density becomes crucial. In this context, we examine strain energy from an engineering standpoint.

To provide a physical interpretation of strain energy, let's consider a differential volume element $\mathrm{d}x\mathrm{d}y\mathrm{d}z$, where we have the normal stress σ_x acting on it, as depicted in Figure 6.4.1.

From Figure 6.4.1, it can be found that the stored energy caused by the normal stress σ_x is equal to the triangular area of the graph defined in Figure 6.4.1:

$$U_0(\varepsilon) = \left(\frac{\sigma_x}{2}\mathrm{d}y\,\mathrm{d}z\right)(\varepsilon_x \mathrm{d}x) = \frac{1}{2}\sigma_x\varepsilon_x \mathrm{d}x\,\mathrm{d}y\,\mathrm{d}z. \qquad (6.4.17)$$

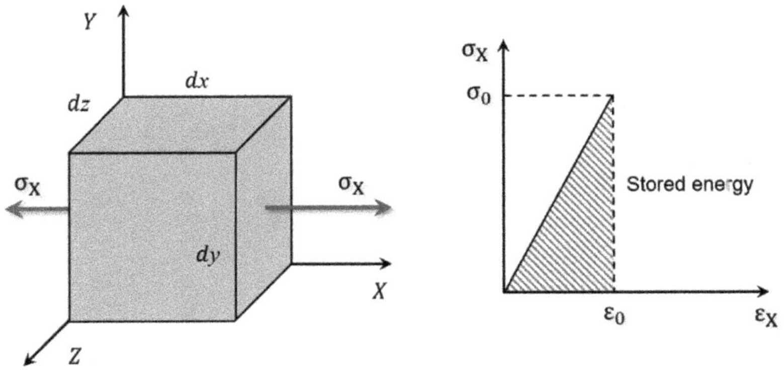

Figure 6.4.1 Element stored energy under normal stress component.

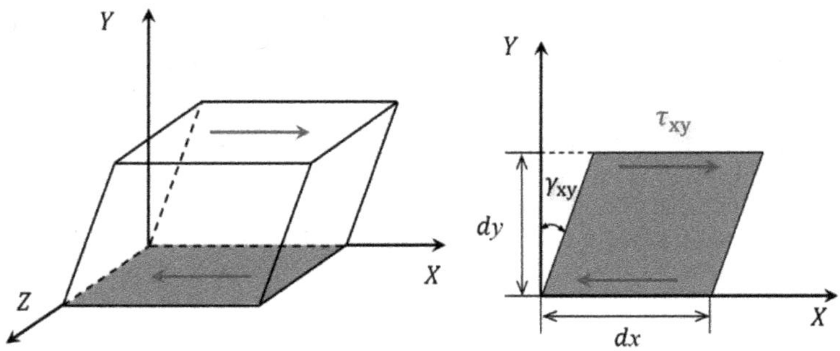

Figure 6.4.2 Element stored energy under shear stress component.

Next, we consider element stored energy under the shear stress component (Figure 6.4.2). For shear stress τ_{xy}, the strain energy is given as follows:

$$U_0(\varepsilon) = \left(\frac{\tau_{xy}}{2}\mathrm{d}x\,\mathrm{d}z\right)(\gamma_{xy}\mathrm{d}y) = \frac{1}{2}\tau_{xy}\gamma_{xy}\mathrm{d}x\,\mathrm{d}y\,\mathrm{d}z. \tag{6.4.18}$$

Similarly, considering other stress components we can now introduce the strain energy per unit volume, Ψ^e, which is known as the strain energy density and is given by

$$\Psi^e = \frac{1}{2}(\sigma_x\varepsilon_x + \sigma_y\varepsilon_y + \sigma_z\varepsilon_z + \tau_{xy}\gamma_{xy} + \tau_{xz}\gamma_{xz} + \tau_{yz}\gamma_{yz}). \tag{6.4.19}$$

Then, the total strain energy in the entire continuum can be evaluated by integrating the strain energy density over the volume

$$U_0(\varepsilon) = \int_V \Psi^e \mathrm{d}V. \tag{6.4.20}$$

Note also that Ψ^e is the elastic potential (the Helmholtz free energy per unit volume):

$$\Psi^e = \frac{1}{2}\boldsymbol{\varepsilon} : \boldsymbol{\sigma}. \tag{6.4.21}$$

Then, using the generalized Hooke's law $\boldsymbol{\sigma} = \mathbf{C} : \boldsymbol{\varepsilon}$,

$$\Psi^e = \frac{1}{2}\boldsymbol{\varepsilon} : \mathbf{C} : \boldsymbol{\varepsilon}. \tag{6.4.22}$$

Thus, considering the linear Hooke's law, we have

$$\Psi^e = \frac{\lambda}{2}\left[(\varepsilon_x + \varepsilon_x + \varepsilon_x)^2 + \mu(\varepsilon_x^2 + \varepsilon_y^2 + \varepsilon_z^2) + 2\mu(\gamma_{xy}^2 + \gamma_{yz}^2 + \gamma_{zx}^2)\right]. \tag{6.4.23}$$

Therefore,

$$\frac{\partial \Psi^e}{\partial \varepsilon_{ij}} = \sigma_{ij} \quad \text{and} \quad \frac{\partial^2 \Psi^e}{\partial \boldsymbol{\varepsilon} \otimes \partial \boldsymbol{\varepsilon}} = \frac{\partial^2}{\partial \boldsymbol{\varepsilon} \otimes \partial \boldsymbol{\varepsilon}}\left(\frac{1}{2}\boldsymbol{\varepsilon} : \mathbf{C} : \boldsymbol{\varepsilon}\right) = \mathbf{C}.$$

We can further split the strain energy density into deviatoric and spherical parts

$$\Psi^e = \frac{\kappa[\mathrm{tr}(\boldsymbol{\varepsilon})]^2}{2} + \mu \boldsymbol{\varepsilon}^{\mathrm{dev}} : \boldsymbol{\varepsilon}^{\mathrm{dev}}, \tag{6.4.24}$$

where $\boldsymbol{\varepsilon} = \boldsymbol{\varepsilon}^{\mathrm{dev}} + \frac{\mathrm{tr}(\boldsymbol{\varepsilon})}{3}\mathbf{I}$. The first term in Equation (6.4.24) represents purely volumetric energy, while the second term represents purely distortional energy. Therefore, we can conclude that the strain energy density allows for an additive decomposition into purely volumetric and distortional parts.

6.5 Special Hyperelasticity Materials and Discussion

Some materials, such as elastomers, polymers, rubber, hydrogels, and biological tissues (arteries, muscles, skin, etc.), are capable of undergoing large deformations without experiencing internal energy dissipation, which is characteristic of elastic processes. These materials are classified as hyperelastic, and purely hyperelastic materials do not retain any memory of their motion history; they are solely dependent on the current values of the state variables.

From a physical perspective, elastic materials (including those with linear elasticity and hyperelasticity) return to their original state once the applied load is removed. In other words, the work done during the loading process is fully recovered during the unloading process, indicating the absence of internal energy dissipation (a reversible process). In this section, we delve deeper into hyperelastic materials for certain substances. Our analysis will be limited to purely mechanical theories, excluding thermodynamic variables, such as temperature and entropy. For a more comprehensive study on hyperelastic constitutive equations, readers are encouraged to consult the works of Alexander (1968), Treloar (1975), Ogden (1984), Morman (1986), Holzapfel (2000), Chaves (2013), Merodio and Ogden (2020). Additionally, for specific hyperelastic materials, such as hydrogels and shape memory polymers, readers can refer to the review papers by Liu *et al.* (2015, 2020, 2021).

6.5.1 *Constitutive Equations for Purely Mechanical Hyperelastic Materials*

In the previous sections, we introduced the general form of a hyperelastic constitutive model. In this context, a hyperelastic material assumes the existence of an energy function known as the Helmholtz free energy per unit reference volume, denoted as Ψ. This energy function is also referred to as the strain energy density, strain energy function, or elastic potential. In hyperelastic materials, the strain energy density or strain energy function, is solely dependent on the deformation gradient, denoted as $\Psi = \Psi(\mathbf{F})$ (for hydrogel materials, the strain energy function may also depend on the deformation gradient and chemical potential/concentration). It should be noted that there is a relationship between the strain energy density, and the Helmholtz free energy per unit mass, $\widetilde{\Psi}(\mathbf{F})$, given by $\Psi = \rho_0 \widetilde{\Psi}(\mathbf{F})$.

During pure deformation processes that do not involve changes in entropy or temperature, there is no internal energy dissipation, which can be expressed as $e_{\text{int}} = 0$. Consequently, for reversible processes, the Clausius–Planck inequality can be written as the following equations:

$$e_{\text{int}} = \mathbf{P} : \dot{\mathbf{F}} - \dot{\Psi} = 0, \rightarrow \dot{\Psi} = \mathbf{P} : \dot{\mathbf{F}}. \tag{6.5.1}$$

Therefore, $\dot{\Psi} = \mathbf{P} : \dot{\mathbf{F}}$ holds for the reference configuration.

Similarly, for the current and reference configurations, we have

$$\dot{\Psi} = \boldsymbol{\sigma} : \mathbf{D}, \tag{6.5.2}$$

$$\dot{\Psi} = \frac{1}{2}\mathbf{S} : \dot{\mathbf{C}}, \tag{6.5.3}$$

where $\boldsymbol{\sigma}$ is the Cauchy stress tensor, $\mathbf{D}$ is the rate-of-deformation tensor, $\mathbf{P}$ is the first Piola–Kirchhoff stress tensor, $\mathbf{S}$ is the second

Piola–Kirchhoff stress tensor, and $\mathbf{C}$ is the right Cauchy–Green deformation tensor.

By taking into account the conjugate relations, we have

$$\int_V \boldsymbol{\sigma} : \mathbf{D}\, \mathrm{d}V = \int_{V_0} J\boldsymbol{\sigma} : \mathbf{D}\, \mathrm{d}V_0 = \int_{V_0} \mathbf{S} : \dot{\mathbf{E}}\, \mathrm{d}V_0 = \int_{V_0} \frac{1}{2}\mathbf{S} : \dot{\mathbf{C}}\, \mathrm{d}V_0$$
$$= \int_{V_0} \boldsymbol{\tau} : \mathbf{D}\, \mathrm{d}V_0 = \int_{V_0} \mathbf{P} : \dot{\mathbf{F}}\, \mathrm{d}V_0 = \int_V \frac{\rho}{\rho_0}\mathbf{P} : \dot{\mathbf{F}}\, \mathrm{d}V. \tag{6.5.4}$$

The change rate of the strain energy density can also be expressed as follows:

$$\dot{\Psi} = \mathbf{P} : \dot{\mathbf{F}} = \mathbf{S} : \dot{\mathbf{E}} = \boldsymbol{\tau} : \mathbf{D}, \tag{6.5.5}$$

In the context of hyperelastic materials, the relationship between the Green–Lagrange strain tensor, denoted as $\mathbf{E}$, and the Kirchhoff stress tensor, denoted as $\boldsymbol{\tau}$, allows us to define a material as hyperelastic if the change rate of the strain energy is equal to the power of the stress. It is important to note that this expression pertains to the reference configuration of the material.

Then, by evaluating the change rate of the strain energy $\boldsymbol{\Psi} = \boldsymbol{\Psi}(\mathbf{F})$, we obtain

$$\dot{\Psi}(\mathbf{F}) = \frac{\partial \Psi(\mathbf{F})}{\partial \mathbf{F}} : \frac{\partial \mathbf{F}}{\partial t} = \frac{\partial \Psi(\mathbf{F})}{\partial \mathbf{F}} : \dot{\mathbf{F}}. \tag{6.5.6}$$

Next, by substituting the above equation into the internal energy dissipation given by the equation, we obtain

$$\mathbf{P} : \dot{\mathbf{F}} = \frac{\partial \Psi(\mathbf{F})}{\partial \mathbf{F}} : \dot{\mathbf{F}} \rightarrow \mathbf{P} = \frac{\partial \Psi(\mathbf{F})}{\partial \mathbf{F}}. \tag{6.5.7}$$

Note that the tensor $\mathbf{P}$ is a function of X and $\mathbf{F}$, and $\mathbf{P}$ is directly dependent on X. We can study non-homogeneous materials. Here, for the sake of simplicity, we omit the material coordinate X.

As discussed previously, the strain energy has to be objective: $\Psi(\mathbf{F}) = \Psi(\mathbf{F}*) = \Psi(\mathbf{Q} \cdot \mathbf{F})$; then, by applying the polar decomposition $\mathbf{F} = \mathbf{R} \cdot \mathbf{U}$ and by adopting the orthogonal tensor $\mathbf{Q} = \mathbf{R}^T$, we can obtain

$$\Psi(\mathbf{F}) = \Psi(\mathbf{Q} \cdot \mathbf{F}) = \Psi(\mathbf{Q} \cdot \mathbf{R} \cdot \mathbf{U}) = \Psi(\mathbf{U}) = \Psi(\mathbf{C}) = \Psi(\mathbf{E}), \tag{6.5.8}$$

where $\mathbf{U}$ is the right-stretch tensor and $\mathbf{R}$ is the polar decomposition rotation tensor. Since the tensors $\mathbf{C}$, $\mathbf{U}$, and $\mathbf{E}$ are directly linked by

$\mathbf{C} = \mathbf{U}^2$ and $\mathbf{E} = \frac{1}{2}(\mathbf{C} - \mathbf{I})$, the strain energy density can also be expressed in terms of the Green–Lagrange strain tensor ($\mathbf{E}$). Then, it is possible to express the constitutive equation for stress in the material description:

$$\dot{\Psi}(\mathbf{C}) = \frac{\partial \Psi(\mathbf{C})}{\partial \mathbf{C}} : \frac{\partial \mathbf{C}}{\partial t} = \frac{\partial \Psi(\mathbf{C})}{\partial \mathbf{C}} : \dot{\mathbf{C}}. \tag{6.5.9}$$

By substituting the above into the internal energy dissipation equation, we obtain

$$\begin{aligned} \dot{e} &= \frac{1}{2}\mathbf{S} : \dot{\mathbf{C}} - \dot{\Psi}(\mathbf{C}) \\ &= \frac{1}{2}\mathbf{S} : \dot{\mathbf{C}} - \frac{\partial \Psi(\mathbf{C})}{\partial \mathbf{C}} : \dot{\mathbf{C}} \\ &= \left(\frac{1}{2}\mathbf{S} - \frac{\partial \Psi(\mathbf{C})}{\partial \mathbf{C}}\right) : \dot{\mathbf{C}} = 0. \end{aligned} \tag{6.5.10}$$

Thus,

$$\mathbf{S} = 2\frac{\partial \Psi(\mathbf{C})}{\partial \mathbf{C}}. \tag{6.5.11}$$

Since we have $\mathbf{E} = \frac{1}{2}(\mathbf{C} - \mathbf{I})$,

$$\mathbf{S} = 2\frac{\partial \Psi(\mathbf{C})}{\partial \mathbf{C}} = \frac{\partial \Psi(\mathbf{E})}{\partial \mathbf{E}}. \tag{6.5.12}$$

Then, if we take the relationships between the stress tensors into account, we can express the constitutive equation for the other stress.

For the Kirchhoff stress tensor,

$$\boldsymbol{\tau} = \mathbf{F} \cdot \mathbf{S} \cdot \mathbf{F}^T = 2\mathbf{F} \cdot \frac{\partial \Psi(\mathbf{C})}{\partial \mathbf{C}} \cdot \mathbf{F}^T = \mathbf{F} \cdot \frac{\partial \Psi(\mathbf{E})}{\partial \mathbf{E}} \cdot \mathbf{F}^T. \tag{6.5.13}$$

For the Cauchy stress tensor,

$$\boldsymbol{\sigma} = J\frac{\partial \Psi(\mathbf{F})}{\partial \mathbf{F}} \cdot \mathbf{F}^{-T}. \tag{6.5.14}$$

For the first Piola–Kirchhoff stress tensor,

$$\mathbf{P} = \boldsymbol{\tau} \cdot \mathbf{F}^{-T} = \mathbf{F} \cdot \mathbf{S} \cdot \mathbf{F}^T \cdot \mathbf{F}^{-T} = \mathbf{F} \cdot \mathbf{S} = \mathbf{F} \cdot 2\frac{\partial \Psi(\mathbf{C})}{\partial \mathbf{C}}. \tag{6.5.15}$$

We should note that the strain energy function Ψ has to satisfy the following conditions:

(1) The normalization condition: $\Psi = \Psi(\mathbf{I}) = 0$, i.e., the strain energy function vanishes when the material has been completely unloaded, i.e., when $\mathbf{F} = \mathbf{I}$.
(2) $\Psi(\mathbf{F}) \geq 0$: The strain energy must increase monotonically with deformation.
(3) The work done is independent of the path.

6.5.2 *The Constitutive Equation in Terms of Invariants*

If the scalar-valued tensor function $\Psi(\mathbf{C})$ is isotropic, it must satisfy the following:

$$\Psi(\mathbf{C}) = \Psi(\mathbf{Q} \cdot \mathbf{C} \cdot \mathbf{Q}^T), \tag{6.5.16}$$

for any orthogonal tensor $\mathbf{Q}$ and $\mathbf{Q} = \mathbf{R}^T$.

Then, if we use the polar decomposition rotation tensor, we can obtain

$$\begin{aligned}\Psi(\mathbf{C}) &= \Psi(\mathbf{R} \cdot \mathbf{C} \cdot \mathbf{R}^T) = \Psi(\mathbf{R} \cdot \mathbf{F}^T \cdot \mathbf{F} \cdot \mathbf{R}^T) = \Psi(\mathbf{V}^T \cdot \mathbf{V}) \\ &= \Psi(\mathbf{V}^2) = \Psi(\mathbf{b}),\end{aligned} \tag{6.5.17}$$

where $\mathbf{V}$ is the left-stretch tensor, which is related to the left Cauchy–Green deformation tensor $\mathbf{b}$.

6.5.2.1 *The constitutive equation in terms of* $\mathbf{C}$ *and* $\mathbf{b}$

We know that the scalar-valued isotropic tensor function, $\Psi(\mathbf{C})$, can be written in terms of the principal invariants of $\mathbf{C} = \mathbf{C}(I_\mathbf{C}, II_\mathbf{C}, III_\mathbf{C})$ or in terms of the invariants of $\mathbf{b}$, i.e.,

$$\Psi(\mathbf{C}) = \Psi(I_\mathbf{C}, II_\mathbf{C}, III_\mathbf{C}) = \Psi(I_\mathbf{b}, II_\mathbf{b}, III_\mathbf{b}), \tag{6.5.18}$$

where

$$I_\mathbf{C} = \mathrm{tr}(\mathbf{C}), \quad II_\mathbf{C} = \frac{1}{2}\{[\mathrm{tr}(\mathbf{C})]^2 - \mathrm{tr}(\mathbf{C}^2)\}, \quad III_\mathbf{C} = \det(\mathbf{C}) = J^2. \tag{6.5.19}$$

We also know that for the scalar-valued tensor function, $\Psi(\mathbf{C}) = \Psi(I_{\mathbf{C}}, II_{\mathbf{C}}, III_{\mathbf{C}})$, or $\Psi(\mathbf{C}) = \Psi(I_{\mathbf{b}}, II_{\mathbf{b}}, III_{\mathbf{b}})$, the following equations are valid:

$$
\begin{aligned}
\frac{\partial \Psi(I_{\mathbf{C}}, II_{\mathbf{C}}, III_{\mathbf{C}})}{\partial \mathbf{C}} &= \frac{\partial \Psi}{\partial I_{\mathbf{C}}}\frac{\partial I_{\mathbf{C}}}{\partial \mathbf{C}} + \frac{\partial \Psi}{\partial II_{\mathbf{C}}}\frac{\partial II_{\mathbf{C}}}{\partial \mathbf{C}} + \frac{\partial \Psi}{\partial III_{\mathbf{C}}}\frac{\partial III_{\mathbf{C}}}{\partial \mathbf{C}} \\
&= \left(\frac{\partial \Psi}{\partial I_{\mathbf{C}}} + \frac{\partial \Psi}{\partial II_{\mathbf{C}}} I_{\mathbf{C}}\right)\mathbf{I} - \left(\frac{\partial \Psi}{\partial II_{\mathbf{C}}}\right)\mathbf{C} \\
&\quad + \left(\frac{\partial \Psi}{\partial III_{\mathbf{C}}} III_{\mathbf{C}}\right)\mathbf{C}^{-1} \\
&= \left(\frac{\partial \Psi}{\partial I_{\mathbf{C}}} + \frac{\partial \Psi}{\partial II_{\mathbf{C}}} I_{\mathbf{C}} + \frac{\partial \Psi}{\partial III_{\mathbf{C}}} II_{\mathbf{C}}\right)\mathbf{I} \\
&\quad - \left(\frac{\partial \Psi}{\partial II_{\mathbf{C}}} + \frac{\partial \Psi}{\partial III_{\mathbf{C}}} I_{\mathbf{C}}\right)\mathbf{C} + \left(\frac{\partial \Psi}{\partial III_{\mathbf{C}}}\right)\mathbf{C}^2 \\
&= \left(\frac{\partial \Psi}{\partial I_{\mathbf{C}}}\right)\mathbf{I} + \left(\frac{\partial \Psi}{\partial II_{\mathbf{C}}} II_{\mathbf{C}} + \frac{\partial \Psi}{\partial III_{\mathbf{C}}} III_{\mathbf{C}}\right)\mathbf{C}^{-1} \\
&\quad - \left(\frac{\partial \Psi}{\partial II_{\mathbf{C}}} III_{\mathbf{C}}\right)\mathbf{C}^{-2}, \qquad (6.5.20)
\end{aligned}
$$

where it holds that

$$
\begin{aligned}
&\frac{\partial I_{\mathbf{C}}}{\partial \mathbf{C}} = \mathbf{I}, \quad \frac{\partial II_{\mathbf{C}}}{\partial \mathbf{C}} = I_{\mathbf{C}}\mathbf{I} - \mathbf{C}^T = I_{\mathbf{C}}\mathbf{I} - \mathbf{C} = II_{\mathbf{C}}\mathbf{C}^{-1} - III_{\mathbf{C}}\mathbf{C}^{-2} \\
&\frac{\partial III_{\mathbf{C}}}{\partial \mathbf{C}} = III_{\mathbf{C}}\mathbf{C}^{-T} = III_{\mathbf{C}}\mathbf{C}^{-1} = \mathbf{C}^2 - I_{\mathbf{C}}\mathbf{C} + II_{\mathbf{C}}\mathbf{I}. \qquad (6.5.21)
\end{aligned}
$$

Using the relationships mentioned above, we can now derive the constitutive equation in terms of the principal invariants of $\mathbf{C}$ as follows:

$$
\begin{aligned}
\mathbf{S} &= 2\left[\left(\frac{\partial \Psi}{\partial I_{\mathbf{C}}} + \frac{\partial \Psi}{\partial II_{\mathbf{C}}} I_{\mathbf{C}}\right)\mathbf{I} - \left(\frac{\partial \Psi}{\partial II_{\mathbf{C}}}\right)\mathbf{C} + \left(\frac{\partial \Psi}{\partial III_{\mathbf{C}}} III_{\mathbf{C}}\right)\mathbf{C}^{-1}\right] \\
&= 2\left[\left(\frac{\partial \Psi}{\partial I_{\mathbf{C}}} + \frac{\partial \Psi}{\partial II_{\mathbf{C}}} I_{\mathbf{C}} + \frac{\partial \Psi}{\partial III_{\mathbf{C}}} II_{\mathbf{C}}\right)\mathbf{I}\right. \\
&\quad \left. - \left(\frac{\partial \Psi}{\partial II_{\mathbf{C}}} + \frac{\partial \Psi}{\partial III_{\mathbf{C}}} I_{\mathbf{C}}\right)\mathbf{C} + \left(\frac{\partial \Psi}{\partial III_{\mathbf{C}}}\right)\mathbf{C}^2\right]
\end{aligned}
$$

$$= 2\left[\left(\frac{\partial\Psi}{\partial I_{\mathbf{C}}}\right)\mathbf{I} + \left(\frac{\partial\Psi}{\partial II_{\mathbf{C}}}II_{\mathbf{C}} + \frac{\partial\Psi}{\partial III_{\mathbf{C}}}III_{\mathbf{C}}\right)\mathbf{C}^{-1}\right.$$
$$\left. - \left(\frac{\partial\Psi}{\partial II_{\mathbf{C}}}III_{\mathbf{C}}\right)\mathbf{C}^{-2}\right]. \tag{6.5.22}$$

Now, if we consider the relationship between the Kirchhoff stress and the second Piola–Kirchhoff stress tensors, $\boldsymbol{\tau} = \mathbf{F}\cdot\mathbf{S}\cdot\mathbf{F}^T$, and the constitutive equation in the reference configuration $\mathbf{S} = 2\frac{\partial\Psi(\mathbf{C})}{\partial\mathbf{C}}$, it is possible to obtain the constitutive equation in the current configuration as follows:

$$\boldsymbol{\tau} = \mathbf{F}\cdot\mathbf{S}\cdot\mathbf{F}^T = \mathbf{F}\cdot 2\frac{\partial\Psi}{\partial\mathbf{C}}\cdot\mathbf{F}^T = 2\frac{\partial\Psi}{\partial\mathbf{b}}\cdot\mathbf{b} = 2\mathbf{b}\cdot\frac{\partial\Psi}{\partial\mathbf{b}}. \tag{6.5.23}$$

Note that $\mathbf{C} = \mathbf{F}^T\cdot\mathbf{F}$ and $\mathbf{b} = \mathbf{F}\cdot\mathbf{F}^T$:

$$\boldsymbol{\tau} = \mathbf{F}\cdot\mathbf{S}\cdot\mathbf{F}^T = 2\mathbf{F}\cdot\left[\left(\frac{\partial\Psi}{\partial I_{\mathbf{C}}} + \frac{\partial\Psi}{\partial II_{\mathbf{C}}}I_{\mathbf{C}}\right)\mathbf{I} - \left(\frac{\partial\Psi}{\partial II_{\mathbf{C}}}\right)\mathbf{C}\right.$$
$$\left. + \left(\frac{\partial\Psi}{\partial III_{\mathbf{C}}}III_{\mathbf{C}}\right)\mathbf{C}^{-1}\right]\cdot\mathbf{F}^T \tag{6.5.24}$$

and

$$\boldsymbol{\tau} = J\boldsymbol{\sigma} = 2\left[\left(\frac{\partial\Psi}{\partial I_{\mathbf{b}}} + \frac{\partial\Psi}{\partial II_{\mathbf{b}}}I_{\mathbf{b}}\right)\mathbf{b} - \left(\frac{\partial\Psi}{\partial II_{\mathbf{b}}}\right)\mathbf{b}^2 + \left(\frac{\partial\Psi}{\partial III_{\mathbf{b}}}III_{\mathbf{b}}\mathbf{I}\right)\right]. \tag{6.5.25}$$

The constitutive equation can also be written in terms of the first Piola–Kirchhoff stress tensor:

$$\mathbf{P} = 2\mathbf{F}\cdot\left[\left(\frac{\partial\Psi}{\partial I_{\mathbf{C}}} + \frac{\partial\Psi}{\partial II_{\mathbf{C}}}I_{\mathbf{C}}\right)\mathbf{I} - \left(\frac{\partial\Psi}{\partial II_{\mathbf{C}}}\right)\mathbf{C} + \left(\frac{\partial\Psi}{\partial III_{\mathbf{C}}}III_{\mathbf{C}}\right)\mathbf{C}^{-1}\right]. \tag{6.5.26}$$

6.5.2.2 *The constitutive equation in terms of Green–Lagrange strain tensor*

Energy can also be written in terms of the Green–Lagrange strain tensor $\mathbf{E}$, and if we are dealing with isotropic materials, the energy constitutive equation can be expressed in terms of the principal invariants of $\mathbf{E}$. We have the following relations:

$$\Psi(\mathbf{E}) = \Psi(I_{\mathbf{E}}, II_{\mathbf{E}}, III_{\mathbf{E}}), \tag{6.5.27}$$

where

$$I_{\mathbf{E}} = \mathrm{tr}(\mathbf{E}), \quad II_{\mathbf{E}} = \frac{1}{2}\{[\mathrm{tr}(\mathbf{E})]^2 - \mathrm{tr}(\mathbf{E}^2)\}, \quad III_{\mathbf{E}} = \det(\mathbf{E}). \tag{6.5.28}$$

Using $\mathbf{S} = \frac{\partial \Psi(\mathbf{E})}{\partial \mathbf{E}}$, we can obtain another one analogous to that obtained previously:

$$\begin{aligned}\mathbf{S} = \Bigg[\left(\frac{\partial \Psi}{\partial I_{\mathbf{E}}} + \frac{\partial \Psi}{\partial II_{\mathbf{E}}} I_{\mathbf{E}} + \frac{\partial \Psi}{\partial III_{\mathbf{E}}} II_{\mathbf{E}}\right)\mathbf{I} - \left(\frac{\partial \Psi}{\partial II_{\mathbf{E}}} + \frac{\partial \Psi}{\partial III_{\mathbf{E}}} I_{\mathbf{E}}\right)\mathbf{E} \\ + \left(\frac{\partial \Psi}{\partial III_{\mathbf{E}}}\right)\mathbf{E}^2\Bigg].\end{aligned} \tag{6.5.29}$$

6.5.2.3 *Series expansion of the energy function*

Let us assume that $\Psi(\mathbf{C})$ is a continuously differentiable function with respect to the $\mathbf{C}$-invariants. It is possible, then, to represent $\Psi(\mathbf{C})$ by means of an infinite power series:

$$\Psi = \Psi(I_{\mathbf{C}}, II_{\mathbf{C}}, III_{\mathbf{C}}) = \sum_{p,q,r=0}^{\infty} c_{pqr}(I_{\mathbf{C}} - 3)^p (II_{\mathbf{C}} - 3)^q (III_{\mathbf{C}} - 1)^r, \tag{6.5.30}$$

where the coefficients c_{pqr} are independent of the deformation.

In Equation (6.5.30), we can note that in an undeformed state, we have $\mathbf{F} = \mathbf{I}$ and $\mathbf{C} = \mathbf{I}$, then $I_{\mathbf{C}} = 3$, $II_{\mathbf{C}} = 3$, $III_{\mathbf{C}} = 1$, which results in $\Psi(\mathbf{C}) = 0$, as expected. It means that the strain energy is zero (normalization condition) for the undeformed state.

6.5.2.4 *Constitutive equations in terms of the principal stretches*

As we have seen previously, for isotropic materials, we can express the strain energy function in terms of the principal stretches, such as $\Psi = \Psi(\lambda_1, \lambda_2, \lambda_3)$. Therefore, the second Piola–Kirchhoff stress tensor in terms of the principal stretches can be written as follows:

$$\mathbf{S} = 2\frac{\partial \Psi(\mathbf{C})}{\partial \mathbf{C}} = 2\frac{\partial \Psi}{\partial \lambda_i}\frac{\partial \lambda_i}{\partial \mathbf{C}} = 2\left[\frac{\partial \Psi}{\partial \lambda_1}\frac{\partial \lambda_1}{\partial \mathbf{C}} + \frac{\partial \Psi}{\partial \lambda_2}\frac{\partial \lambda_2}{\partial \mathbf{C}} + \frac{\partial \Psi}{\partial \lambda_3}\frac{\partial \lambda_3}{\partial \mathbf{C}}\right]. \tag{6.5.31}$$

Let us now suppose that $\widehat{\mathbf{N}}^\alpha$ and $\widehat{\mathbf{n}}^\alpha$ are the principal directions (eigenvectors) of the right-stretch tensor $\mathbf{U}$ and the left-stretch tensor $\mathbf{V}$, respectively, where $\alpha = 1, 2, 3$.

We have

$$\frac{1}{2\lambda_\alpha}\widehat{\mathbf{N}}^\alpha \otimes \widehat{\mathbf{N}}^\alpha = \frac{\partial \lambda_\alpha}{\partial \mathbf{C}}. \tag{6.5.32}$$

Then, by using the second Piola–Kirchhoff stress tensor expression, we will have

$$\mathbf{S} = \sum_{\alpha=1}^{3} \frac{1}{\lambda_\alpha}\frac{\partial \Psi}{\partial \lambda_\alpha}\widehat{\mathbf{N}}^\alpha \otimes \widehat{\mathbf{N}}^\alpha = \sum_{\alpha=1}^{3} S_\alpha \widehat{\mathbf{N}}^\alpha \otimes \widehat{\mathbf{N}}^\alpha, \tag{6.5.33}$$

where S_α are the eigenvalues of the second Piola–Kirchhoff stress tensor.

Then, as regards the Cauchy stress tensor, we have

$$\begin{aligned}\boldsymbol{\sigma} &= \sum_{\alpha=1}^{3} J^{-1}\frac{1}{\lambda_\alpha}\frac{\partial \Psi}{\partial \lambda_\alpha}(\mathbf{F}\cdot\widehat{\mathbf{N}}^\alpha \otimes \widehat{\mathbf{N}}^\alpha \cdot \mathbf{F}^T) \\ &= \sum_{\alpha=1}^{3} J^{-1}\frac{1}{\lambda_\alpha}\frac{\partial \Psi}{\partial \lambda_\alpha}(\mathbf{F}\cdot\widehat{\mathbf{N}}^\alpha \otimes \mathbf{F}\cdot\widehat{\mathbf{N}}^\alpha).\end{aligned} \tag{6.5.34}$$

Moreover, if we take the equation $\mathbf{F}\cdot\widehat{\mathbf{N}}^\alpha = \lambda_\alpha \widehat{\mathbf{n}}^\alpha$ into account, we have the following relation:

$$\boldsymbol{\sigma} = \sum_{\alpha=1}^{3} J^{-1}\lambda_\alpha \frac{\partial \Psi}{\partial \lambda_\alpha}\widehat{\mathbf{n}}^\alpha \otimes \widehat{\mathbf{n}} = \sum_{\alpha=1}^{3} \sigma_\alpha \widehat{\mathbf{n}}^\alpha \otimes \widehat{\mathbf{n}}, \tag{6.5.35}$$

where σ_α are the eigenvalues of the Cauchy stress tensor.

We can also conclude that in isotropic materials, the tensors $\mathbf{C}$ and $\mathbf{S}$ are coaxial, meaning they have the same principal directions.

Since $\mathbf{C}$ and $\mathbf{S}$ are coaxial, $\mathbf{C}\cdot\mathbf{S} = \mathbf{S}\cdot\mathbf{C}$, we can determine the eigenvalues of $\mathbf{C}$ by considering the principal directions of $\mathbf{S}$ using one of the equations mentioned above:

$$S_\alpha = 2\left[\left(\frac{\partial\Psi}{\partial I_\mathbf{C}}\right) + \left(\frac{\partial\Psi}{\partial II_\mathbf{C}} II_\mathbf{C} + \frac{\partial\Psi}{\partial III_\mathbf{C}} III_\mathbf{C}\right)\lambda_\alpha^{-2} - \left(\frac{\partial\Psi}{\partial II_\mathbf{C}} III_\mathbf{C}\right)\lambda_\alpha^{-4}\right]. \tag{6.5.36}$$

The first Piola–Kirchhoff stress tensor is given by

$$\mathbf{P} = \mathbf{F}\cdot\mathbf{S} = \sum_{\alpha=1}^{3} P_\alpha \widehat{\mathbf{n}}^\alpha \otimes \widehat{\mathbf{N}}^\alpha \tag{6.5.37}$$

$$P_\alpha = 2\lambda_\alpha \left[\left(\frac{\partial\Psi}{\partial I_\mathbf{C}}\right) + \left(\frac{\partial\Psi}{\partial II_\mathbf{C}} II_\mathbf{C} + \frac{\partial\Psi}{\partial III_\mathbf{C}} III_\mathbf{C}\right)\lambda_\alpha^{-2} - \left(\frac{\partial\Psi}{\partial II_\mathbf{C}} III_\mathbf{C}\right)\lambda_\alpha^{-4}\right]. \tag{6.5.38}$$

We can also calculate the derivatives of $I_\mathbf{C}$ with respect to λ_α. They are

$$I_\mathbf{C} = \lambda_1^2 + \lambda_2^2 + \lambda_3^2 \to \frac{\partial I_c}{\partial \lambda_\alpha} = 2\lambda_\alpha. \tag{6.5.39}$$

Similarly, we can obtain the derivatives of $II_\mathbf{C}$ and $III_\mathbf{C}$ with respect to λ_α to get

$$\frac{\partial II_\mathbf{C}}{\partial \lambda_\alpha} = 2\lambda_\alpha (II_\mathbf{C}\lambda_\alpha^{-2} - III_\mathbf{C}\lambda_\alpha^{-4}), \tag{6.5.40}$$

$$\frac{\partial III_\mathbf{C}}{\partial \lambda_\alpha} = 2\lambda_\alpha (III_\mathbf{C}\lambda_\alpha^{-2}). \tag{6.5.41}$$

Therefore,

$$\frac{\partial\Psi(I_\mathbf{C}, II_\mathbf{C}, III_\mathbf{C})}{\partial\lambda_\alpha} = 2\lambda_\alpha \left[\left(\frac{\partial\Psi}{\partial I_\mathbf{C}}\right) + \left(\frac{\partial\Psi}{\partial II_\mathbf{C}} II_\mathbf{C} + \frac{\partial\Psi}{\partial III_\mathbf{C}} III_\mathbf{C}\right)\lambda_\alpha^{-2} - \left(\frac{\partial\Psi}{\partial II_\mathbf{C}} III_\mathbf{C}\right)\lambda_\alpha^{-4}\right]. \tag{6.5.42}$$

Additionally, according to the above derivation, we can further draw the conclusion that

$$P_\alpha = \frac{\partial \Psi(I_C, II_C, III_C)}{\partial \lambda_\alpha} = \lambda_\alpha S_\alpha. \tag{6.5.43}$$

Then, it holds that

$$\mathbf{P} = \sum_{\alpha=1}^{3} P_\alpha \widehat{\mathbf{n}}^\alpha \otimes \widehat{\mathbf{N}}^\alpha = \sum_{\alpha=1}^{3} \lambda_\alpha S_\alpha \widehat{\mathbf{n}}^\alpha \otimes \widehat{\mathbf{N}}^\alpha. \tag{6.5.44}$$

Note that P_α are not the eigenvalues of $\mathbf{P}$. The Cauchy stress tensor is related to the first Piola–Kirchhoff stress tensor by means of $\boldsymbol{\sigma} = J^{-1}\mathbf{P} \cdot \mathbf{F}^T$, after which the eigenvalues of $\boldsymbol{\sigma}$ are given by

$$\sigma_\alpha = J^{-1} \lambda_\alpha \frac{\partial \Psi}{\partial \lambda_\alpha}. \tag{6.5.45}$$

Then, in isotropic materials, the Kirchhoff stress tensor ($\boldsymbol{\tau}$) and the left-stretch tensor ($\mathbf{V}$) have the same principal directions, and if we consider that $\boldsymbol{\tau} = J\boldsymbol{\sigma}$, we can obtain

$$\boldsymbol{\tau} = \sum_{\alpha=1}^{3} \lambda_\alpha^2 S_\alpha \widehat{\mathbf{n}}^\alpha \otimes \widehat{\mathbf{n}}^\alpha = \sum_{\alpha=1}^{3} \tau_\alpha \widehat{\mathbf{n}}^\alpha \otimes \widehat{\mathbf{n}}^\alpha. \tag{6.5.46}$$

Thus, we can conclude that the principal values of the tensors $\mathbf{S}$, $\boldsymbol{\sigma}$, $\boldsymbol{\tau}$, are interrelated by

$$S_\alpha = \frac{J}{\lambda_\alpha^2} \sigma_\alpha = \frac{1}{\lambda_\alpha^2} \tau_\alpha = \frac{1}{\lambda_\alpha} \frac{\partial \Psi}{\partial \lambda_\alpha}. \tag{6.5.47}$$

6.6 Compressible Materials

In compressible hyperelastic materials, which experience a change in volume during the deformation process, it is appropriate to separate the deformation into two components: isochoric motion (volume preserving) and dilatational transformation (pure volume change). To do this, we consider the multiplicative decomposition of the deformation gradient as follows:

$$\mathbf{F} = \widetilde{\mathbf{F}} \cdot \mathbf{F}^{\text{vol}}, \tag{6.6.1}$$

where $\widetilde{\mathbf{F}}$ show an isochoric transformation and $\mathbf{F}^{\text{vol}}$ describes a dilatational transformation; therefore, we have

$$\widetilde{\mathbf{F}} = J^{-1/3}\mathbf{F}, \quad \mathbf{F}^{\text{vol}} = J^{1/3}\mathbf{I}, \tag{6.6.2}$$

$$\widetilde{\mathbf{C}} = J^{-2/3}\mathbf{C}, \quad \mathbf{C}^{\text{vol}} = J^{2/3}\mathbf{I}, \quad \widetilde{\mathbf{b}} = J^{-2/3}\mathbf{b}, \quad \mathbf{b}^{\text{vol}} = J^{2/3}\mathbf{I}, \tag{6.6.3}$$

and

$$\widetilde{J} = |\widetilde{\mathbf{F}}| = 1, \quad J^{\text{vol}} = |\mathbf{F}^{\text{vol}}| = J. \tag{6.6.4}$$

Through further derivation, we can use $\frac{\partial J}{\partial \mathbf{C}} = \frac{J}{2}\mathbf{C}^{-1}$ and obtain

$$\frac{\partial J^{-2/3}}{\partial \mathbf{C}} = -\frac{1}{3}J^{-2/3}\mathbf{C}^{-1}, \tag{6.6.5}$$

$$\begin{aligned} \frac{\partial \widetilde{\mathbf{C}}}{\partial \mathbf{C}} &= \frac{\partial (J^{-2/3}\mathbf{C})}{\partial \mathbf{C}} = J^{-2/3}\frac{\partial \mathbf{C}}{\partial \mathbf{C}} + \mathbf{C} \otimes \frac{\partial J^{-2/3}}{\partial \mathbf{C}} \\ &= J^{-2/3}\mathbf{II} - \frac{1}{3}J^{-2/3}\mathbf{C} \otimes \mathbf{C}^{-1} = J^{-2/3}\boldsymbol{\Theta}^T, \end{aligned} \tag{6.6.6}$$

where $\mathbf{II}$ is the fourth-order unit tensor and $\boldsymbol{\Theta}$ is a fourth-order tensor and is known as the projection tensor with respect to the reference configuration:

$$\boldsymbol{\Theta}^{\text{T}} = \mathbf{II} - \frac{1}{3}\mathbf{C} \otimes \mathbf{C}^{-1}, \quad \boldsymbol{\Theta} = \mathbf{II} - \frac{1}{3}\mathbf{C}^{-1} \otimes \mathbf{C}, \tag{6.6.7}$$

or the component form is

$$\frac{\partial \widetilde{C}_{ij}}{\partial C_{kl}} = J^{-2/3}\left(II_{ijkl} - \frac{1}{3}C_{ij}C_{kl}^{-1}\right). \tag{6.6.8}$$

We define a stress tensor, $\bar{\boldsymbol{\sigma}}^{\text{vol}}$, which is analogous to the Cauchy stress tensor in the intermediate configuration by means of the transformation $\mathbf{F}^{\text{vol}}$.

Thus, the corresponding stress tensor is

$$\bar{\boldsymbol{\sigma}}^{\mathrm{vol}} = \frac{\partial \Psi(J^{\mathrm{vol}})}{\partial J^{\mathrm{vol}}}\mathbf{I} = \frac{\partial \Psi(J)}{\partial J}\mathbf{I}. \tag{6.6.9}$$

We define $\widetilde{\widetilde{\mathbf{S}}}$ to be a stress tensor in the intermediate configuration caused by the transformation $\widetilde{\mathbf{F}}$:

$$\widetilde{\widetilde{\mathbf{S}}} = 2\frac{\partial \Psi(\widetilde{\mathbf{C}})}{\partial \widetilde{\mathbf{C}}}. \tag{6.6.10}$$

We now observe additive decomposition of the strain energy function in two parts, namely, isochoric and volumetric, i.e.,

$$\Psi(\mathbf{F}) = \widetilde{\Psi}(\widetilde{\mathbf{F}}) + \Psi^{\mathrm{vol}}(\mathbf{F}^{\mathrm{vol}}); \quad \Psi(\mathbf{C}) = \widetilde{\Psi}(\widetilde{\mathbf{C}}) + \Psi^{\mathrm{vol}}(\mathbf{C}^{\mathrm{vol}}). \tag{6.6.11}$$

We can further derive

$$\dot{\Psi}(\mathbf{C}) = J^{-2/3}\Theta : \frac{\partial \widetilde{\Psi}(\widetilde{\mathbf{C}})}{\partial \widetilde{\mathbf{C}}} : \dot{\mathbf{C}} + \frac{J}{2}\frac{\mathrm{d}\Psi^{\mathrm{vol}}(J)}{\mathrm{d}J}\mathbf{C}^{-1} : \dot{\mathbf{C}}. \tag{6.6.12}$$

Considering a purely elastic material, its internal energy dissipation is zero. The stress tensor can be

$$\begin{aligned} \mathbf{S} &= 2\frac{\partial \Psi(\mathbf{C})}{\partial \mathbf{C}} = 2\frac{\partial[\widetilde{\Psi}(\widetilde{\mathbf{C}}) + \Psi^{\mathrm{vol}}(\mathbf{C}^{\mathrm{vol}})]}{\partial \mathbf{C}} \\ &= 2\frac{\partial \widetilde{\Psi}(\widetilde{\mathbf{C}})}{\partial \mathbf{C}} + 2\frac{\partial \Psi^{\mathrm{vol}}(\mathbf{C}^{\mathrm{vol}})}{\partial \mathbf{C}} = \widetilde{\mathbf{S}} + \mathbf{S}^{\mathrm{vol}}, \end{aligned} \tag{6.6.13}$$

where

$$\mathbf{S}^{\mathrm{vol}} = 2\frac{\partial \Psi^{\mathrm{vol}}(C^{\mathrm{vol}})}{\partial \mathbf{C}} = 2\frac{\partial \Psi^{\mathrm{vol}}(J)}{\partial J}\frac{\partial J}{\partial \mathbf{C}} = J\frac{\partial \Psi^{\mathrm{vol}}(J)}{\partial J}\mathbf{C}^{-1}, \tag{6.6.14}$$

$$\widetilde{\mathbf{S}} = 2\frac{\partial \widetilde{\Psi}(\widetilde{\mathbf{C}})}{\partial \mathbf{C}} = 2\frac{\partial \widetilde{\Psi}(\widetilde{\mathbf{C}})}{\partial \widetilde{\mathbf{C}}} : \frac{\partial \widetilde{\mathbf{C}}}{\partial \mathbf{C}} = J^{-2/3}\Theta : \widetilde{\widetilde{\mathbf{S}}}. \tag{6.6.15}$$

In addition, with the constitutive equation for hydrostatic pressure (Holzapfel, 2000), we have

$$\mathbf{p} = \frac{\mathrm{D}\Psi^{\mathrm{vol}}(J)}{\mathrm{D}J}. \tag{6.6.16}$$

6.7 Incompressible Materials

Many polymers, according to Holzapfel (2000), can undergo large deformations without exhibiting any volume change. Therefore, these materials can be considered incompressible, meaning that the continuum is characterized by isochoric motion, and the following condition holds:

$$\det(\mathbf{F}) = J = \lambda_1\lambda_2\lambda_3 = 1, \quad J^2 = III_{\mathbf{C}} = III_{\mathbf{b}} = 1. \tag{6.7.1}$$

In incompressible materials, for which $J = 1$, the stress state is not fully determined by the strain state. This is because in an incompressible body, we can add hydrostatic stress (pressure) to the current stress state without altering the strain state. It should be noted that in isotropic materials, a hydrostatic state only produces volumetric deformations. Consequently, in incompressible materials, the volumetric deformation is always zero for any hydrostatic state. Furthermore, it is important to mention that the energy is unaffected by the volumetric part. Therefore, for an incompressible case, the following relationship holds:

$$\widetilde{\mathbf{F}} = \mathbf{F}, \quad \mathbf{F}^{\text{vol}} = \mathbf{I}, \quad \widetilde{\mathbf{C}} = \mathbf{C}, \quad \mathbf{C}^{\text{vol}} = \mathbf{I}. \tag{6.7.2}$$

Then, the hydrostatic stress state is given by

$$\boldsymbol{\sigma}^{\text{hyd}} = -p\mathbf{I}, \quad \sigma_{ij}^{\text{hyd}} = -p\delta_{ij}. \tag{6.7.3}$$

Then, for incompressible materials, we have

$$\mathbf{S} = 2\frac{\partial\Psi(\mathbf{C})}{\partial\mathbf{C}} - Jp\mathbf{C}^{-1}. \tag{6.7.4}$$

Next, to solve a problem with a constraint ($J = 1$), we can introduce the Lagrange multiplier γ, which must satisfy the following:

$$\hat{\Psi} = \Psi(\mathbf{C}) + \gamma(J - 1). \tag{6.7.5}$$

Thus,

$$\mathbf{S} = 2\frac{\partial\Psi(\mathbf{C})}{\partial\mathbf{C}} - J\gamma\mathbf{C}^{-1}. \tag{6.7.6}$$

Now, if we compare (6.7.4) with (6.7.6), we can conclude that

$$\gamma = -p = \frac{\sigma_{kk}}{3}, \tag{6.7.7}$$

where p (pressure) is an unknown function to be determined by the incompressibility condition.

Similarly, when we consider the incompressibility condition ($J = 1$), we can summarize that the constitutive equation for stress in an incompressible continuum can be expressed as follows:

$$\begin{aligned}
\mathbf{S} &= 2\frac{\partial \Psi(\mathbf{C})}{\partial \mathbf{C}} - p\mathbf{C}^{-1},\\
\mathbf{P} &= \frac{\partial \Psi(\mathbf{F})}{\partial \mathbf{F}} - p\mathbf{F}^{-T},\\
\sigma &= \frac{\partial \Psi(\mathbf{F})}{\partial \mathbf{F}} \cdot \mathbf{F}^T - p\mathbf{I} = \mathbf{F} \cdot \left(\frac{\partial \Psi(\mathbf{F})}{\partial \mathbf{F}}\right)^T - p\mathbf{I}.
\end{aligned} \tag{6.7.8}$$

In isotropic incompressible hyperelastic materials, the scalar-valued tensor function $\Psi = \Psi(\mathbf{C}) = \Psi(\mathbf{b})$ can be expressed in terms of the invariants $\Psi = \Psi(I_\mathbf{C}, II_\mathbf{C}) = \Psi(I_\mathbf{b}, II_\mathbf{b})$ or in terms of the principal invariants of the Green–Lagrange strain tensor:

$$\Psi = \Psi(I_\mathbf{E}, II_\mathbf{E}). \tag{6.7.9}$$

Then, the constitutive equation for stress in hyperelastic materials becomes

$$\begin{aligned}
\mathbf{S} &= \frac{\partial \Psi(I_\mathbf{E}, II_\mathbf{E})}{\partial \mathbf{E}} - p\frac{\partial (III_\mathbf{E})}{\partial \mathbf{E}}\\
&= \frac{\partial \Psi}{\partial I_\mathbf{E}}\frac{\partial I_\mathbf{E}}{\partial \mathbf{E}} + \frac{\partial \Psi}{\partial II_\mathbf{E}}\frac{\partial II_\mathbf{E}}{\partial \mathbf{E}} - p\frac{\partial III_\mathbf{E}}{\partial \mathbf{E}}.
\end{aligned} \tag{6.7.10}$$

Consider the relationships between the principal invariants of the tensors $\mathbf{E}$ and $\mathbf{C}$:

$$\begin{aligned}
I_\mathbf{E} &= \frac{1}{2}(I_\mathbf{C} - 3), \quad II_\mathbf{E} = \frac{1}{4}(-2I_\mathbf{C} + II_\mathbf{C} + 3),\\
III_\mathbf{E} &= \frac{1}{8}(III_\mathbf{C} - II_\mathbf{C} + I_\mathbf{C} - 1),
\end{aligned} \tag{6.7.11}$$

$$\begin{aligned}
I_\mathbf{C} &= 2I_\mathbf{E} + 3, \quad II_\mathbf{C} = 4II_\mathbf{E} + 4I_\mathbf{E} + 3,\\
III_\mathbf{C} &= 8III_\mathbf{E} + 4II_\mathbf{E} + 2I_\mathbf{E} + 1.
\end{aligned} \tag{6.7.12}$$

Thus,

$$
\begin{aligned}
\mathbf{S} &= \frac{\partial \Psi}{\partial I_{\mathbf{C}}} 2\mathbf{I} + \frac{\partial \Psi}{\partial II_{\mathbf{C}}} [4(I_{\mathbf{E}}\mathbf{I} - \mathbf{E}) + 4\mathbf{I}] \\
&\quad - p[8III_{\mathbf{E}}\mathbf{E}^{-1} + 4(I_{\mathbf{E}}\mathbf{I} - \mathbf{E}) + 2\mathbf{I}] \\
&= \frac{\partial \Psi}{\partial I_{\mathbf{C}}} 2\mathbf{I} + \frac{\partial \Psi}{\partial II_{\mathbf{C}}} 4[(I_{\mathbf{E}} + 1)\mathbf{I} - \mathbf{E}] \\
&\quad - 2p[(2I_{\mathbf{E}} + 1)\mathbf{I} - 2\mathbf{E} + 4III_{\mathbf{E}}\mathbf{E}^{-1}].
\end{aligned} \tag{6.7.13}
$$

Now, if we take into account the fact that $III_{\mathbf{C}} = 1$ in the equation in (6.7.11), we can then express $III_{\mathbf{E}}$ as a function of $I_{\mathbf{E}}$ and $II_{\mathbf{E}}$, i.e.,

$$
III_{\mathbf{E}} = -\frac{1}{4}(2II_{\mathbf{E}} + I_{\mathbf{E}}). \tag{6.7.14}
$$

Then, by using the equation, the constitutive equation for isotropic incompressible materials becomes

$$
\boldsymbol{\sigma} = \left[2\left(\frac{\partial \Psi}{\partial I_{\mathbf{b}}} + \frac{\partial \Psi}{\partial II_{\mathbf{b}}} I_{\mathbf{b}} \right) \mathbf{b} - 2\frac{\partial \Psi}{\partial II_{\mathbf{b}}} I_{\mathbf{b}}^2 \right] - p\mathbf{I}. \tag{6.7.15}
$$

Note that we can still express the constitutive equation for incompressible hyperelastic materials in terms of principal stretches, using the equations shown earlier,

$$
\sigma_\alpha = p + \lambda_\alpha \frac{\partial \Psi}{\partial \lambda_\alpha}, \quad \alpha = 1, 2, 3. \tag{6.7.16}
$$

In incompressible materials, it holds that $III_{\mathbf{C}} = 1$, and the energy function $\Psi = \Psi(I_{\mathbf{C}}, II_{\mathbf{C}})$ can also be represented by a power series; thus,

$$
\Psi = \Psi(I_{\mathbf{C}}, II_{\mathbf{C}}) = \sum_{p,q=0}^{3} c_{pq}(I_{\mathbf{C}} - 3)^p (II_{\mathbf{C}} - 3)^q. \tag{6.7.17}
$$

Therefore, according to previous derivations, we can derive the constitutive equations for different material models.

6.8 Examples of Hyperelastic Models

In this textbook, we would like to introduce and discuss some hyperelastic material models that are commonly used in the literature to simulate the phenomenological behavior of different materials. These models are particularly applicable to polymer materials, including rubber and hydrogels.

6.8.1 *The Neo-Hookean Material Model*

As a widely used constitutive model for polymer and rubber materials, the neo-Hookean material model provides a simple representation of the material's behavior. In this model, the strain energy function is expressed in terms of the isochoric part of the right Cauchy–Green deformation tensor, denoted as $\mathbf{C}$. The neo-Hookean strain energy function is given by

$$\Psi(\mathbf{C}) = \frac{\mu}{2}(I_{\mathbf{C}} - 3) = c_1(I_{\mathbf{C}} - 3), \tag{6.8.1}$$

where $c_1 = \frac{\mu}{2}$. The parameter μ was originally determined through statistical mechanics (Treloar, 1944) by $\mu = \frac{Nk}{2}\theta$, where N is the number of polymer chains per unit of the reference volume, k is the Boltzmann constant, and θ is the temperature. However, in a recent study, the parameter μ has been determined experimentally and is known as the shear modulus $\mu = G$.

According to the formulas discussed in the previous section, we can derive the stress constitutive equation for the neo-Hookean material model as follows:

$$\boldsymbol{\sigma} = -p\mathbf{I} + 2c_1\mathbf{F}\cdot\mathbf{F}^T = -p\mathbf{I} + 2c_1\mathbf{b}. \tag{6.8.2}$$

In engineering, the neo-Hookean model provides a reasonable prediction of the constitutive behavior of natural rubber or hydrogels for moderate strains. This model is widely used due to its simplicity and ability to capture the elastic response of these materials under deformation. It is particularly effective when applied to materials that exhibit nearly incompressible behavior and small to moderate deformations. While the neo-Hookean model may not capture all the intricacies of the material's behavior at large strains or complex loading conditions, it serves as a useful approximation for many practical engineering applications involving rubber and hydrogels.

6.8.2 *The Ogden Material Model*

In many problems, it is convenient to describe deformation using stretches. The Ogden material model provides a mathematical representation of the strain energy function in terms of the principal stretches. It is widely used to characterize the behavior of hyperelastic materials, such as elastomers and biological tissues. The strain energy function for the Ogden model is given by the following expression:

$$\begin{aligned}\Psi(\lambda_1, \lambda_2, \lambda_3) = &\sum_{p=1}^{M} a_p(\lambda_1^{\alpha_p} + \lambda_2^{\alpha_p} + \lambda_3^{\alpha_p} - 3) \\ &+ \sum_{p=1}^{N} b_q[(\lambda_1\lambda_2)^{\beta_q} + (\lambda_1\lambda_3)^{\beta_q} + (\lambda_2\lambda_3)^{\beta_q} - 3] \\ &+ h(\lambda_1\lambda_2\lambda_3), \end{aligned} \tag{6.8.3}$$

where M, a_p, b_q are positive constants, $a_p \geq 0$, $b_q \geq 0$ and h is a one-variable convex function.

For incompressible materials, the Ogden material model can be simplified into a more concise form. It still expresses the strain energy function in terms of the principal stretches and is given by the following equation:

$$\Psi(\lambda_1, \lambda_2, \lambda_3) = \sum_{p=1}^{N} \frac{\mu_p}{\alpha_p}(\lambda_1^{\alpha_p} + \lambda_2^{\alpha_p} + \lambda_3^{\alpha_p} - 3), \tag{6.8.4}$$

where N, μ_p, α_p are material constants. In general, the shear modulus in the reference configuration becomes

$$2\mu = \sum_{p=1}^{N} \mu_p\alpha_p, \tag{6.8.5}$$

where $\mu_p\alpha_p > 0$. As an example, Holzapfel (2000) provided the following values for the constants when $N = 3$:

$$\begin{gathered}\alpha_1 = 1.3, \quad \alpha_2 = 5.0, \quad \alpha_3 = -2.0, \\ \mu_1 = 6.3 \times 10^5(\mathrm{N \cdot m^{-2}}), \quad \mu_2 = 0.012 \times 10^5(\mathrm{N \cdot m^{-2}}), \\ \mu_3 = 0.1 \times 10^5(\mathrm{N \cdot m^{-2}}).\end{gathered} \tag{6.8.6}$$

Then, when $N = 1$ and $\alpha = 2$, the equation in strain energy yields

$$\Psi = \frac{\mu}{2}(\lambda_1^2 + \lambda_2^2 + \lambda_3^2 - 3) = \frac{\mu}{2}(I_C - 3), \tag{6.8.7}$$

which is the neo-Hookean material model.

Recently, the Ogden material model has been subjected to further research and discussion. One notable variant is the Hadamard material model, which is a simplified version of the Ogden model. In the Hadamard model, Equation (6.8.3) is modified by setting $M = N = 1$ and $\alpha_1 = \beta_1 = 2$, resulting in a reduced form of the equation:

$$\Psi(\mathrm{C}) = a_1(I_{\mathrm{C}} - 3) + b_1(II_{\mathrm{C}} - 3) + h(J). \tag{6.8.8}$$

Then, the constitutive equation for the second Piola–Kirchhoff stress becomes

$$\mathbf{S} = 2\frac{\partial \Psi(\mathbf{C})}{\partial \mathbf{C}} = 2\left[a_1\mathbf{I} + b_1(II_{\mathrm{C}}\mathbf{C}^{-1} - III_{\mathrm{C}}\mathbf{C}^{-2}) + h'(J)\frac{\partial J}{\partial \mathbf{C}}\right] \tag{6.8.9}$$

and

$$\frac{\partial J}{\partial \mathbf{C}} = \frac{\partial}{\partial \mathbf{C}}\left[(III_{\mathrm{C}})^{1/2}\right] = \frac{1}{2}J\mathbf{C}^{-1}. \tag{6.8.10}$$

Finally, the second Piola–Kirchhoff stress tensor may also be rewritten as

$$\mathbf{S} = 2\left[a_1\mathbf{I} + \left(b_1 II_{\mathrm{C}} + \frac{1}{2}h'(J)J\right)\mathbf{C}^{-1} - b_1 J^2\mathbf{C}^{-2}\right]. \tag{6.8.11}$$

The Ogden model is a highly versatile hyperelastic model that describes the Helmholtz free energy per reference volume in terms of the applied principal stretches, as discussed earlier. The Helmholtz free energy in the Ogden model can also be expressed in various forms. By combining experimental results, the material constants can be determined. In recent years, these constitutive models have been widely employed in studying both soft and hard living tissues.

6.8.3 *The Mooney–Rivlin Material Model*

The Mooney–Rivlin material model was initially developed to simulate rubber-like materials. However, it is now widely used to model biological tissue-like materials as well. The strain energy density for this model can be expressed as follows:

$$\Psi(\lambda_1, \lambda_2, \lambda_3) = \frac{\mu_1}{2}(\lambda_1^2 + \lambda_2^2 + \lambda_3^2 - 3) - \frac{\mu_2}{2}(\lambda_1^{-2} + \lambda_2^{-2} + \lambda_3^{-2} - 3). \tag{6.8.12}$$

Actually, this model has the same energy expression as that provided previously by Equation (6.8.3) of the Ogden material model. Then, with the parameter values as $N = 2$, $\alpha_1 = 2$, $\alpha_2 = -2$ and with the constraint $\lambda_1, \lambda_2, \lambda_3 = 1$ (incompressibility), this model can be obtained from the Ogden material model. Note that

$$\lambda_1^2 + \lambda_2^2 + \lambda_3^2 = I_{\tilde{\mathbf{C}}},$$

$$\lambda_1^{-2} + \lambda_2^{-2} + \lambda_3^{-2} = \frac{\lambda_2^2\lambda_3^2 + \lambda_1^2\lambda_3^2 + \lambda_1^2\lambda_2^2}{\lambda_1^2\lambda_2^2\lambda_3^2} = \frac{II_{\mathbf{C}}}{III_{\mathbf{C}}} = II_{\mathbf{C}}. \tag{6.8.13}$$

Since we have the constraint $III_{\mathbf{C}} = 1$, we can summarize the strain energy density as follows:

$$\Psi(\mathbf{C}) = \frac{\mu_1}{2}(I_{\mathbf{C}} - 3) - \frac{\mu_2}{2}(II_{\mathbf{C}} - 3) = c_1(I_{\mathbf{C}} - 3) - c_2(II_{\mathbf{C}} - 3). \tag{6.8.14}$$

Then, the terms $(I_{\mathbf{C}} - 3)$, $(II_{\mathbf{C}} - 3)$ ensure that the strain energy is zero when there is no deformation ($\mathbf{E} = 0$) since in this scenario, we will obtain $I_{\mathbf{C}} = 3$ and $II_{\mathbf{C}} = 3$.

In the special case of $c_2 = 0$, we revert to the neo-Hookean material model.

Using the previous formula, the second Piola–Kirchhoff stress tensor for the Mooney–Rivlin material model can be derived, and it becomes

$$\begin{aligned}
\mathbf{S} = 2\frac{\partial\Psi(\mathbf{C})}{\partial\mathbf{C}} &= 2\left[\left(\frac{\partial\Psi}{\partial I_{\mathbf{C}}} + \frac{\partial\Psi}{\partial II_{\mathbf{C}}}I_{\mathbf{C}}\right)\mathbf{I} - \left(\frac{\partial\Psi}{\partial II_{\mathbf{C}}}\right)\mathbf{C}\right. \\
&\quad \left. + \left(\frac{\partial\Psi}{\partial III_{\mathbf{C}}}III_{\mathbf{C}}\right)\mathbf{C}^{-1}\right] \\
&= 2\left[\left(\frac{\partial\Psi}{\partial I_{\mathbf{C}}} + \frac{\partial\Psi}{\partial II_{\mathbf{C}}}I_{\mathbf{C}}\right)\mathbf{I} - \left(\frac{\partial\Psi}{\partial II_{\mathbf{C}}}\right)\mathbf{C}\right] \\
&= 2[(c_1 + c_2 I_{\mathbf{C}})\mathbf{I} - c_2\mathbf{C}].
\end{aligned} \tag{6.8.15}$$

And the Cauchy stress tensor can be obtained as follows:

$$\boldsymbol{\sigma} = -p\mathbf{I} + 2c_1\mathbf{b} - 2c_2\mathbf{b}^{-1}. \tag{6.8.16}$$

6.8.4 *The Yeoh Material Model*

The Yeoh material model is commonly employed to simulate isotropic incompressible materials. In the Yeoh material model, the strain energy density can be expressed using a series expansion as follows:

$$\Psi(I_{\mathbf{C}}, II_{\mathbf{C}}, III_{\mathbf{C}}) = \sum_{p,q,r=1}^{N} c_{pqr}(I_{\mathbf{C}} - 3)^p (II_{\mathbf{C}} - 3)^q (III_{\mathbf{C}} - 1)^r. \tag{6.8.17}$$

Then, by considering the incompressible material, $III_{\mathbf{C}} = 1$, and also by discarding the second invariant, we obtain:

$$\Psi(I_{\mathbf{C}}) = \sum_{p=1}^{N=3} c_p(I_{\mathbf{C}} - 3)^p, \tag{6.8.18}$$

with which we can obtain the strain energy density for the Yeoh material model as follows:

$$\Psi(I_{\mathbf{C}}) = c_1(I_{\mathbf{C}} - 3) + c_2(I_{\mathbf{C}} - 3)^2 + c_3(I_{\mathbf{C}} - 3)^3, \tag{6.8.19}$$

where c_1, c_2, c_3 are material constants.

For the Yeoh material model, the second Piola–Kirchhoff stress tensor becomes

$$\begin{aligned} \mathbf{S} = 2\frac{\partial \Psi(\mathbf{C})}{\partial \mathbf{C}} &= 2\left[\left(\frac{\partial \Psi}{\partial I_{\mathbf{C}}} + \frac{\partial \Psi}{\partial II_{\mathbf{C}}} I_{\mathbf{C}}\right)\mathbf{I} - \left(\frac{\partial \Psi}{\partial II_{\mathbf{C}}}\right)\mathbf{C} \right. \\ &\quad \left. + \left(\frac{\partial \Psi}{\partial III_{\mathbf{C}}} III_{\mathbf{C}}\right)\mathbf{C}^{-1}\right] \\ &= 2\left(\frac{\partial \Psi}{\partial I_{\mathbf{C}}}\right)\mathbf{I} = 2[c_1 + 2c_2(I_{\mathbf{C}} - 3) + 3c_3(I_{\mathbf{C}} - 3)^2]\mathbf{I}. \end{aligned} \tag{6.8.20}$$

6.8.5 *The Arruda–Boyce Material Model*

The Arruda–Boyce material model, also known as the eight-chain model, is specifically designed to account for the strain-dependent shear modulus, denoted as G, observed in certain polymers. This model is commonly employed in polymer research and analysis. The strain energy density for the Arruda–Boyce material model can be expressed as follows:

$$\Psi(\mathbf{C}) = \mu_0 \sum_{p=1}^{N} \frac{c_p}{\lambda_{\text{lock}}^{2p-2}} (I_{\mathbf{C}}^p - 3^p), \tag{6.8.21}$$

where μ_0 is the initial shear modulus, c_p are constants obtained by statistical theory, and λ_{lock} and N are material constants. Then, if we consider that $N = 3$, we can obtain

$$\begin{aligned}\Psi(\mathbf{C}) &= \mu_0 \left[c_1(I_{\mathbf{C}} - 3) + \frac{c_2}{\lambda_{\text{lock}}^2}(I_{\mathbf{C}}^2 - 9) + \frac{c_3}{\lambda_{\text{lock}}^4}(I_{\mathbf{C}}^3 - 27) \right] \\ &= \mu_0 \left[\frac{1}{2}(I_{\mathbf{C}} - 3) + \frac{1}{20\lambda_{\text{lock}}^2}(I_{\mathbf{C}}^2 - 9) + \frac{11}{1050\lambda_{\text{lock}}^4}(I_{\mathbf{C}}^3 - 27) \right].\end{aligned} \tag{6.8.22}$$

6.8.6 *The Gent Model*

The Gent material model is considered a straightforward extension of the neo-Hookean material model, aimed at capturing the finite extensibility of the polymeric chains within an elastomer network. The strain energy density in the Gent model, proposed by Gent in 1996, is characterized by the following logarithmic function:

$$\Psi(I_{\mathbf{C}}) = \frac{-\mu}{2} \Xi \ln \left[1 - \frac{I_{\mathbf{C}} - 3}{\Xi} \right], \tag{6.8.23}$$

where μ, Ξ are material constants and Ξ is the constant that measures the limited value of $(I_{\mathbf{C}} - 3)$. For example, the important parameter Ξ represents the maximum value of $I_{\mathbf{C}}$ with the energy that grows to infinity as $I_{\mathbf{C}} \to \Xi$. To better understand its mechanical meaning, we may recall a simple result that states that $I_{\mathbf{C}}$ "is equal to three times the square of the stretch ratio of an infinitesimal line element averaged over all possible orientations." As a consequence, Ξ can be seen as a parameter (and natural) measure of the average contour length of the chains composing the polymeric network.

The stress–strain relation for Equation (6.8.23) is easily obtained as

$$\boldsymbol{\sigma} = -p\mathbf{I} + \frac{\mu}{1 - I_{\mathbf{C}}/\Xi}\mathbf{b}. \tag{6.8.24}$$

6.9 Newtonian Fluids

Fluids can exist in two forms: gases and liquids. In this section, we discuss the constitutive relations for fluids that exhibit a characteristic property: Stress is directly proportional to velocity gradients, or, in other words, strain rates. The proportionality factor in this relationship is referred to as the viscosity of the fluid, and the fundamental principle governing this behavior is known as Newton's law of viscosity. Fluids that follow Newton's law of viscosity are referred to as Newtonian fluids.

For such fluids, the constitutive equations for stress cannot be derived solely from the condition resulting from the entropy inequality, which is typically used for solids. Instead, the physics of Newtonian fluids requires the symmetric part of the velocity gradient tensor, denoted by $\mathbf{D}$, to be considered an argument in the constitutive equations. This is in contrast to solids, where the deformation gradient tensor, $\mathbf{F}$, is used.

In fluid mechanics, the Eulerian description is commonly employed to derive all equations of mechanics. The Eulerian description focuses on describing the flow properties at fixed points in space as functions of time, rather than tracking individual fluid particles. This approach is particularly suitable for analyzing fluid behavior and studying fluid flow phenomena.

For viscous fluids, the total stress tensor, $\boldsymbol{\sigma}$, is decomposed into two components: the equilibrium stress and the deviatoric stress. When considering the conditions resulting from the entropy inequality, it is possible to derive constitutive relations for compressible fluids by treating the equilibrium stress as the thermodynamic pressure, denoted by $p(\rho, \theta)$. However, for incompressible fluids, the thermodynamic pressure is equivalent to the mechanical pressure, $p(\theta)$.

It's important to note that the entropy inequality only imposes the condition that the work done by the deviatoric stress must be positive, but it does not provide a specific constitutive relation for it. As a result, a functional form for the deviatoric stress, $\boldsymbol{\sigma}$, is assumed for compressible fluids. The specific form of the constitutive relation depends on the nature of the fluid and the mathematical model being used:

$$\boldsymbol{\sigma} = -p(\rho, \theta)\mathbf{I} + \mathfrak{S}(\mathbf{D}). \qquad (6.9.1)$$

However, for incompressible fluids,

$$\boldsymbol{\sigma} = -p(\theta)\mathbf{I} + \mathfrak{S}(\mathbf{D}), \tag{6.9.2}$$

where ρ, θ are the spatial density and the absolute temperature, respectively. A fluid is said to be incompressible if the volume change is zero:

$$\nabla \cdot \mathbf{v} = 0. \tag{6.9.3}$$

A fluid is considered inviscid when its viscosity is zero. An ideal fluid, on the other hand, is characterized by being both incompressible and having zero viscosity. The constitutive equation for an ideal fluid is the most general form and can be expressed as follows:

$$\boldsymbol{\sigma} = -p(\rho, \theta)\mathbf{I}. \tag{6.9.4}$$

For viscous incompressible fluids, the constitutive equation for the stress tensor in fluid motion is assumed to follow a general form, as given by Equation (6.9.1). Similar to isotropic materials, isotropic fluids are characterized by shear stress–strain rate relations that can be expressed as follows:

$$\mathfrak{S}(\mathbf{D}) = \boldsymbol{\tau} = \mathfrak{J} : \mathbf{D}. \tag{6.9.5}$$

Here, $\boldsymbol{\tau}$ is the viscous stress tensor, $\mathfrak{J}$ denotes the fourth-order tensor of viscosities, and $\mathbf{D}$ is the strain rate tensor (symmetric part of the velocity gradient tensor $\mathbf{L}$):

$$\mathbf{D} = \frac{1}{2}(\nabla\mathbf{v} + (\nabla\mathbf{v})^T) \quad \text{or} \quad \mathrm{D}_{ij} = \frac{1}{2}\left(\frac{\partial v_i}{\partial x_j} + \frac{\partial v_j}{\partial x_i}\right), \tag{6.9.6}$$

where $\mathbf{v}$ is the velocity vector.

In the majority of cases, a viscous fluid is considered an isotropic fluid, for which the constitutive relation can be expressed as follows:

$$\boldsymbol{\sigma} = -p(\rho, \theta)\mathbf{I} + \boldsymbol{\tau}, \quad \boldsymbol{\tau} = 2\mu(\rho, \theta)\mathbf{D} + \lambda(\rho, \theta)\mathrm{tr}(\mathbf{D})\mathbf{I}, \tag{6.9.7}$$

Or, in rectangular Cartesian component form,

$$\sigma_{ij} = -p\left(\rho, \theta\right)\delta_{ij} + \tau_{ij}, \quad \tau_{ij} = 2\mu D_{ij} + \lambda D_{kk}\delta_{ij}, \tag{6.9.8}$$

where μ and λ are the Lamé parameters that have the meaning of bulk viscosity and shear viscosity, respectively.

We can express them in terms of the deviatoric components of stress and the rate-of-deformation tensors as

$$\boldsymbol{\sigma}' = \boldsymbol{\sigma} - \widetilde{\sigma}\mathbf{I}, \quad \mathbf{D}' = \mathbf{D} - \frac{1}{3}\mathrm{tr}(\mathbf{D})\mathbf{I}, \quad \widetilde{\sigma} = \frac{1}{3}\mathrm{tr}(\boldsymbol{\sigma}). \tag{6.9.9}$$

We note that $\sigma'_{ii} = 0$ and $D'_{ii} = 0$. Then, the Newtonian constitutive equation takes the form

$$\begin{aligned} \boldsymbol{\sigma}' &= 2\mu\mathbf{D}' + \left(\tfrac{2}{3}\mu + \lambda\right)\mathrm{tr}(\mathbf{D}) - (\widetilde{\sigma} + p)\,\mathbf{I}, \\ \sigma'_{ij} &= 2\mu D'_{ij} + \left(\tfrac{2}{3}\mu + \lambda\right) D_{kk}\delta_{ij} - (\widetilde{\sigma} + p)\,\delta_{ij}. \end{aligned} \tag{6.9.10}$$

From the above equations,

$$(2\mu + 3\lambda)D_{kk}\delta_{ij} - 3(\widetilde{\sigma} + p) = 0. \tag{6.9.11}$$

Therefore,

$$\boldsymbol{\sigma}' = 2\mu\mathbf{D}', \quad \sigma'_{ij} = 2\mu D'_{ij}. \tag{6.9.12}$$

Note that the mean stress $\widetilde{\sigma}$ is equal to the thermodynamic pressure p if and only if one of the following two conditions is satisfied ($D_{kk} = \nabla \cdot \mathbf{v}$):

$$\begin{aligned} \nabla \cdot \mathbf{v} &= 0, \\ K = 2\mu + 3\lambda &= 0. \end{aligned} \tag{6.9.13}$$

For the first equation, the fluid is incompressible, and for the second equation, known as the Stokes equation, it assumes that the Stokes condition holds. However, in general, the Stokes condition may not hold. Therefore, the constitutive equation for viscous, isotropic, incompressible fluids can be simplified to

$$\begin{aligned} \boldsymbol{\sigma} &= -p\mathbf{I} + \boldsymbol{\tau}, & \boldsymbol{\tau} &= 2\mu\mathbf{D}, \\ \sigma_{ij} &= -p\delta_{ij} + \tau_{ij}, & \tau_{ij} &= 2\mu D_{ij}. \end{aligned} \tag{6.9.14}$$

For inviscid fluids, the constitutive equation for the stress tensor has the form

$$\boldsymbol{\sigma} = -p\mathbf{I}, \quad \sigma_{ij} = -p\delta_{ij}. \tag{6.9.15}$$

Generalized Newtonian fluids can be classified into two groups: (1) inelastic fluids, or fluids without memory, and (2) viscoelastic fluids, where memory effects are significant. In inelastic fluids, the viscosity depends on the rate of deformation of the fluid, similar to nonlinear elastic solids. Viscoelastic fluids exhibit time-dependent "memory," meaning that the motion of a material point depends not only on the current stress state but also on the deformation history of the material element. This dependence on history results in complex constitutive equations.

The constitutive equation for the stress tensor in a generalized Newtonian fluid can be expressed as

$$\boldsymbol{\sigma} = -p\mathbf{I} + \boldsymbol{\tau}, \quad \sigma_{ij} = -p\delta_{ij} + \tau_{ij}, \tag{6.9.16}$$

where $\boldsymbol{\tau}$ is known as the viscous or extra stress tensor. For different fluid types, we can use different models.

6.10 Heat Transfer

Heat transfer can occur through one or more of the three basic forms: conduction, convection, and radiation. Conduction heat transfer refers to the transfer of heat within a medium due to a diffusion process. According to Fourier's law, the heat flow is proportional to the temperature gradient, and the proportionality parameter is called the thermal conductivity. It's important to note that for heat conduction to occur, there must be temperature differences between neighboring points.

Convection heat transfer, on the other hand, involves the energy transport influenced by the motion of a fluid. The convection heat transfer between two dissimilar media follows Newton's law of cooling, which states that the heat flow is proportional to the temperature difference between the two media. The proportionality parameter in this case is known as the convection heat transfer coefficient or film conductance. For heat convection to take place, there must be a fluid or another medium capable of transporting energy to and from the primary medium.

Radiation, unlike the previously mentioned transport processes, operates through a different mechanism. It is an electromagnetic process that allows energy transfer at the speed of light through regions of space without any matter. Thermal radiation describes the exchange of radiant energy between surfaces or between a region and its surroundings. The Stefan–Boltzmann law governs this radiation and states that the transmitted radiant energy is proportional to the temperature difference raised to the fourth power. The proportionality parameter in this case is known as the Stefan–Boltzmann parameter.

6.10.1 *Fourier's Heat Conduction Law*

For heat conduction, we consider a rigid body heated by an outside source and ignore the motion of the body. Now, the Helmholtz free energy $\psi = e - \theta\eta$ can be defined as

$$\psi_0 = -\frac{\alpha}{2}(\theta - \theta_0)^2 - \beta(\theta - \theta_0) + \gamma(\theta_0). \tag{6.10.1}$$

Thus, the entropy of the body can be expressed as

$$\eta_0 = -\frac{\partial \psi_0}{\partial \theta} = \alpha(\theta - \theta_0) + \beta. \tag{6.10.2}$$

As there is no deformation (rigid body), the stress will be irrelevant, so we have

$$\mathbf{S} = \rho_0 \frac{\partial \psi_0}{\partial \mathbf{E}} = 0. \tag{6.10.3}$$

The Fourier heat conduction law states that the heat flow $\mathbf{q}$ is related to the temperature gradient by the relation

$$\mathbf{q} = -\mathbf{k} \cdot \nabla\theta, \tag{6.10.4}$$

where $\mathbf{k}$ is the thermal conductivity tensor of order two. The negative sign indicates that heat flows downhill on the temperature scale.

We can define specific heat as

$$c = \frac{\partial e}{\partial \theta} = \theta \frac{\partial \eta_0}{\partial \theta} = \alpha\theta. \tag{6.10.5}$$

Using equations of conservation of energy

$$\begin{aligned} \rho_0 \dot{e}_0 &= \rho_0 \frac{\partial e_0}{\partial \theta}\dot{\theta} = \rho_0 c\dot{\theta} \\ &= \mathrm{Div}\mathbf{q}_0 + r_0 = \mathrm{Div}(-k\nabla\theta) + r_0, \end{aligned} \tag{6.10.6}$$

where r_0 is the internal heat generation per unit mass.

Therefore, the classic heat equation becomes

$$\rho_0 c \frac{\partial \theta}{\partial t} - \nabla \cdot k\nabla\theta = r_0. \tag{6.10.7}$$

6.10.2 *Newton's Law of Cooling*

At a solid–fluid interface, the heat flux is related to the difference between the temperature θ at the interface and that in the fluid θ_{fluid}:

$$q_n \equiv \widehat{\mathbf{n}} \cdot \mathbf{q} = h(\theta - \theta_{\text{fluid}}), \tag{6.10.8}$$

where $\widehat{\mathbf{n}}$ is the unit normal to the surface of the body and h is known as the heat transfer coefficient or film conductance. This relation is known as Newton's law of cooling.

6.10.3 *Stefan–Boltzmann Law*

The heat flow from surface 1 to surface 2 by radiation is governed by the Stefan–Boltzmann law:

$$q_n = \xi(\theta_1^4 - \theta_2^4), \tag{6.10.9}$$

where θ_1, θ_2 are the temperatures of surfaces 1 and 2, respectively, and ξ is the Stefan–Boltzmann constant. Again, this equation also defines a boundary condition on the surface 1 of a body.

6.11 Summary

This chapter focused on the discussion of constitutive equations for solids and fluids as well as heat transfer in solids. It covered topics such as Hookean solids, Newtonian fluids, and heat transfer in solids. The constitutive models for solids and fluids are derived using the entropy inequality and conditions resulting from it, which have been extensively explained in Chapter 5. The chapter begins with an overview of constitutive rules or axioms, frame indifference, and the constraints imposed by the entropy inequality. From there, general constitutive relations for the stress tensor, entropy, and heat flux are derived. Specific topics covered include the generalized Hooke's law for linear elastic solids, Newtonian relations for viscous fluids, and the Fourier heat conduction equation for heat transfer in solids. The generalized Hooke's law is further specialized to monoclinic materials, orthotropic materials, and isotropic materials based on material symmetries. Additionally, constitutive relations for nonlinear elastic solids, generalized Newtonian fluids, and heat transfer are discussed for a comprehensive understanding.

Furthermore, with the emergence of new soft and smart materials, we delved into the constitutive equations of hyperelastic materials, also known as Green-elastic materials. Different models for hyperelastic materials were explored, emphasizing the presence of a Helmholtz free-energy potential. This potential provides the stress as its derivative with respect to strain and the heat flux vector as its derivative with respect to temperature. Special hyperelastic materials that have gained significant attention in the past few decades are discussed in detail. We begin by presenting the general form of hyperelastic constitutive models and then focus on purely mechanical hyperelastic materials.

Deriving constitutive equations for fluids or solid materials can be a complex task. The presentation in this chapter aimed to provide a simplified overview, considering the introductory nature of the course. For a more detailed and advanced study of the subject, readers are encouraged to consult reference books such as those written by Prof. J.N. Reddy and Prof. Raymond Ogden *et al.* The author hopes that this chapter will serve as a general guide for readers interested in exploring the new developments of constitutive models for novel materials, including hydrogels, shape memory polymers, magnetically smart materials, and more.

Further Reading

More details study for hyperelastic constitutive equations, readers may refer to following work: Alexander (1968), Treloar (1975), Ogden (1984), Morman (1986), Holzapfel (2000), Chaves (2013), Merodio & Ogden, (2020). For special hyperelastic materials, such as hydrogels and shape memory polymers, readers may refer to review paper (Liu *et al.*, 2015, 2020, 2021).

General References

Alexander, H. (1968). A constitutive relation for rubber-like material. *Int. J. Eng. Sci.* 6, 549–563.

Chaves, E.W.V. (2013). *Notes on Continuum Mechanics* (Springer, Dordrecht).

Holzapfel, G.A. (2000). *Nonlinear Solid Mechanics* (John Wiley & Sons Ltd., England).

Huang, R., Zheng, S.J., Liu, Z.S., Ng, T.Y. (2020). Recent advances of the constitutive models of smart materials- hydrogels and shape memory polymers. *Int. J. Appl. Mech.* 12(2), 2050014. DOI: 10.1142/S1758825120500143.

Lei, J.C., Li, Z.Q., Xu, S., Liu, Z.S. (2021). Recent advances of hydrogel network models for studies on mechanical behaviors. *Acta Mech. Sin.* 37, 01058-2. DOI: 10.1007/s10409-021-01058-2.

Liu, Z.S., Toh, W., Ng, T.Y. (2015). Advances in mechanics of soft materials — A review of large deformation behavior of hydrogel. *Int. J. Appl. Mech.* 7(5), 1530001. DOI: 10.1142/S1758825115300011.

Merodio, J., Ogden, R. (2020). *Constitutive Modelling of Solid Continua* (Springer, Cham).

Oden, J.T. (2011). *An Introduction to Mathematical Modeling: A Course in Mechanics* (John Wiley & Sons Inc., New Jersey, USA).

Ogden, R.W. (1984). *Non-Linear Elastic Deformations* (Dover Publications Inc., New York).

Reddy, J.N. (2013). *An Introduction to Continuum Mechanics* (Cambridge University Press, New York, USA).

Reddy, J.N. (2017). *Principles of Continuum Mechanics: Conservation and Balance Laws with Applications* (Cambridge University Press, New York, USA).

Treloar, L.R.G. (1975). *The Physics of Rubber Elasticity* (Clarendon Press, Oxford).

Problems

6.1. The components of a stress tensor at a point in a body made of structural steel are

$$[\boldsymbol{\sigma}] = \begin{bmatrix} 42 & 12 & 30 \\ 12 & 15 & 0 \\ 30 & 0 & -5 \end{bmatrix} \text{MPa}.$$

Assuming that the Lamê constants for structural steel are $\lambda = 207\,\text{GPa}$ and $\mu = 79.6\,\text{GPa}$, determine the principal invariants of the strain tensor.

6.2. Given an isotropic linear elastic material whose elastic properties are $E = 71\,\text{GPa}$ and $G = 26.6\,\text{GPa}$, find the strain tensor components and the strain energy density at the point in which the stress state, in the Cartesian basis, is represented by

$$[\boldsymbol{\sigma}] = \begin{bmatrix} 20 & -4 & 5 \\ -4 & 0 & 10 \\ 5 & 10 & 15 \end{bmatrix} \text{MPa}.$$

6.3. Given the strain energy potential

$$\psi\left(\mathbf{E}\right) = \frac{1}{2}(\text{tr}(\mathbf{E}))^2 + \mu(\text{tr}(\mathbf{E} \cdot \mathbf{E}),$$

(1) determine the second Piola–Kirchhoff stress tensor $\mathbf{S}$ in terms of the Green strain tensor $\mathbf{E}$.
(2) if it is a case of infinitesimal deformations, the strain energy potential becomes

$$\psi(\boldsymbol{\epsilon}) = \frac{1}{2}(\text{tr}(\boldsymbol{\epsilon}))^2 + \mu(\text{tr}(\boldsymbol{\epsilon} \cdot \boldsymbol{\epsilon}),$$

then determine the strain energy function $\psi(\boldsymbol{\sigma})$ in terms of the stress tensor $\boldsymbol{\sigma}$.

6.4. For the Navier equations, show that for an isotropic, incompressible solid with infinitesimal deformations (i.e., $\boldsymbol{\sigma} \approx \mathbf{S}$ and $\mathbf{F} \cdot \mathbf{S} \approx \mathbf{S}$), the equation of motion $\nabla \cdot \boldsymbol{\sigma} + \rho_0 \mathbf{b} = \rho_0 \ddot{\mathbf{u}} = \rho_0 \mathbf{a}$ can be expressed in the following form:

$$\rho_0 \frac{\partial^2 \mathbf{u}}{\partial t^2} = \rho_0 \mathbf{f} - \nabla p + (\mu + \lambda)\, \nabla\left(\nabla \cdot \mathbf{u}\right) + \mu\, \nabla^2 \mathbf{u}.$$

6.5. Given the following motion of an isotropic continuum,

$$\mathbf{x} = \mathbf{x}(\mathbf{X}, t) = (X_1 + kt^2\left(X_2\right)^2)\mathbf{e}_1 + (X_2 + ktX_2)\mathbf{e}_2 + (X_3)\mathbf{e}_3,$$

determine the components of the viscous stress tensor as a function of position and time.

Chapter 7

Constitutive Models of Soft Materials: Hydrogels and Shape Memory Polymers

Table of Contents

7.1 Introduction of Hydrogels and Shape Memory Polymers

In the previous chapters, we discussed the constitutive models for the general continuum. In this chapter, we focus on the applications of these models and delve into the process of deriving constitutive models specifically for soft materials, such as hydrogels and shape memory polymers (SMPs).

Soft machines based on soft materials are poised to become the next generation of robots. These machines are designed to be more flexible, adaptable, and responsive to their environment and various stimuli, including mechanical, chemical (pH), thermal, optical, and magnetic. They are constructed using soft materials such as polymers, hydrogels, SMPs, dielectric elastomers (DEs), and liquid crystal elastomers. This construction enables them to bend, stretch, and deform, similar to biological organisms. Soft machines possess the capability to navigate complex environments, interact with delicate objects, and perform tasks that are currently challenging or impossible for traditional rigid or hard robots. Furthermore, they can provide improved safety and a more comfortable human interaction experience. It is important to highlight that soft machines have the potential to revolutionize industries such as healthcare, manufacturing, and transportation, playing a significant role in the future of robotics and automation.

Hydrogels and SMPs are smart materials that possess remarkable and captivating properties, making them ideal for future applications in soft machines (Liu *et al.*, 2015). In this chapter, the author's objective is to explore the utilization of continuum mechanics in solving the deformation of hydrogels and SMP structures. To study the deformation of these materials, constitutive equations will be essential, as they serve as illustrative examples of typical smart materials.

7.1.1 *Advances of the Constitutive Models of Hydrogels*

In recent years, hydrogels have gained global recognition as the most intelligent soft material, demonstrating immense potential for various applications. They have been employed as actuators responsive to physiological cues (Beebe *et al.*, 2000) and have played a crucial role in the development of soft electronic devices (Keplinger *et al.*, 2013). Highly flexible and stretchable hydrogels, known for their exceptional biocompatibility, hold great promise in biomedical science, soft robotics, and human–machine interaction (Huang *et al.*, 2020). Furthermore, functional hydrogels and composite materials have been engineered to meet diverse requirements, such as pH- and temperature-sensitive hydrogels for drug delivery applications (Ding *et al.*, 2016).

To further advance the utilization of hydrogels as smart materials and provide guidance for the aforementioned applications (Hu *et al.*, 2014, 2017; Liu *et al.*, 2010, 2013; Toh *et al.*, 2015, 2016), it is crucial to investigate their mechanical properties and performance. Researchers in mechanics should have the capability to simulate and program the mechanical behavior of hydrogels. Therefore, it is necessary to establish suitable modeling methods for hydrogels using continuum mechanics. While multi-scale modeling approaches (nanoscale, meso-scale, and continuum methods) have also emerged and thrived in this field, this book primarily focuses on continuum modeling. Each of these modeling methodologies has its own advantages and disadvantages.

Over the past decade, the primary modeling methods for hydrogels have been macro or continuum methods, including the finite element method (FEM) (Hong *et al.*, 2009) and the meshfree method (Liu and Cheng, 2018), both of which are based on continuum mechanics theories.

In the continuum realm, constitutive theories for hydrogels are formulated based on a statistical understanding of the polymer network–water microstructure within hydrogels. These theories enable the prediction of hydrogel behavior in response to various stimuli, encompassing neutral gels, salt concentration-sensitive gels, pH-sensitive gels, temperature-sensitive gels, photothermal-sensitive gels, and magnetic field-sensitive hydrogels. Figure 7.1.1 provides schematic representations of hydrogels under different external stimuli.

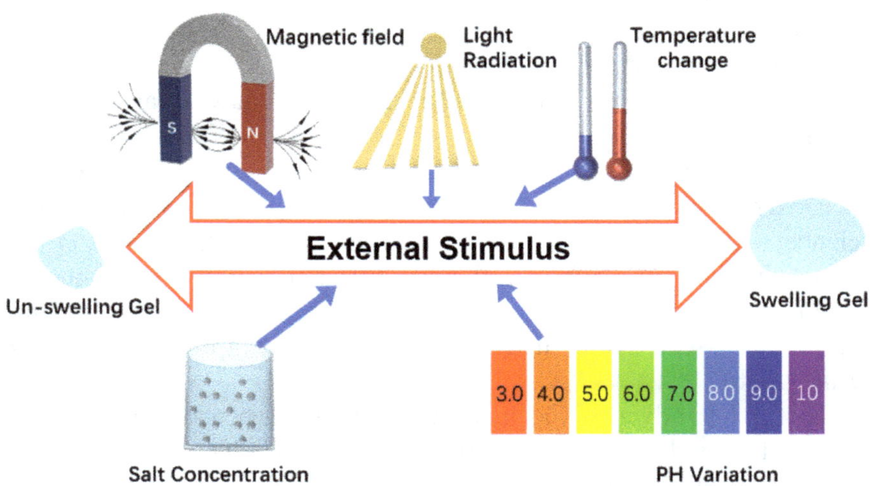

Figure 7.1.1 Schematic diagrams of hydrogels under different external stimuli (un-swelling: deswollen; swelling: swollen).

To accurately capture the hyperelasticity (Chester *et al.*, 2015; Hong *et al.*, 2009) and viscoelasticity (Mao *et al.*, 2017) of hydrogels, a range of numerical methods have been employed, including FEMs, meshless methods, and phase-field methods. These methodologies utilize well-established constitutive theories that were discussed in Chapter 6.

Furthermore, researchers are devoted to unraveling the fundamental mechanisms behind large deformations (Lei *et al.*, 2020) and energy dissipation (Lei *et al.*, 2019) through the construction of atomic structure models or coarse-grained polymer network models. Molecular dynamics (MD), Monte Carlo (MC), and coarse-grained molecular dynamics (CGMD) methods have been employed to develop structural models of hydrogels and simulate various aspects, including the nature of cross-linking, interactions between the solvent and polymer, as well as the mechanical response of the deformed polymer network.

To bridge the gap between micro-scale and macro-scale modeling, meso-scale modeling approaches have been proposed to enhance our understanding of the mechanical behavior of hydrogels. In certain cases, the meso-scale approach may provide more effective and realistic results compared to micro- and macro-scale methods. However, due to space limitations, this chapter focuses primarily on the continuum modeling of hydrogels. For a comprehensive overview of multi-scale modeling approaches for hydrogels, including simulation methods ranging from micro-scale to macro-scale, readers are referred to the author's recent review papers (Liu *et al.*, 2015; Huang *et al.*, 2020).

7.1.2 *Advances of the Constitutive Models of Shape Memory Polymers*

In recent years, another extensively researched type of soft matter has been SMPs. SMPs belong to the class of stimulus-responsive smart materials that have the remarkable ability to revert to their original (permanent) shape from a programmed temporary shape when exposed to changes in their surrounding environment, including temperature, light, pH, and electricity. When compared to traditional shape memory materials, such as shape memory alloys and shape memory ceramics, SMPs offer several advantages. These include being lightweight and cost-effective, exhibiting good biocompatibility, and, most notably, having the ability to recover from large deformations (Leng *et al.*, 2009).

These advantages have paved the way for diverse applications harnessing the potential of SMPs (He *et al.*, 2015, 2017a, 2018). Examples of these applications include functional textiles (Hu and Chen, 2010), aircraft equipment and aerospace structures (Behl *et al.*, 2010), self-healing materials, and adaptive biomedical devices. The unique properties of SMPs make them highly attractive for a wide range of innovative uses.

In earlier studies, researchers have examined the shape memory behaviors of SMPs from specific perspectives of interest (Liu *et al.*, 2014, 2019). However, to fully unlock the potential of SMPs for various applications, it is crucial to establish a comprehensive understanding of the intrinsic mechanisms underlying them. Thus, in this chapter, our aim is to integrate diverse theories by discussing different representative constitutive models, with a particular focus on thermal-sensitive SMPs. These models can be broadly categorized into two main groups: rheological models and phenomenological models.

Rheological models are based on viscoelastic modeling approaches that incorporate rate- and temperature-dependent parameters. Early thermoviscoelastic constitutive models often consisted of classical spring and dashpot elements, along with a friction modulus that qualitatively represented the shape memory effect (SME) of SMPs. One notable early viscoelastic model was proposed by Tobushi *et al.* (1997, 2001), who introduced an irreversible slip element in the Maxwell spring-damper system to describe the general shape memory process of SMPs. Building upon the framework of the spring-dashpot system, several other viscoelastic models were subsequently developed and extended to describe the large three-dimensional (3D) deformation of SMPs (Li *et al.*, 2015).

To better characterize the rate-dependent and temperature-dependent performance of amorphous SMPs, researchers further developed thermoviscoelastic models that combined relaxation behaviors with the viscoelastic behaviors of these SMPs (Nguyen *et al.*, 2008). In an effort to simplify the prediction process and provide a simple yet effective SMP model, Pan and Liu (2018) introduced novel fractional viscoelastic constitutive models by simplifying the model parameters. These models offer a streamlined approach while still capturing the essential characteristics of SMP behavior.

In the study of viscoelastic models for the thermally activated SME, Xiao *et al.* (2015) developed a finite deformation viscoelastic model with multiple relaxation processes. This model effectively captures the temperature memory effect and multi-shape memory effect observed in Nafion, an amorphous polymer known for its broad glass transition region. The model provides a suitable description of the shape memory performance exhibited by amorphous thermoplastics. However, it is important to note that viscoelastic models are generally not applicable for simulating the shape memory performance of polymers with a temporary shape programmed below the glass transition region.

Although previous rheological models have been successful in evaluating the thermomechanical properties of SMPs and capturing the rate and temperature dependence of the SME, they have faced challenges in establishing a direct connection between phase transition mechanisms and SME as well as providing a clear physical interpretation. As a result, the phenomenological phase transition approach was introduced and has been widely investigated as an alternative method. This approach aims to bridge the gap by offering a more direct and physically meaningful description of the phase transition processes underlying the shape memory behavior of SMPs.

The first phenomenological model of SMPs was introduced by Liu *et al.* (2006). This model considered SMPs as a mixture of different phases, with the transformation between these phases being temperature-dependent. Building on this approach, subsequent researchers developed their own models with unique assumptions. Qi *et al.* (2008) redefined the glassy phase of SMPs to improve the accuracy of their three-phase transition models. Lu *et al.* (2019) proposed a cooperative domain model to describe the glass transition and relaxation behaviors of SMPs, with a specific focus on the triple-shape memory effect in multiple phase SMPs. Furthermore, comprehensive phenomenological models based on the phase transition concept have been developed by Reese *et al.* (2010), Li *et al.* (2017b), and Lu *et al.* (2018). Previous studies utilizing these phase transition models have demonstrated that phenomenological models can offer a clear physical interpretation of the relationship between the glass transition and the SME. However, incorporating viscosity- and rate-dependency effects into this framework has proven to be challenging.

Subsequently, researchers attempted to integrate both the viscoelasticity and phase transition of SMPs in constitutive models. Li *et al.* (2017a) proposed a phase-evolution-based thermomechanical constitutive model that can capture the SME in amorphous SMPs while considering the viscoelastic properties of polymers and the phase transition phenomenon. Building upon this work, Li and Liu (2018) further improved the model, enabling precise predictions of rate-dependent shape memory behaviors and incorporating a clear physical interpretation of creep and stress relaxation in SMPs.

Despite the significant research and interest in SMPs, their low modulus and limited recovery stress have posed limitations on their practical use and hindered further development. To address this challenge, researchers have proposed approaches to enhance and reinforce the mechanical properties of SMPs. One such approach is the incorporation of spherical particles into shape memory polymer composites (SMPCs). Pan *et al.* (2019) conducted a study on the mechanical properties and SME of SMPCs reinforced with spherical particles. They utilized a representative volume element generated using the random sequential adsorption algorithm to investigate these properties.

Given the aforementioned context, the subsequent sections present the constitutive models for hydrogels and SMPs.

7.2 Large Deformation of Hydrogels

Based on continuum mechanics, we introduce the theory of large deformation to model hydrogels. Hydrogels exhibit variations in their response based on the type of stimulus they are exposed to. Nonetheless, a generalized theory has been developed to describe various types of hydrogels, including neutral gels, salt concentration-sensitive gels, pH-sensitive gels, temperature-sensitive gels, photothermal-sensitive gels, and magnetic-sensitive gels. Although each of these theories has its own unique models and formulations, they share a common foundation in their basic formulations.

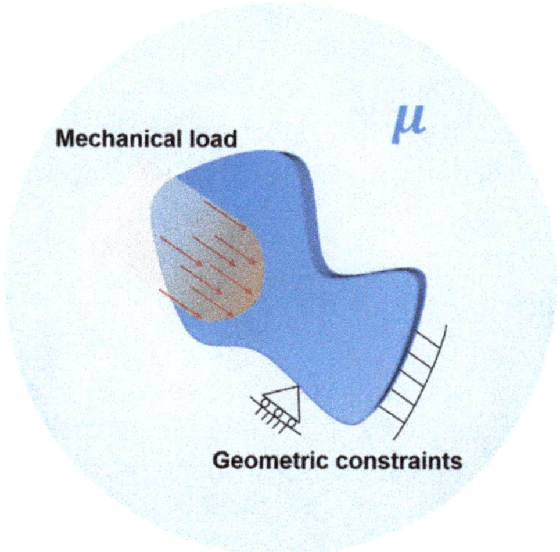

Figure 7.2.1 A gel is in contact with a solvent of a fixed chemical potential and is subjected to a mechanical load and a geometric constraint.

7.2.1 *The Basic Formulas of Constitutive Models of Hydrogels*

First, let's consider a general loading scenario for a hydrogel under external loading and in an external environment. In Figure 7.2.1, a hydrogel is subjected to geometric constraints and is attached to a body force f_i, while a traction T_i is maintained at a chemical potential μ. It is important to note that different types of hydrogels may experience different physical constraints. For instance, in the case of a magnetic-sensitive gel, there might be a nearby wire carrying an alternating current I, which induces a magnetic field B within the gel. The work done on the hydrogel by the mechanical load and the solvent can be represented as $P\delta l$ and $\mu\delta N$, respectively. δl is the displacement induced by the external force P, and δN is the change in solvent molecules induced by μ. Furthermore, it is worth mentioning that different types of hydrogels may exhibit different forms of work. For instance, in the case of a magnetic-sensitive gel, the work done through the magnetic field $B\delta M$ should be taken into account within the system, where δM is the change in the magnetic moment.

For large deformations of hydrogels, we consider two distinct states: the reference state and the current state (or the state of the hydrogels at time t). We can choose any state as the reference state, such as the stress-free dry network of the hydrogel, and assign a coordinate $\mathbf{X}$ to each small portion of the network in the reference state. In a deformed state, this portion of the network moves to a new position with the coordinate $x_i(\mathbf{X}, t)$ at time t. The deformation gradient is denoted by

$$F_{iK} = \frac{\partial x_i(\mathbf{X}, t)}{\partial X_K} \quad \text{or} \quad \mathbf{F} = \frac{\partial \mathbf{x}(\mathbf{X}, t)}{\partial \mathbf{X}}. \tag{7.2.1}$$

In the deformation process, the deformation gradient $\mathbf{F}$ can be decomposed multiplicatively for different constitutive models. In the case of hydrogel deformation, with respect to the dry network, the state of free swelling can be characterized by the deformation gradient

$$\mathbf{F}_0 = \begin{bmatrix} \lambda_0 & 0 & 0 \\ 0 & \lambda_0 & 0 \\ 0 & 0 & \lambda_0 \end{bmatrix}. \tag{7.2.2}$$

Practically, it is often more convenient to use the initial stress-free state of an isotropically pre-swollen hydrogel as the reference state. In this case, the deformation gradient of the initial state is denoted as $\mathbf{F}_0 = \lambda_0 \mathbf{I}$, where $\mathbf{I}$ is the identity matrix. The total deformation gradient in the current state can be decomposed into

$$\mathbf{F} = \mathbf{F}'\mathbf{F}_0 \quad \text{or} \quad \mathbf{F} = \mathbf{F}_\text{d}\mathbf{F}_0, \tag{7.2.3}$$

where $\mathbf{F}'$ or $\mathbf{F}_\text{d}$ is the deformation gradient of the current state relative to the free-swelling state, and $\det \mathbf{F} = \det \mathbf{F}' \det \mathbf{F}_0 = \lambda_0^3 \det \mathbf{F}'$.

Figure 7.2.1 illustrates a polymer network in contact with a solvent, subjected to a mechanical load and geometric constraints, and held at a constant temperature. To simplify the problem, we can consider the stress-free dry network as the reference state. In this reference state, each small part of the network is named after its coordinate $\mathbf{X}$. Let $\text{d}V(\mathbf{X})$ represent an element of volume, $A(\mathbf{X})$ represent an element of area, and $N_K(\mathbf{X})$ represent the unit vector normal to the element of area. In the deformed state, let $C(\mathbf{X})\text{d}V(\mathbf{X})$ represent the number of solvent molecules in the element of volume. The field $x_i(\mathbf{X})$ describes the deformation of the network, the field $C(\mathbf{X})$

describes the distribution of the solvent molecules in the hydrogel, and the combination of these two fields describes the state of the gel.

In a deformed state, let $B_i(\mathbf{X})\mathrm{d}V(\mathbf{X})$ be the mechanical force applied on the element of volume and $T_i(\mathbf{X})\mathrm{d}A(\mathbf{X})$ be the mechanical force applied on the element of area. When the network deforms by a small amount, $\delta x_i(\mathbf{X})$, the field of mechanical load does the work $\int B_i\delta x_i \mathrm{d}V + \int T_i \delta x_i \mathrm{d}A$.

We consider the external solvent, in its pure liquid state, as the reference state. In this state, the chemical potential of the solvent is assumed to be zero. The liquid solvent is treated as incompressible, with a volume per molecule denoted by v and a vapor pressure denoted by p_0. When the solvent is subjected to a pressure p greater than the vapor pressure ($p > p_0$), the chemical potential of the solvent molecules is $v(p - p_0)$. On the other hand, when the solvent is subjected to a pressure p that is less than the vapor pressure ($p < p_0$), the solvent reaches equilibrium and transitions into a gas phase, which is assumed to be an ideal gas. In this case, the chemical potential of the solvent molecules is $\mu = kT(p/p_0)$, where k is the Boltzmann constant and T is the absolute temperature, and kT is measured in energy units. When the concentration field within the hydrogel changes by $\delta C(\mathbf{X})$, work is done by the external solvent, given by $\mu \int \delta C \mathrm{d}V$.

Let $W\mathrm{d}V(\mathbf{X})$ be the Helmholtz free energy of the hydrogel in the element of volume. We assume that the free-energy density of the hydrogel is a function of the deformation gradient and the concentration $W(\mathbf{F}, C)$. When the hydrogel equilibrates with the solvent and the mechanical load, the chemical potential of the solvent molecules is homogeneous in the external solvent and in the hydrogel:

$$\mu = \frac{\partial W(\mathbf{F}, C)}{\partial C}. \tag{7.2.4}$$

This is the thermodynamic equation which will be derived in the following section.

When the network equilibrates with the solvent and the mechanical load, the change in the free energy of the hydrogel equals the sum of the work done by the mechanical force and the solvent, namely,

$$\int \delta W \mathrm{d}V = \int B_i \delta x_i \mathrm{d}V + \int T_i \delta x_i \mathrm{d}S + \mu \int \delta C \mathrm{d}V. \tag{7.2.5}$$

The equilibrium condition is that this equation holds for arbitrary changes, $\delta\mathbf{x}$ and δC.

Introduce another free-energy function $\hat{W}$ by using a Legendre transformation:

$$\hat{W} = W(\mathbf{F}, C) - \mu C. \tag{7.2.6}$$

Once the function $W(\mathbf{F}, C)$ is prescribed and the differential is taken, (7.2.4) becomes an algebraic equation, from which we can express C as a function of $\mathbf{F}$ and μ. Consequently, (7.2.6) defines $\hat{W}$ as a function of the deformation gradient of the network and the chemical potential of the solvent molecules: $\hat{W}(\mathbf{F}, \mu)$.

Combining (7.2.5) and (7.2.6) gives

$$\int \delta\hat{W}\mathrm{d}V = \int B_i\delta x_i\mathrm{d}V + \int T_i\delta x_i\mathrm{d}A. \tag{7.2.7}$$

As noted above, when the network equilibrates with the solvent and the mechanical load, the chemical potential of the solvent molecules inside the hydrogel becomes homogenous and is equal to the chemical potential of the external solvent, μ. Indeed, the chemical potential plays a role analogous to that of the temperature. The equilibrium condition (7.2.7) takes the same form as that for a hyperelastic solid. Once the function $\hat{W}(\mathbf{F}, \mu)$ is prescribed, we can implement an FEM. Note that since the theory does not use an intrinsic length scale, the field can only depend on lengths originating from the boundary conditions.

Following a tradition in continuum mechanics, we now reduce the equilibrium condition of variational forms to that of differential forms. We have assumed that the free-energy density takes the functional form $W(\mathbf{F}, C)$. When associated with a small change in the deformation gradient of the network, δF_{iK}, and a small change in the concentration of the solvent molecules, δC, the free-energy density changes by

$$\delta W = \frac{\partial W(\mathbf{F}, C)}{\partial F_{iK}}\delta F_{iK} + \frac{\partial W(\mathbf{F}, C)}{\partial C}\delta C. \tag{7.2.8}$$

Substituting (7.2.8) into the equilibrium condition (7.2.5) and applying the divergence theorem, we obtain

$$\int \left(\frac{\partial}{\partial X_K} \frac{\partial W}{\partial F_{iK}} + B_i \right) \delta x_i \mathrm{d}V + \int \left(T_i - \frac{\partial W}{\partial F_{iK}} N_K \right) \delta x_i \mathrm{d}A$$
$$+ \int \left(\mu - \frac{\partial W}{\partial C} \right) \delta C \mathrm{d}V = 0. \tag{7.2.9}$$

In equilibrium, (7.2.9) holds for the arbitrary changes δx_i and δC, so that the quantity in each pair of parentheses in (7.2.9) vanishes. Consequently, the equilibrium condition is equivalent to (7.2.5), along with

$$\frac{\partial}{\partial X_K} \frac{\partial W(\mathbf{F}, C)}{\partial F_{iK}} + B_i = 0 \tag{7.2.10}$$

in the volume of the gel and

$$\frac{\partial W(\mathbf{F}, C)}{\partial F_{iK}} N_K = T_i \tag{7.2.11}$$

on the surface of the gel.

Define nominal stress as the work conjugate to the deformation gradient so that

$$s_{iK} = \frac{\partial W(\mathbf{F}, C)}{\partial F_{iK}}. \tag{7.2.12}$$

The nominal stress expressions given by Equations (7.2.10) and (7.2.11) have a familiar interpretation as the conditions for mechanical equilibrium. Using (7.2.4) and (7.2.12), we rewrite (7.2.8) as

$$\delta W = s_{iK} \delta F_{iK} + \mu \delta C. \tag{7.2.13}$$

Combining (7.2.6) and (7.2.13) gives

$$\delta \hat{W} = s_{iK} \delta F_{iK} - C \delta \mu, \tag{7.2.14}$$

so that

$$s_{iK} = \frac{\partial \hat{W}(\mathbf{F}, \mu)}{\partial F_{iK}} \tag{7.2.15}$$

and

$$C = -\frac{\partial \hat{W}(\mathbf{F}, \mu)}{\partial \mu}. \tag{7.2.16}$$

We assume that all molecules within a gel are incompressible and that the volume of the gel is the sum of the volumes of the dry network and the pure liquid solvent. This assumption is based on the work by Hong *et al.* (2009):

$$1 + vC = \det \mathbf{F}, \tag{7.2.17}$$

where ν is the nominal volume of a solvent molecule. As mentioned earlier, we have made the assumption that the two fields, $C(\mathbf{X})$ and $x_i(\mathbf{X})$, vary independently. However, Equation (7.2.17) introduces a constraint between these two fields. To incorporate this constraint, we introduce a Lagrange multiplier field, denoted by $\Pi(1 + vC - \det \mathbf{F})$, into the free-energy function $W(\mathbf{F}, C)$. By replacing $W(\mathbf{F}, C)$ with $W(\mathbf{F}, C) + \Pi(1 + vC - \det \mathbf{F})$ in all the previous equations, we treat $\mathbf{F}$ and C as independent fields.

The next step involves defining the free-energy density $W(\mathbf{F}, C)$. According to Flory and Rehner (1943), for the basic formulation of the theory, we assume that the total free-energy density can be decomposed into a linear sum of the two component densities:

$$W(F_{iK}, C) = W_{\text{str}}(F_{iK}) + W_{\text{mix}}(C). \tag{7.2.18}$$

For different types of hydrogels, various energy densities can be included in Equation (7.2.18). In the equation, the free-energy density of network stretch is assumed to follow a Gaussian form, as derived by Wall (1943):

$$W_{\text{str}} = \frac{1}{2} NkT[\mathbf{F} : \mathbf{F} - 3 - 2\log(\det \mathbf{F})], \tag{7.2.19}$$

where N is the cross-link density in the reference state, $\mathbf{F} = F_{iK}$, and $k = 1.3806488 \times 10^{-23} \text{m}^2 \cdot \text{kg} \cdot \text{s}^{-2} \cdot \text{K}^{-1}$ is the Boltzmann constant.

In addition to Equation (7.2.19), Chester and Anand (2010) have proposed an alternative form of the free-energy density of network stretch. This form incorporates a more realistic representation of the network stretch, considering the limited extensibility of the polymer network. It is expressed as follows:

$$W_{\rm str} = -NkT\left\{-\lambda_{\rm L}^2\left[\left(\frac{\overline{\lambda}}{\lambda_{\rm L}}\right)\beta + \log\left(\frac{\beta}{\sinh\beta}\right) - \frac{1}{\lambda_{\rm L}}\beta_0 - \log\left(\frac{\beta_0}{\sinh\beta_0}\right)\right] + \frac{\lambda_{\rm L}}{3}\beta_0\log(\det\mathbf{F})\right\}, \tag{7.2.20}$$

where $\overline{\lambda} = \sqrt{\mathrm{tr}(\mathbf{F}^{\rm T}\mathbf{F})/3}$, $\lambda_{\rm L}$ is the network locking stretch parameter, $\beta = L^{-1}(\overline{\lambda}/\lambda_{\rm L})$, $\beta_0 = L^{-1}(1/\lambda_{\rm L})$, and L^{-1} is the inverse of the Langevin function $L(x) = \coth x - x^{-1}$.

In Equation (7.2.18), there are both enthalpic and entropic contributions to the free-energy density of mixing. We assume the Flory–Huggins form (Flory, 1942; Huggins, 1941)

$$W_{\rm mix} = kT\left(C\log\left(\frac{\nu C}{1+\nu C}\right) + \frac{\chi C}{1+\nu C}\right), \tag{7.2.21}$$

where χ is the interaction parameter.

The partial differential derivative of the free-energy density can produce the nominal stress

$$s_{iK} = \frac{\partial W}{\partial F_{iK}}. \tag{7.2.22}$$

Here, we have presented the fundamental formulas of hydrogel theory, which can be applied to various types of hydrogels. Specifically, based on fundamental deformation theory, constitutive models for different types of hydrogels can be derived. These models cover neutral gels, salt concentration-sensitive gels, pH-sensitive gels, temperature-sensitive gels, photothermal-sensitive gels, and magnetic-sensitive gels. Depending on the specific type of hydrogel, distinct energy density functions can be incorporated into Equation (7.2.18), or modifications can be made to the equation to account for different stimuli.

7.2.2 *Constitutive Model for Neutral Hydrogels*

In the field of hydrogels, neutral gel is the most commonly studied type of gel. It is considered the most fundamental type of hydrogel, as its only stimulus is exposure to water. Consequently, the constitutive model for neutral gels is based on the fundamental formulas discussed earlier in this section. Many research groups have extensively investigated the neutral gel model due to its simplicity and relevance to various applications.

The free energy due to stretching a network of polymers is taken to be (Hong *et al.*, 2009)

$$W_{\text{str}} = \frac{1}{2}NkT(\lambda_1^2 + \lambda_2^2 + \lambda_3^2 - 3 - 2\log\lambda_1\lambda_2\lambda_3) \tag{7.2.23}$$

Let $s_i (i = 1,\ 2,\ 3)$ be the three principal nominal stresses. Equation (7.2.22) is specialized to

$$s_1 = NkT(\lambda_1 - \lambda_1^{-1}) - \Pi\lambda_2\lambda_3, \tag{7.2.24}$$

and

$$s_2 = NkT(\lambda_2 - \lambda_2^{-1}) - \Pi\lambda_1\lambda_3,\quad s_3 = NkT(\lambda_3 - \lambda_3^{-1}) - \Pi\lambda_1\lambda_2, \tag{7.2.25}$$

$$\mu = kT\left[\log\frac{\nu C}{1+\nu C} + \frac{1}{1+\nu C} + \frac{\chi}{(1+\nu C)^2}\right] + \Pi\nu. \tag{7.2.26}$$

The general form of the constitutive equations can be expressed as

$$\frac{s_{iK}}{kT/v} = Nv(F_{iK} - H_{iK}) + \left[J\log\left(1 - \frac{1}{J}\right) + 1 + \frac{\chi}{J} - \frac{\mu}{kT}J\right]H_{iK}, \tag{7.2.27}$$

where s_{iK} is the component of nominal stress and H_{iK} is the component of the inverse of $\mathbf{F}$.

Equations (7.2.24)–(7.2.27) represent the equations of state for the neutral gel. These equations mathematically describe the mechanical behaviors exhibited by the neutral gel, including phenomena such as free swelling and deformation under uniaxial tension. The model proposed by Hong *et al.* (2009) provides a comprehensive framework for understanding and predicting the mechanical response of neutral gels under different conditions.

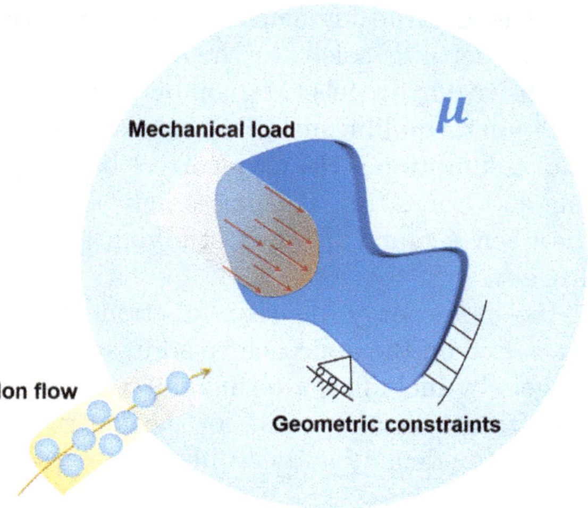

Figure 7.2.2 A gel is in contact with a solvent with a fixed salt concentration and is subjected to a mechanical load and geometric constraint, while ions flow from external sources into the gel through a field of pumps.

7.2.3 *Constitutive Model of Salt Concentration-Sensitive Hydrogels*

When a polyelectrolyte network is immersed in an ionic solution, it absorbs the solution and undergoes swelling, leading to the formation of a salt concentration-sensitive gel. In addition to the geometric constraints and mechanical loads experienced by the gel, it is also influenced by the stimulus of salt concentration, as depicted in Figure 7.2.2. The chemical potential equilibrium between the interior and exterior of the gel is crucial for achieving thermodynamic equilibrium. To describe this phenomenon, the nominal concentration C^a is defined according to Zheng and Liu (2019). This parameter serves as an important characteristic of the salt concentration-sensitive gel and plays a role in its constitutive modeling and understanding its mechanical behavior.

$$C^a = c^a J, \tag{7.2.28}$$

where $J = \det\mathbf{F}$.

It is important to acknowledge that in many studies (Hong *et al.*, 2008, 2009; Liu *et al.*, 2010; Marcombe *et al.*, 2010), the nominal concentration C^a has been assumed to be independent of J.

This assumption holds true for neutral gels, where the concentration in the theory pertains solely to the solvent. However, for salt concentration-sensitive hydrogels (Marcombe *et al.*, 2010), due to the constraints of Donnan equilibrium, C^a is indeed related to J. Therefore, the original assumption is clearly incorrect based on the previous analysis (Zheng and Liu, 2019). It is necessary to consider the interdependence between C^a and J when studying salt concentration-sensitive hydrogels.

Based on the free-energy density function discussed in Section 7.2.2, we can extend the approach to address salt concentration-sensitive hydrogels by including a term that considers the influence of ions. This additional term accounts for the contribution of ions to the overall free-energy density and can be expressed as follows:

$$W = W_{\text{str}} + W_{\text{mix}} + W_{\text{ion}}, \tag{7.2.29}$$

where W_{ion} is the free-energy density of mixing the solvent and ions.

W_{ion}, which differs from that of the neutral gel, is assumed as follows:

$$W_{\text{ion}} = kT\left[C^+\left(\log\frac{C^+}{c^+_{\text{ref}}J} - 1\right) + C^-\left(\log\frac{C^-}{c^-_{\text{ref}}J} - 1\right)\right], \tag{7.2.30}$$

where c^a_{ref} is a reference value of the concentration of species a; here, we take c^a_{ref} to be c_0, the concentration in the salt solution. The unit of C^a is $[\text{m}^{-3}]$, rendering vC^a a dimensionless parameter.

To specify the relationship between the true concentration c^a and J, we introduce the well-known Donnan equation:

$$\frac{c^+}{c_0} = \frac{c_0}{c^-}, \tag{7.2.31}$$

where c_0 is the true concentration of the salt solution.

Furthermore, electroneutrality requires that (Liu *et al.*, 2010)

$$C_0 + C^- = C^+, \tag{7.2.32}$$

where C_0 is the fixed charges in the gel.

Combining Equations (7.2.28), (7.2.31), and (7.2.32) yields

$$\frac{C_0}{J} + c^- = c^+. \tag{7.2.33}$$

Using Equations (7.2.31) and (7.2.32), we obtain

$$c^+ = \frac{C_0}{2J} + \frac{1}{2}\sqrt{\frac{C_0^2}{J^2} + 4c_0^2}, \tag{7.2.34}$$

$$c^- = -\frac{C_0}{2J} + \frac{1}{2}\sqrt{\frac{C_0^2}{J^2} + 4c_0^2}. \tag{7.2.35}$$

Through the use of the Donnan equation, the function W has been reduced so that it depends on only two independent variables, i.e., $W(J, c_0)$. Additionally, by enforcing the condition of molecular incompressibility as a constraint, the theory determines the true stress as follows:

$$\sigma_{ij} = \frac{F_{jK}}{J}\frac{\partial W}{\partial F_{iK}} - \frac{\mu}{v}\delta_{ij}, \tag{7.2.36}$$

where μ is the chemical potential in the salt solution and can be specified as

$$\mu = -2kTvc_0. \tag{7.2.37}$$

From Equations (7.2.34) and (7.2.35), we obtain

$$\frac{\partial c^+}{\partial J} = -\frac{C_0}{2J^2} - \frac{1}{2}\frac{C_0^2}{J^3}\frac{1}{\sqrt{\frac{C_0^2}{J^2} + 4c_0^2}}, \tag{7.2.38}$$

$$\frac{\partial c^-}{\partial J} = \frac{C_0}{2J^2} - \frac{1}{2}\frac{C_0^2}{J^3}\frac{1}{\sqrt{\frac{C_0^2}{J^2} + 4c_0^2}}. \tag{7.2.39}$$

Using the function $W(J, c_0)$ and Equations (7.2.34)–(7.2.36), we obtain

$$\begin{aligned}\frac{\sigma_{ij}}{kT/v} &= \frac{Nv}{J}(F_{iK}F_{jK} - \delta_{ij}) + \left(\log\frac{J-1}{J} + \frac{1}{J} + \frac{\chi}{J^2} + 2\nu c_0\right)\delta_{ij} \\ &\quad + \nu\delta_{ij}\left[c^+\left(\log\frac{c^+}{c_0} - 1\right) + c^-\left(\log\frac{c^-}{c_0} - 1\right)\right. \\ &\quad \left. + J\left(\frac{\partial c^+}{\partial J}\log\frac{c^+}{c_0} + \frac{\partial c^-}{\partial J}\log\frac{c^-}{c_0}\right)\right].\end{aligned} \tag{7.2.40}$$

The model described is capable of accurately representing the mechanical deformation of salt concentration-sensitive gels, encompassing phenomena such as free swelling and constrained swelling. Moreover, the model can be seamlessly integrated into the FEM code through the utilization of an ABAQUS subroutine. This integration enables numerical simulations and analysis of the mechanical behavior exhibited by the gel, facilitating comprehensive investigations and evaluations.

7.2.4 *Constitutive Model of pH-Sensitive Hydrogel*

For pH-sensitive hydrogels, which comprise soft materials containing acidic groups in equilibrium with an aqueous solution and experiencing mechanical forces, it is necessary to incorporate an additional term in the free-energy density function related to the dissociation of acidic groups. This consideration results in the following expression for the free-energy density (Marcombe *et al.*, 2010):

$$W = W_{\text{str}} + W_{\text{mix}} + W_{\text{ion}} + W_{\text{dis}}, \tag{7.2.41}$$

where W_{dis} is due to dissociating the acidic groups.

It should be noted that, due to the consideration of acidic groups, the W_{ion} of a pH-sensitive gel is more complicated than that of a salt concentration-sensitive gel, namely,

$$\begin{aligned} W_{\text{ion}} = kT \Bigg[& C^{\text{H}^+} \left(\log \frac{C^{\text{H}^+}}{c_{\text{ref}}^{\text{H}^+} J} - 1 \right) + C^+ \left(\log \frac{C^+}{c_{\text{ref}}^+ J} - 1 \right) \\ & + C^- \left(\log \frac{C^-}{c_{\text{ref}}^- J} - 1 \right) \Bigg], \end{aligned} \tag{7.2.42}$$

where C^{H^+} is the nominal concentration of the hydrogen ion.

The free-energy density part due to the dissociation of the acidic groups is taken to be

$$\begin{aligned} W_{\text{dis}} = kT & \left[C^{\text{A}^-} \log \left(\frac{C^{\text{A}^-}}{C^{\text{A}^-} + C^{\text{AH}}} \right) + C^{\text{AH}} \log \left(\frac{C^{\text{AH}}}{C^{\text{A}^-} + C^{\text{AH}}} \right) \right] \\ & + \gamma C^{\text{A}^-}, \end{aligned} \tag{7.2.43}$$

where γ is the increase in the enthalpy when an acidic group dissociates and C^{A^-} and C^{AH} are the nominal concentrations of the fixed charges and the associated acidic groups, respectively.

Using the function W specified above in Equation (7.2.41), the stress becomes

$$\frac{\sigma_{ij}}{kT/v} = \frac{Nv}{J}(F_{iK}F_{jK} - \delta_{ij}) + \left(\log\frac{J-1}{J} + \frac{1}{J} + \frac{\chi}{J^2}\right)\delta_{ij}$$
$$- v\delta_{ij}[c^{\mathrm{H}^+} + c^+ + c^- - \bar{c}^{\mathrm{H}^+} - \bar{c}^+ - \bar{c}^-], \qquad (7.2.44)$$

where $\bar{c}^{\mathrm{H}^+}, \bar{c}^+$, and $\bar{c}^-$ are the concentrations of the external solution.

7.2.5 *Constitutive Model of Temperature-Sensitive Hydrogel*

Temperature-sensitive hydrogels, commonly known as PNIPAM hydrogels, are a specific type of hydrogel that exhibits substantial changes in volume in response to temperature changes. These hydrogels are characterized by their transparency, elasticity, and high flexibility. One of their remarkable properties is the abrupt macromolecular transition from a hydrophilic structure to a hydrophobic one at the lower critical solution temperature (LCST). As the temperature surpasses the critical threshold, the hydrogel undergoes a phase transition. This temperature-dependent transition results in a discontinuous change in the equilibrium water content within the hydrogel, as illustrated in Figure 7.2.3.

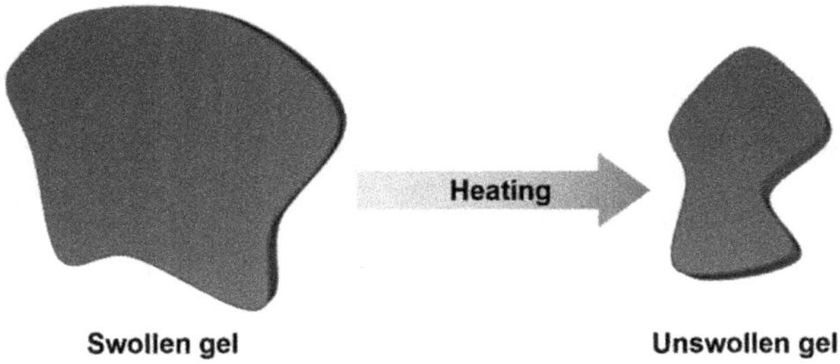

Figure 7.2.3 Schematic illustration of the swollen state to the collapsed state of temperature sensitive hydrogel.

The free-energy density of temperature-sensitive hydrogels is similar to that of neutral gels, which includes the contributions from stretch and mixing. However, the key difference lies in the presence of an interaction parameter, denoted as χ. This parameter is experimentally determined and plays a crucial role in the free-energy density function, as described by Huggins (1964):

$$\chi = \chi_0 + \chi_1\phi, \tag{7.2.45}$$

where $\chi_0 = A_0 + B_0T$, $\chi_1 = A_1 + B_1T$, and $\phi = \frac{1}{1+\nu C}$.

Here, for the PNIPAM gel, we use the following fitting parameters (Afroze *et al.*, 2000):

$$A_0 = -12.947, \quad B_0 = 0.04496\,\mathrm{K}^{-1}, \quad A_1 = 17.92, \quad \text{and}$$
$$B_1 = -0.0569\,\mathrm{K}^{-1}. \tag{7.2.46}$$

We can also adopt the differential equation to obtain nominal stress. For the purpose of this study, we only consider a uniaxial loading case in direction 3. In this case,

$$\lambda_1 = \lambda_2 = \sqrt{\frac{V}{V_0\lambda_3}}, \tag{7.2.47}$$

where V is the volume of the gel and V_0 is the volume in the referential state.

Under uniaxial load, we obtain

$$\frac{\partial W(\lambda_1, \lambda_3, T)}{\partial \lambda_1} = 0, \tag{7.2.48}$$

$$\frac{\partial W(\lambda_1, \lambda_3, T)}{\partial \lambda_3} = s, \tag{7.2.49}$$

where s is the stress due to the uniaxial load.

Combining Equations (7.2.24)–(7.2.27), (7.2.48), and (7.2.49), we arrive at

$$N\nu(\lambda_1^2 - 1) + \left(\frac{V}{V_0}\right)\log\left[1 - \left(\frac{V}{V_0}\right)^{-1}\right]$$
$$+ 1 + (\chi_0 - \chi_1)\left(\frac{V}{V_0}\right)^{-1} + 2\chi_1\left(\frac{V}{V_0}\right)^{-2} = 0, \tag{7.2.50}$$

$$\frac{1}{\lambda_3}\left\{N\nu(\lambda_3^2-1)+\left(\frac{V}{V_0}\right)\log\left[1-\left(\frac{V}{V_0}\right)^{-1}\right]\right.$$
$$\left.+1+(\chi_0-\chi_1)\left(\frac{V}{V_0}\right)^{-1}+2\chi_1\left(\frac{V}{V_0}\right)^{-2}\right\}=\frac{s\nu}{kT}. \quad (7.2.51)$$

Indeed, a distinctive characteristic of temperature-sensitive hydrogels is the occurrence of a phase transition. Unlike other types of gels discussed previously, temperature-sensitive hydrogels undergo a transition between different phases. When subjected to uniaxial loading, a stress can be attributed to two distinct stretches, representing the process of phase transition within the hydrogel. This unique behavior arises from the structural changes induced by temperature and the corresponding variations in the hydrogel's equilibrium water content.

7.2.6 *Constitutive Model of Photothermal-Sensitive Hydrogels*

The photothermal-sensitive gel is a type of temperature-sensitive hydrogel that contains light-absorbing nanoparticles, as shown in Figure 7.2.4. In the case of a photothermal-sensitive gel, an additional term for the free-energy density, W_p, is introduced into the

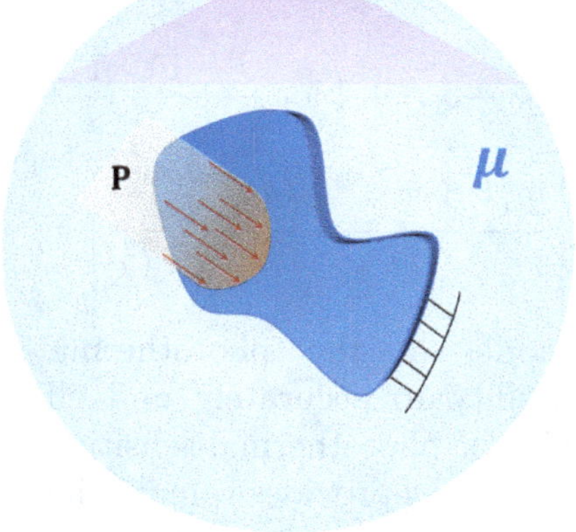

Figure 7.2.4 A hydrogel domain subjected to external weight **P**, exposed to an external solvent of fixed chemical potential μ, and irradiated with light.

free-energy density function of the temperature-sensitive hydrogel. This is due to the photochemical reactions that occur within the gel, as described by Toh *et al.* (2014a):

$$W = W_{\rm str} + W_{\rm mix} + W_{\rm p}, \tag{7.2.52}$$

where $W_{\rm p}$ is the free energy of the photochemical reaction.

The free-energy density $W_{\rm p}$ resulting from photochemical reactions is expressed as

$$W_{\rm p} = C_{\rm p}\left[hf + kT\log\left(\frac{C_{\rm p}}{C_{\rm g,0}}\right)\right], \tag{7.2.53}$$

where hf corresponds to the energy transition of an electron into the excited state and the logarithmic term corresponds to the entropy changes associated with the transition; $C_{\rm p}$ and $C_{\rm g,0}$ are considered nominal reference values, given that the concentration of excited particles is low ($C_{\rm p}/C_{\rm g,0} \sim 10^{-10}$).

$C_{\rm p}$ can be expressed in terms of swelling ratio and light intensity:

$$C_{\rm p} = \left[\frac{c^{(\rm w)}}{J} + \frac{c^{(\rm network)} - c^{(\rm w)}}{J^2}\right]\frac{\alpha_{\rm c} I_0}{hf}, \tag{7.2.54}$$

where $c^{(\rm w)}$ and $c^{(\rm network)}$ are the volumetric heat capacities of water and the network, respectively, $\alpha_{\rm c}$ is the proportionality constant related to the heat capacity of the gel, and I_0 is the light intensity.

Using the function W specified above, Equation (7.2.27) becomes

$$\begin{aligned}\frac{\sigma_{ij}}{kT/v} &= \frac{Nv}{J}(F_{iK}F_{jK} - \delta_{ij}) + \left(\log\frac{J-1}{J} + \frac{1}{J} + \frac{\chi_0 - \chi_1}{J^2} + \frac{\chi_1}{J^3}\right)\delta_{ij} \\ &\quad + \nu\frac{\alpha_{\rm c} I_0}{hf}\left[\frac{2(c^{(\rm network)} - c^{(\rm w)})}{J^3} + \frac{c^{(\rm w)}}{J^2}\right]\delta_{ij} - \frac{\mu}{kT}\delta_{ij}\end{aligned} \tag{7.2.55}$$

The developed model of the photothermal-sensitive gel has demonstrated its ability to accurately and efficiently predict the deformation behavior of photothermal-sensitive gels, even for complex geometries. This model provides valuable insights and predictive capabilities for understanding and designing photothermal-sensitive gels in various applications.

7.2.7 *The Constitutive Model of Magnetic-Sensitive Hydrogels*

Magnetic-sensitive hydrogels, which incorporate magnetic nanoparticles, such as superparamagnetic iron oxide nanoparticles (SPIONs), have garnered significant interest from researchers due to their remarkable capacity for substantial deformations under remote control. Extensive studies conducted by Hu *et al.* (2018) and Zhao *et al.* (2019) have explored and demonstrated the potential of magnetic-sensitive gels in achieving precise shape changes and actuation through the application of external magnetic fields.

Referring to Figure 7.2.5, a hydrogel is subjected to geometrical constraints and is influenced by a body force f_i and traction T_i. It is maintained at a specific chemical potential μ. Additionally, a wire carrying alternating current I is placed nearby, generating a magnetic field B within the gel. In this scenario, the work done on the gel is attributed to the mechanical load $P\delta l$, the solvent $\mu\delta N$, and the magnetic field $B\delta M$.

To enhance the model for magnetic-sensitive gels, we can further extend the approach by incorporating a term related to the magnetization. This term takes the response of the gel to the magnetic field into account, which is an important factor in capturing

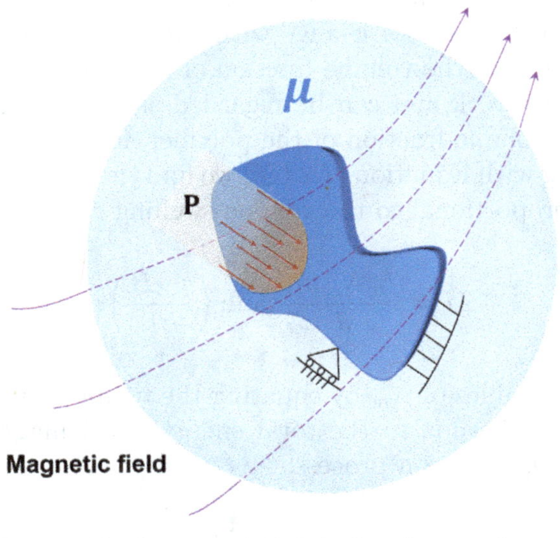

Figure 7.2.5 External loads on a magnetic hydrogel exposed to a magnetic field.

the unique behavior and deformation characteristics exhibited by magnetic-sensitive hydrogels:

$$W = W_{\mathrm{str}}(F_{iK}) + W_{\mathrm{mix}}(C) + W_{\mathrm{mag}}(M). \tag{7.2.56}$$

We assume the simplest case of a paramagnetic system with a spin 1/2 ground state and no orbital angular momentum. Under this assumption, W_{mag} has the following form:

$$W_{\mathrm{mag}} = -N_{\mathrm{m}}kT\left\{\log\left[2\cosh\left(\frac{\mu_{\mathrm{B}}B}{kT}\right)\right]\right\}, \tag{7.2.57}$$

where N_{m} is the number of magnetic particles per unit reference volume.

In a gel with SPIONs, the magnetization is proportional to the magnetic particle concentration and takes the form of a hyperbolic tangent function (Stöhr and Siegmann, 2006), i.e.,

$$M = \phi_{\mathrm{m}}N_{\mathrm{m}}\mu_{\mathrm{B}}\tanh\left(\frac{\mu_{\mathrm{B}}B}{kT}\right). \tag{7.2.58}$$

Given that ϕ_{m}, the concentration of magnetic particles within the polymer network, does not change with swelling, we can write $f_{\mathrm{m}} + f_{\mathrm{p}} = 1$, where f_{m} is the volume fraction of magnetic particles within the polymer network and can be regarded as a material parameter and f_{p} is the volume fraction of the polymer network.

Combining with Equation (7.2.58), we find that the magnetization is inversely proportional to the volume swelling ratio J:

$$M = \frac{f_{\mathrm{m}}N_{\mathrm{m}}\mu_{\mathrm{B}}}{J}\tanh\left(\frac{\mu_{\mathrm{B}}B}{kT}\right). \tag{7.2.59}$$

We obtain the values of N_{m} by equating the temperature rise during magnetic hyperthermia to the total energy of all magnetic dipoles during the magnetization process:

$$N_{\mathrm{m}}\mu_{\mathrm{B}}B\tanh\left(\frac{\mu_{\mathrm{B}}B}{kT}\right) = \rho c\Delta\theta. \tag{7.2.60}$$

where $\Delta\theta$ is the temperature difference and, for SPION gels, $\rho = 1480\,\mathrm{kg}\cdot\mathrm{m}^{-3}$ and $c \approx 2230\,\mathrm{J}\cdot\mathrm{kg}^{-1}\cdot\mathrm{K}^{-1}$. The nominal stress is thus

$$\begin{aligned}\frac{s_{iK}}{kT_0/v} &= N\nu\frac{T}{T_0}(F_{iK} - H_{iK}) \\ &\quad + \frac{T}{T_0}\left[\log\left(\frac{J-1}{J}\right) + \frac{1}{J} + \frac{\chi_0 - \chi_1}{J^2} + \frac{2\chi_1}{J^3}\right] JH_{iK} \\ &\quad - \bar{\mu}^{\mathrm{s}} JH_{iK} + N_{\mathrm{m}}\nu f_{\mathrm{m}}\frac{\bar{B}\tanh\left(\bar{B}\frac{T_0}{T}\right)}{J^2} JH_{iK}. \end{aligned} \tag{7.2.61}$$

where $F_{iK}H_{jK} = \delta_{ij}$ and $\overline{B} = \frac{\mu^{\mathrm{s}} B_{\mathrm{mag}}}{k_B T}$ is the dimensionless strength of the magnetic field.

We have discussed above the constitutive models of various types of hydrogels. These developed models have demonstrated their effectiveness in accurately and efficiently predicting the deformation behavior of different types of gels, even in complex geometries. By incorporating the appropriate energy density functions and considering specific stimuli or factors, such as salt concentration, pH, temperature, photochemical reaction, and magnetic field, these models enable a comprehensive understanding of the mechanical response and deformation of hydrogels. These predictions are valuable for various applications and engineering designs involving hydrogel materials.

7.3 Constitutive Models of Shape Memory Polymers

As a rapidly emerging type of smart material, SMPs have garnered significant research interest and found extensive applications in various industrial sectors over the past few decades. To comprehensively investigate the mechanical behavior and underlying mechanisms of SMP structures, it is crucial to propose robust and suitable constitutive models that accurately describe the SME. SMPs, unlike other shape memory materials, can be triggered by diverse stimuli such as light, electricity, water/moisture, and magnetism. While each type of SMP requires specific considerations for its unique external stimulus effects, the intrinsic deformation mechanisms of SMPs generally follow similar principles to those of thermally induced SMPs.

Therefore, most theoretical studies on SMP materials have focused on thermally induced SMPs.

The examination and understanding of thermally induced SMPs can be approached through various methods, including investigating stress–strain relationships under different conditions and their dependence on temperature, time, strain rate, and other factors. Constitutive models for thermally induced SMPs can generally be classified into two categories: rheological models based on viscoelastic theory, with rate- or temperature-dependent property parameters, and micromechanical phenomenological models, which are based on the concept of phase transition. In the following sections, we discuss the constitutive models of SMPs from these two perspectives.

Additionally, we also delve into the constitutive model of water-triggered shape memory hydrogels (SMHs) in this section.

7.3.1 *Rheological Models of Shape Memory Polymer*

Rheological models constitute an important and valuable approach to studying SMPs that exhibit thermally induced behavior. This model incorporates temperature-dependent viscosity and modulus parameters, allowing for a comprehensive understanding of SMPs' complex response. By utilizing multiple springs and dashpot elements, this model accurately captures the SMEs demonstrated by SMPs. Additionally, it effectively characterizes the viscoelastic properties of SMPs, including creep and stress relaxation. The temperature dependence of the model parameters enables the evaluation of mechanical properties that vary with temperature, time, strain rate, and other relevant factors. Overall, rheological models provide a robust framework for analyzing the behavior of SMPs and their response to thermal stimuli.

7.3.1.1 *Basic viscoelastic model*

The earlier researchers laid the foundation for describing the thermomechanical behavior of SMPs by utilizing linear viscoelastic models and making appropriate modifications. Tobushi *et al.* (1997) introduced a rheological four-element model that combined spring-dashpot elements with a slip unit to effectively capture the thermoviscoelastic behavior of SMPs undergoing small 1D deformations.

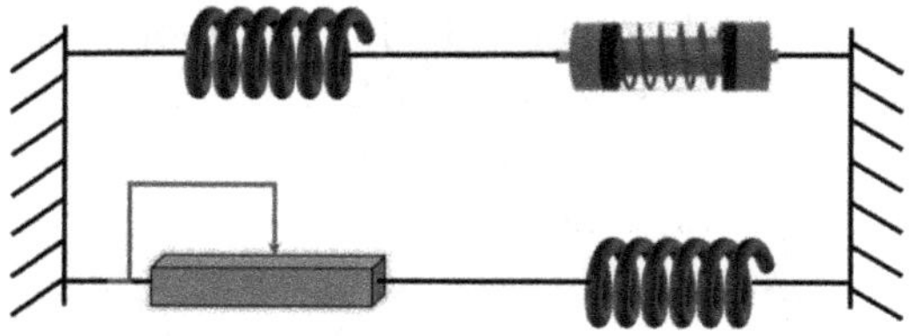

Figure 7.3.1 The basic four-element model of SMPs.

Figure 7.3.1 illustrates the utilization of a standard linear viscoelastic model with spring-dashpot elements to characterize the linear viscoelasticity and overall mechanical behavior of SMPs. These models provided a valuable framework for understanding and analyzing the mechanical response of SMPs in early studies.

Meanwhile, the slip mechanism, resulting from internal friction, is introduced to describe the creep recovery strain above and below the glass transition temperature region. In addition to capturing the general viscoelastic behavior using these elements, the thermal expansion due to temperature changes during a complete thermal cycle is also taken into account in this constitutive model. The stress–strain relationship for this model can be expressed as follows:

$$\dot{\varepsilon} = \frac{\dot{\sigma}}{E} + \frac{\sigma}{\eta} - \frac{\varepsilon - \varepsilon_{\mathrm{s}}}{\tau} + \alpha \dot{T}, \tag{7.3.1}$$

$$\varepsilon_{\mathrm{s}} = c(\varepsilon_{\mathrm{c}} - \varepsilon_{\mathrm{l}}), \tag{7.3.2}$$

where $\dot{\sigma}$, $\dot{\varepsilon}$, and $\dot{T}$ denote the stress rate, strain rate, temperature rate, respectively. The key material parameters E, η, τ, and α are the elastic modulus, viscosity, relaxation time, and heat expansion coefficient, respectively, while ε_{c} and ε_{l} denote the creep strain and its critical value, respectively. Besides, based on the observation of creep tests of SMPs, the irrecoverable creep strain ε_{s} due to slip (when force is greater than internal friction) is assumed to be in a proportional relationship with the creep strain.

To calibrate the parameters of the proposed constitutive model, Tobushi *et al.* (1996a, 1996b) conducted a series of experimental tests on SMPs from the polyurethane series. These experiments revealed distinct mechanical performance while uncovering a general law applicable to SMPs. It was observed that the mechanical properties of SMPs in the glass transition region exhibit significant variation, with material coefficients highly dependent on temperature. Based on the results of dynamic mechanical tests, the elastic modulus E can be described by a single exponential function of temperature, given by the equation

$$E = E_{\mathrm{g}} \exp\left\{a_E\left(\frac{T_{\mathrm{g}}}{T} - 1\right)\right\}, \tag{7.3.3}$$

where T_{g} represents the glass transition temperature, E_{g} denotes Young's modulus value when $T = T_{\mathrm{g}}$, and a_E is the slope of the straight line obtained through fitting of the experiment data. Similarly, the variation curves of other mechanical coefficients, namely, η, τ, α, and ε_{l} (viscosity, relaxation time, heat expansion coefficient, and the critical value of creep strain, respectively) due to the glass transition will basically coincide with those of E. Therefore, to express the deformation performance of SMPs at the glass transition region, all material parameters can be expressed in the same manner as

$$G = G_{\mathrm{g}} \exp\left\{a_G\left(\frac{T_{\mathrm{g}}}{T} - 1\right)\right\}. \tag{7.3.4}$$

Here, the material parameters E, τ, λ, α, and ε_{l} are all accounted for by G and expressed as exponential functions of temperature. G_{g} is the distinctive value of G when the temperature is in the glass transition region, and a_G denotes the corresponding slope of each straight line as observed in experimental data.

The aforementioned constitutive model has been demonstrated to provide excellent agreement with the observed thermomechanical behaviors in experiments for certain SMPs. This linear constitutive model offers a straightforward approach to effectively predicting material properties such as shape fixity, shape recovery, and recovery stress. However, it should be noted that the validity of this simple model is limited to small one-dimensional (1D) deformation cases, as it accurately captures the thermomechanical properties only up to 10% strain. In order to account for relatively large deformations in SMPs, Tobushi *et al.* (2001) introduced nonlinear terms for stress as exponential functions in both the elastic and viscous components within the framework of the earlier linear constitutive equations.

The detailed stress–strain relationship can be expressed as follows:

$$\dot{\varepsilon} = \frac{\dot{\sigma}}{E} + m\left(\frac{\sigma - \sigma_{\mathrm{y}}}{k}\right)^{m-1}\frac{\dot{\sigma}}{K} + \frac{\sigma}{\eta} + \frac{1}{b}\left(\frac{\sigma}{\sigma_{\mathrm{c}}} - 1\right)^{n} - \frac{\varepsilon - \varepsilon_{\mathrm{s}}}{\tau} + \alpha\dot{T}, \tag{7.3.5}$$

$$\varepsilon_{\mathrm{s}} = S(\varepsilon_{\mathrm{c}} + \varepsilon_{\mathrm{p}}). \tag{7.3.6}$$

This new constitutive model adds nonlinear terms of stress as a power function to the previous linear model framework; σ_{y} and σ_{c} correspond to the yield stress and creep limit, respectively. Defined in the same manner as the linear model, the irrecoverable creep strain ε_{s} is assumed to be proportional to the creep strain at a ratio of S. However, a remaining plastic strain denoted by ε_{p} at the recovery stage, which corresponds to the large pre-deformation, must also be considered in the model. Similar to Equation (7.3.1), the material parameters E, $k, \sigma_{\mathrm{y}}, \mu$, $\sigma_{\mathrm{c}}, \tau$, and S involved in this model would be accounted for by a single exponential function of temperature. Other material parameters, including m, n, b, and α, have a weak dependence on temperature and are therefore assumed to be temperature-independent for simplicity. In general, the proposed nonlinear model is applied to calculate several results of different thermomechanical tests and could well express the general properties of the SMPs in the strain range of practical use (up to 20% maximum strain). Besides, this model could effectively characterize the working performance of SMPs, such as their working temperature, SME, tightening force, and response speed, which could be helpful in the design of SMP elements. Similarly, Morshedian *et al.* (2005) combined a Kelvin unit and a dashpot element in series to establish a mechanical model to describe the stress–strain–time relationship of the cross-linked PE SMP.

Inspired by the same framework, Li *et al.* (2015) introduced a simplified three-element model and successfully simulated the stress–strain–temperature behavior of polyurethane-based SMPs during both free and constrained strain recovery processes. This model combines a standard Kelvin element with a spring element in series, resulting in an overall three-element (two springs and one dashpot) model framework. The 1D constitutive equations for this model can be derived as follows:

$$\sigma + \frac{\mu(T)}{(E_1(T) + E_2(T))} \frac{\mathrm{d}\sigma}{\mathrm{d}t} = \frac{\mu(T)}{(1 + E_1(T)/E_2(T))} \left(\frac{\mathrm{d}\varepsilon}{\mathrm{d}t} - \alpha \frac{\mathrm{d}T}{\mathrm{d}t} \right) + \frac{1}{(1/E_1(T) + 1/E_2(T))} (\varepsilon - \alpha(T - T_0)). \tag{7.3.7}$$

This constitutive model was subsequently implemented as a user material subroutine (UMAT) in ABAQUS and extended to a 3D isotropic solid formulation to simulate the shape memory behavior of SMPs. It is important to mention that the parameters, including the glass transition temperature T_g, the coefficient of thermal expansion α in units of K^{-1}, the elastic modulus $E(T_g)$ at T_g, the retardation time $\tau(T_g)$ at T_g, and the viscosity $\eta(T_g)$ at T_g, were determined based on experimental data obtained earlier (Tobushi *et al.*, 1997). When compared to the experimental data, this model demonstrates improved accuracy in predicting both free and constrained shape recovery processes. In summary, this model offers efficient prediction capabilities for SMP response using simplified modal parameters, making it highly valuable for various engineering applications.

These early thermo-constitutive models employed the basic dashpot and spring elements, which, through various arrangements, successfully captured the key characteristics of SMP material's mechanical behavior. These simple yet effective models provide significant convenience for basic modeling and simulation needs in various engineering applications.

7.3.1.2 *Thermoviscoelastic models of SMPs*

Although previous models based on well-known standard linear viscoelastic elements provide a simple method to quantitatively represent the general mechanical properties of SMPs, these constitutive models mainly focus on infinitesimal strains. In order to account for large strain deformation behaviors and consider the viscoelastic properties and thermomechanical considerations of SMPs, Diani *et al.* (2006) developed a 3D thermoviscoelastic constitutive model. In this model, the deformation change during a typical thermomechanical loading cycle of the SMP is correlated with changes in entropy and internal energy. Based on thermodynamics, the Helmholtz free energy of the SMP is decomposed as follows:

$$W = U(\mathbf{F}^{e}) - \eta_0(\mathbf{F})T, \tag{7.3.8}$$

where the entropy η_0 is dependent on the total deformation gradient $\mathbf{F}$, and the internal energy is simply a function of viscous deformation $\mathbf{F}^{v}$ (or, equivalently, $\mathbf{F}^{e}$). The free energy in this model is then applied in a neo-Hookean law, as expressed in Chapter 6, and the Clausius–Duhem inequality is introduced as the thermodynamic requirement for the evolution of the overall deformation.

In the 3D thermoviscoelastic model (Diani *et al.*, 2006), which is based on the thermodynamic considerations of SMPs to represent the thermomechanical behaviors in the context of finite strain, the deformation gradient is assumed to be a mixture contributed by changes of entropy and internal energy. Therefore, the deformation gradient could be multiplicatively decomposed into a viscous part and an elastic part on the rheological basis and expressed as follows:

$$\left\{\begin{array}{ll}\mathbf{F}_{\mathrm{m}} = \mathbf{F}^{\mathrm{e}} & \text{(entropy or elastic branch)} \\ \mathbf{F}_{\mathrm{m}} = \mathbf{F}^{\mathrm{e}}\mathbf{F}^{\mathrm{v}} & \text{(internal energy or viscoelastic branch)}\end{array}\right\}. \tag{7.3.9}$$

In the above equation, the deformations from entropy and internal energy are expressed in different ways. Therefore, the total Cauchy stress due to changes in entropy and internal energy can be expressed accordingly as

$$\left\{\begin{array}{ll}\boldsymbol{\sigma}^{\eta} = \frac{E^{r}}{6}\frac{T}{T_{\mathrm{h}}}\mathbf{F}^{\mathrm{e}}\mathbf{F}^{\mathrm{eT}} - p\mathbf{I} & \text{(stress from entropy branch)} \\ \boldsymbol{\sigma}^{U} = \mathbf{L}^{\mathrm{e}}\log(\mathbf{V}^{\mathrm{e}}) & \text{(stress from internal energy branch)}\end{array}\right\}, \tag{7.3.10}$$

where p is a Lagrange multiplier dependent on the boundary conditions, $\mathbf{L}^{\mathrm{e}}$ is the elastic constant tensor assumed to be temperature-independent, and $\mathbf{V}^{\mathrm{e}}$ is the left stretch tensor decomposed from the deformation gradient $\mathbf{F}^{\mathrm{e}}$ or, equivalently, $\mathbf{F}^{\mathrm{v}}$. To compute $\boldsymbol{\sigma}^{U}$, one can introduce the evolution of $\mathbf{F}^{\mathrm{v}}$ based on earlier observations and the mechanical dissipation in the form of a velocity gradient corresponding to $\mathbf{F}^{\mathrm{v}}$ into the equations. All other material parameters, including Young's modulus and thermal expansion coefficient, can be estimated based on actual experimental testing for both above and below T_g. Generally, this model can accurately estimate the remaining strain during stress release and provide a useful framework to predict the thermomechanical response of SMPs undergoing large deformation.

Previous rheological models mainly discussed the mechanical performance of SMPs with temperature dependence. Later on, researchers began to investigate the effects of both temperature and rate on polymer viscosity, including stress relaxation, creep retardation time, and loading rate. Buckley *et al.* (2007) introduced the Kohlrausch–Williams–Watts equation, an empirical formula for the creep curve of rubbery materials, into the thermoviscoelastic models of shape memory materials. This incorporation successfully described the temperature dependence of the polymer's retardation time. This approach can be used to predict shape recovery during the heating recovery process by first measuring the thermoviscoelastic response of SMPs in the linear viscoelastic region.

Subsequently, researchers found that two important factors determined the rate dependence of the shape memory response of amorphous SMPs: structure relaxation in the glass transition region (below T_g) and stress relaxation over the entire temperature range. Structure relaxation mainly describes the rate dependence on temperature and pressure, while stress relaxation focuses on the rate dependence on mechanical loading changes. Building upon a linear thermoviscoelastic rheological model, the nonlinear formulation of the Adam–Gibbs model was introduced to characterize the temperature and rate dependences on structural relaxation. Additionally, a modified Eyring temperature-dependent flow rule was adopted in the model to simulate the stress relaxation response spanning the glass transition region. By considering nonequilibrium processes for both structural and stress relaxation, this model can provide a good fit for the stress-free strain temperature response and the strain rate-dependent stress–strain response of SMPs.

7.3.1.3 *Fractional viscoelastic constitutive model*

Classical viscoelastic models, such as the generalized Maxwell model and the Kevin model, typically involve differential operators of integer orders. These models establish exponential relationships between the relaxation modulus and time. However, many types of SMPs

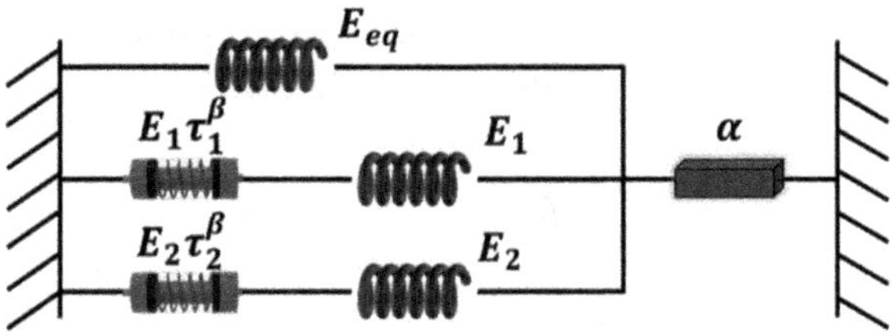

Figure 7.3.2 Schematic diagram of the generalized fractional viscoelastic model.

exhibit relaxation behavior of a power-law nature, which requires a considerable number of material parameters to be determined through experiments. For instance, the previously discussed model by Diani *et al.* (2006) involves 31 material parameters.

In an effort to describe complex viscoelastic behavior with fewer parameters, Pan and Liu (2018) employed the fractional viscoelastic model to systematically investigate the thermomechanical properties of SMPs. They conducted a series of thermomechanical experiments to validate the model parameters. Figure 7.3.2 schematically illustrates the proposed model. The mechanical branches consist of two fractional Maxwell elements (representing the nonequilibrium branches) and a Hookean spring (representing the equilibrium branch), all connected in parallel. The model assumes that thermal expansion occurs independently of mechanical behavior and is defined as follows:

$$\varepsilon_T = \alpha(T - T_0). \tag{7.3.11}$$

Following the rules of fractional calculus, the fractional differential equation for each Maxwell element in this model can be expressed as follows:

$$\frac{\mathrm{D}^{\beta_{\mathrm{FM}}}\sigma_{\mathrm{FM}}}{\mathrm{D}t^{\beta_{\mathrm{FM}}}} + \frac{1}{\tau^{\beta_{\mathrm{FM}}}}\sigma_{\mathrm{FM}} = E\frac{\mathrm{D}^{\beta_{\mathrm{FM}}}\varepsilon_{\mathrm{FM}}}{\mathrm{D}t^{\beta_{\mathrm{FM}}}}, \quad 0 < \beta_{\mathrm{FM}} < 1, \tag{7.3.12}$$

where E is the stiffness of the spring, τ is the relaxation time, and β_{FM} is a decimal between zero and one. σ_{FM} and $\varepsilon_{\mathrm{FM}}$ are the stress and strain in a fractional Maxwell element, respectively.

The corresponding explicit stress–strain relationship can be derived by Laplace transformation as:

$$\sigma_{\mathrm{FM}}(t) = E\int_{t_0}^{t} E_\beta\left(-\left(\frac{(t-\xi)}{\tau}\right)^{\beta_{\mathrm{FM}}}\right)\frac{\mathrm{d}\varepsilon_{\mathrm{FM}}(\xi)}{\mathrm{d}\xi}\mathrm{d}\xi + E_\beta\left(-\left(\frac{t-t_0}{\tau}\right)^{\beta_{\mathrm{FM}}}\right)\sigma_{\mathrm{FM}}(t_0), \tag{7.3.13}$$

$$E_\beta(x) = \sum_{n=0}^{\infty}\frac{x^n}{\Gamma(\beta_{\mathrm{FM}}n+1)}, \tag{7.3.14}$$

where E_β is the Mitting–Leffler function and n belongs to the set of integers. Finally, the total mechanical stress σ_{M} is derived by adding all branches in the model:

$$\sigma_M(t) = \sigma_{\mathrm{eq}}(t) + \sum_{i=1}^{m}\sigma_i(t) = E_{\mathrm{eq}}\varepsilon_M(t) + \sum_{i=1}^{2}\left[E_i\int_{t_0}^{t}E_\beta\left(-\left(\frac{(t-\xi)}{\tau_i}\right)^{\beta_{\mathrm{FM}}}\right)\frac{\mathrm{d}\varepsilon_M(\xi)}{\mathrm{d}\xi}\mathrm{d}\xi + E_\beta\left(-\left(\frac{t-t_0}{\tau_i}\right)^{\beta_{\mathrm{FM}}}\right)\sigma_i(t_0)\right]. \tag{7.3.15}$$

Pan and Liu (2018) also conducted several thermomechanical experiments to validate the model parameters. By shifting the storage modulus–frequency curves measured in Figure 7.3.3, they were able to determine the shift factors.

As demonstrated in Table 7.3.1, the proposed fractional constitutive model requires only 11 material parameters to be determined. This represents a significant reduction in comparison to previous complex models. Despite having fewer parameters, this model is able to accurately capture the thermomechanical behaviors of SMPs, exhibiting excellent agreement with experimental results of shape memory free recovery.

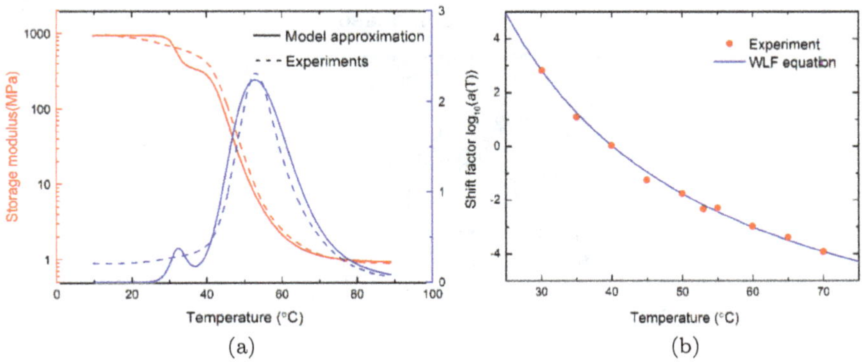

Figure 7.3.3 (a) Storage modulus and tanδ master curves of the SMP obtained by horizontally shifting the frequency sweep tests at a reference temperature of 40°C and (b) WLF equation approximation of the shift factors.

Table 7.3.1 Material parameters which need be determined.

Material Parameters	E_{eq}	E_1	E_2	τ_1	τ_2	β_{FM}	c_1	c_2	T_r	α_r	α_g
Values	0.9 MPa	335.77 MPa	596.56 MPa	0.6065 s	0.0008 s	0.793	9.91	45.23°C	40°C	2.1e−4	3.2e−5

7.3.2 *Phenomenological Models of SMPs*

A typical phenomenological model for SMPs adopts the "meso-mechanical approach," which involves decomposing SMPs into multiple continuous structures, or "phases." Each phase can undergo transformations when subjected to certain external stimuli, such as temperature changes, thereby exhibiting corresponding properties of the SMP. In this type of model, it is commonly assumed that the deformation of the phase above the glass transition temperature T_g is considered "active," while the phase below T_g is considered "frozen."

These phases are assumed to deform in parallel, and the rule of mixtures is applied as a mechanical constraint to calculate the stress response by considering the contributions from individual phases in SMPs. By employing the phenomenological model, the concept of phase transition can be effectively linked with the SME, providing a clearer and more comprehensive understanding of the deformation mechanism in SMPs. This approach allows for a more in-depth

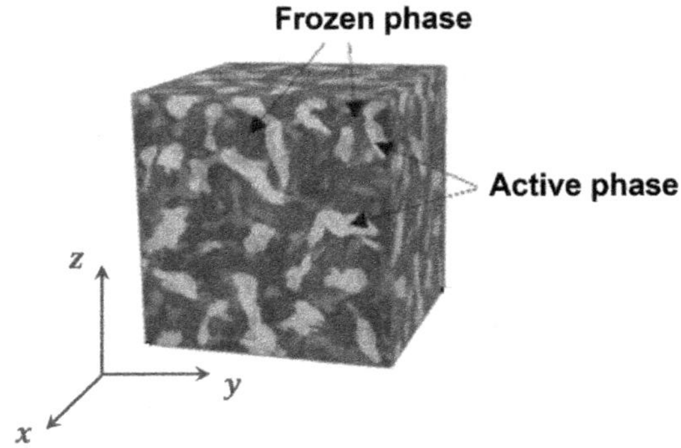

Figure 7.3.4 Schematic diagram of the two-phase mixture of SMPs.

exploration of how SMPs respond to external stimuli and recover their original shapes.

7.3.2.1 *Classic phenomenological constitutive model*

The earliest phenomenological 3D model for temperature-activated SMPs was proposed by Liu *et al.* (2006). In this work, the structure of the SMP is regarded as a mixture of two phases: the frozen phase (dark-shaded region in Figure 7.3.4), where the deformation is primarily influenced by internal energy changes and the high-temperature entropic deformation is completely restricted; and the active phase (light-shaded region in Figure 7.3.4), where the polymer exhibits free entropic conformational motion.

The frozen phase corresponds to the predominant phase of a polymer in its glassy state, while the active phase primarily represents the rubbery state. By adjusting the proportion of these two phases, the extensive conformational motion at high temperatures can be locked within the frozen phase and subsequently released as the temperature is restored. This mechanism enables the complete deformation cycle of an SMP.

In this model, the strain energy is decomposed into thermal, elastic, and frozen entropic (stored) strain components based on the different phases. The evolution of the microstructure is described by utilizing the frozen volume fraction as an internal variable. To simplify the model, the volume fraction is assumed to be solely dependent on temperature, and the stress in the two phases is considered to be equal, even though the SMP as a whole is heterogeneous in nature.

The total strain ε can be mathematically expressed as follows:

$$\varepsilon = \left(\frac{1}{V}\int_0^{v_{\mathrm{frz}}} \varepsilon_{\mathrm{f}}^{\mathrm{e}}(\mathbf{X})\mathrm{d}v\right) + (\phi_{\mathrm{f}}\varepsilon_{\mathrm{f}}^{\mathrm{i}} + (1-\phi_{\mathrm{f}})\varepsilon_{\mathrm{a}}^{\mathrm{e}}) + (\phi_{\mathrm{f}}\varepsilon_{\mathrm{f}}^{\mathrm{T}} + (1-\phi_{\mathrm{f}})\varepsilon_{\mathrm{a}}^{\mathrm{T}}), \tag{7.3.16}$$

where the subscripts "f" and "a" denote the frozen and active phases, respectively. The superscripts "e," "i," and "T" correspond to the average of the frozen (stored) entropic strain, the internal energetic strain, and the thermal strain, respectively. The frozen volume fraction ϕ_{f} is defined by the rules of mixtures. For simplicity, the total deformation is decomposed into three parts; refer to the right-hand side of Equation (7.3.16). The first part is the frozen entropic (stored) strain ε_{s}, and the second part is defined as a mechanical strain ε_{m} that follows the generalized Hooke's law since the nonlinearity is neglected for small deformations. The third part is defined as the thermal strain ε_{T} and assumed to be dependent on the equivalent homogeneous thermal expansion coefficient.

From free strain recovery experiments, the frozen fraction ϕ_{f} can be found to be the strain ratio $\varepsilon^*/\varepsilon_{\mathrm{pre}}$ if the thermal and internal energetic strains are neglected. The modified strain ε^* reflects the real strain stored in the frozen phase, and $\varepsilon_{\mathrm{pre}}$ is defined as the predeformation strain in the preload process. Consequently, ϕ_{f} could be expressed as a phenomenological function of temperature, and the detailed formula can be written as

$$\phi_{\mathrm{f}} = 1 - \frac{1}{1 + c_{\mathrm{f}}(T_{\mathrm{h}} - T)^n \frac{\varepsilon^*}{\varepsilon_{\mathrm{pre}}}} \tag{7.3.17}$$

where the two variables c_{f} and n are dependent on temperature and can be determined by fitting the strain ratio $\varepsilon^*/\varepsilon_{\mathrm{pre}}$.

It is important to note that in this model, the change in ϕ_{f} (frozen volume fraction) is solely dependent on temperature, while the influence of the cooling or heating rate is neglected. Furthermore, the Young's modulus E in this model is correlated with ϕ_{f}, and its 1D form is expressed as

$$E = \frac{1}{\frac{\phi_{\mathrm{f}}}{E_{\mathrm{i}}} + \frac{1-\phi_{\mathrm{f}}}{E_{\mathrm{e}}}}, \tag{7.3.18}$$

where E_{i} is the modulus corresponding to the glassy state at low temperature and E_{e} the modulus corresponding to the entropic deformation at the rubbery state. Also, E_{i} is considered a temperature-independent constant, while E_{e} is defined as the linear function of absolute temperature $E_{\mathrm{e}} = 3NkT$.

Based on the earlier definition, the overall constitutive equation for SMPs in a thermomechanical cycle in 1D form can be expressed as

$$\sigma = \frac{\varepsilon - \varepsilon_{\mathrm{s}} - \varepsilon_{\mathrm{T}}}{\dfrac{\phi_{\mathrm{f}}}{E_{\mathrm{i}}} + \dfrac{1-\phi_{\mathrm{f}}}{E_{\mathrm{e}}}} = E\left(\varepsilon - \varepsilon_{\mathrm{s}} - \int_{T_{\mathrm{h}}}^{T} \alpha \, \mathrm{d}T\right). \tag{7.3.19}$$

Here, the coefficient of thermal expansion α is defined as $\dfrac{\mathrm{d}\varepsilon_{\mathrm{T}}}{\mathrm{d}T}$, and the parameters ϕ_{f}, E_{i}, and E_{e} can all be derived from curve fitting and are considered only temperature-dependent in this model. For example, for an epoxy resin, the following coefficients can be adopted: $\alpha = 1.42 \times 10^{-6}T - 3.16 \times 10^{-4}(\mathrm{K}^{-1})$, $n = 4$, $c_{\mathrm{f}} = 2.76 \times 10^{-5}(\mathrm{K}^{-4})$, $N = 9.86 \times 10^{-4}(\mathrm{mol} \cdot \mathrm{cm}^{-3})$, and $E_{\mathrm{i}} = 813\,\mathrm{MPa}$.

Overall, this work presents a fundamental framework of a phenomenological model for temperature-activated SMPs, with a particular focus on epoxy resin. It should be noted that the model does not take into account rate dependence or large deformations beyond $\pm 10\%$.

By utilizing 1D experimental data, the function describing the frozen fraction can be determined, providing insights into the micromechanics and underlying physics of the glass transition and the SME. The proposed constitutive model demonstrates the ability to predict the uniaxial stress responses under different thermomechanical conditions, given appropriate fitting parameters.

7.3.2.2 *Phenomenological models of SMP considering rate effect*

Following a similar concept to the previous model proposed by Liu *et al.* (2006), Li *et al.* (2017b) introduced a novel phase-evolution-based thermomechanical constitutive model to describe the shape memory behaviors of amorphous SMPs. In the study, they developed phenomenological models for SMPs that take the rate effect

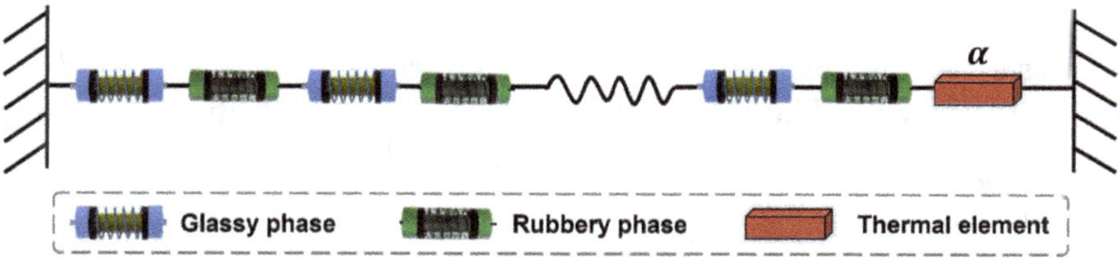

Figure 7.3.5 Schematic representation of the proposed constitutive model.

into account. The detailed framework of the models is depicted in Figure 7.3.5.

The phase transition of materials is a continuous process and can therefore be divided into small domains. Here, each rubbery phase has the volume fraction $\Delta\gamma_{\mathrm{r}}^{i}$ and each glassy phase has the volume fraction $\Delta\gamma_{\mathrm{g}}^{j}$, which correspond to the ith rubbery phase and the jth glassy phase, respectively. The total volume fractions satisfy $\Sigma\Delta\gamma_{\mathrm{r}}^{i} + \Sigma\Delta\gamma_{\mathrm{g}}^{j} = 1$, and the total strain can be given as

$$\varepsilon_{\text{total}} = \Sigma\Delta\gamma_{\mathrm{r}}^{i}\varepsilon_{\text{rubbery}}^{i} + \Sigma\Delta\gamma_{\mathrm{g}}^{j}\varepsilon_{\text{glassy}}^{j} + \varepsilon_{\mathrm{T}}, \tag{7.3.20}$$

where ε_{T} is the thermal strain, $\varepsilon_{\text{rubbery}}^{i}$ is the strain in the ith rubbery phase domain with a volume fraction of $\Delta\gamma_{\mathrm{r}}^{i}$, and $\varepsilon_{\text{glassy}}^{j}$ is the strain in the jth glassy phase domain with a volume fraction of $\Delta\gamma_{\mathrm{g}}^{i}$. During a complete evolution cycle, the rubbery phase domain is assumed to undergo a mechanical deformation $\varepsilon_{\text{r-mechanics}}$ at the loading phase. During temperature reduction, the frozen deformation is locked in the glassy state and is denoted by $\varepsilon_{\text{frozen}}$. The residual mechanical deformation in the glassy phase domain is denoted by $\varepsilon_{\text{g-mechanics}}$. With the above analysis, the contributions of the mechanical strain and frozen strain to the total strain can be expressed as follows:

$$\varepsilon_{\text{total}} = \Sigma\Delta\gamma_{\mathrm{r}}^{i}\varepsilon_{\text{r-mechanics}}^{i} + \Sigma\Delta\gamma_{\mathrm{g}}^{j}(\varepsilon_{\text{g-mechanics}}^{j} + \varepsilon_{\text{frozen}}^{j}) + \varepsilon_{\mathrm{T}}. \tag{7.3.21}$$

For simplicity, the volume fraction of the glassy phase would be replaced by $\gamma = \Sigma\Delta\gamma_{\mathrm{g}}^{j}$; then, the fraction of the rubbery phase can be obtained as $\Sigma\Delta\gamma_{\mathrm{r}}^{i} = 1 - \gamma$. The total strain can be further generalized as

$$\varepsilon_{\text{total}} = \varepsilon_{\mathrm{m}} + \varepsilon_{\mathrm{f}} + \varepsilon_{\mathrm{T}}, \tag{7.3.22}$$

where $\varepsilon_{\mathrm{m}} = (1-\gamma)\varepsilon_{\text{r-mechanics}} + \gamma\varepsilon_{\text{g-mechanics}}$ represents the total mechanical strain in the materials and $\varepsilon_{\mathrm{f}} = \Sigma\Delta\gamma_{\mathrm{g}}^{j}\varepsilon_{\text{frozen}}^{j}$ represents the total frozen strain in the materials.

From these definitions, the author derived a series of equations to describe the mechanical behaviors during a complete thermal mechanical cycle. The constitutive equations of SMPs during cooling and heating processes are summarized as follows:

$$\begin{cases} \sigma_{\text{total}} = \dfrac{\varepsilon_{\text{total}} - \varepsilon_{\text{f}} - \varepsilon_{\text{T}}}{\dfrac{\gamma}{E_{\text{g}}} + \dfrac{1-\gamma}{E_{\text{r}}}} \\ \dfrac{d\varepsilon_{\text{f}}}{\text{d}T} = \dfrac{\text{d}\gamma}{\text{d}T}[1 - f(T)] \dfrac{\varepsilon_{\text{total}} - \varepsilon_{\text{f}} - \varepsilon_{\text{T}}}{E_{\text{r}}\left(\dfrac{\gamma}{E_{\text{g}}} + \dfrac{1-\gamma}{E_{\text{r}}}\right)} \end{cases}. \tag{7.3.23}$$

Under the same boundary conditions, the stress evolution paths during heating closely align with the stress–temperature curves observed during cooling, which is consistent with experimental observations. In their work, Li *et al.* (2017a) proposed a phase-evolution-based constitutive model that shares similarities with previous phenomenological models. However, the frozen strain in these models is assumed to be solely dependent on temperature. In reality, it takes time for the strain to freeze, and this simplification may compromise the reliability of the method.

To address this limitation, Li *et al.* (2017b) also discussed an improved constitutive equation in their work by introducing a time factor into the evolution of the frozen strain. By replacing the frozen strain with the actual frozen strain $\varepsilon_{\text{f-real}}$, the updated model can be expressed as follows:

$$\begin{cases} \sigma_{\text{total}} = \dfrac{\varepsilon_{\text{total}} - \varepsilon_{\text{f}} - \varepsilon_{\text{T}}}{\dfrac{\gamma}{E_{\text{g}}} + \dfrac{1-\gamma}{E_{\text{r}}}} \\ \dfrac{d\varepsilon_{\text{f}}}{\text{d}T} = \dfrac{\text{d}\gamma}{\text{d}T}[1 - f(T)] \dfrac{\varepsilon_{\text{total}} - \varepsilon_{\text{f}} - \varepsilon_{\text{T}}}{E_{\text{r}}\left(\dfrac{\gamma}{E_{\text{g}}} + \dfrac{1-\gamma}{E_{\text{r}}}\right)} \\ \varepsilon_{\text{f-real}} = \varepsilon_{\text{f}} - \int_0^t \dot{\varepsilon}_{\text{f}} e^{\frac{-(t-a)}{\tau}} \text{d}a \end{cases}. \tag{7.3.24}$$

To assess the validity and applicability of the proposed model, Li *et al.* (2017b) conducted simulations to replicate the shape memory performance under various loading modes and boundary conditions. The simulation outcomes were found to align with experimental results, demonstrating that the model is suitable for different types of SMPs.

This model serves a dual purpose: predicting the strain or stress response of SMPs under free strain conditions and reproducing shape memory behaviors under diverse external constraints. It offers the capability to accurately forecast the behavior of SMPs, not only in terms of their mechanical response but also their ability to recover their original shapes when subjected to different external constraints.

7.3.3 *Combining Viscoelasticity & Phase Transitions for SMPs*

We have discussed several representative models of SMPs based on two constitutive modeling approaches, each of which has its own strengths and weaknesses. In order to overcome these limitations, researchers have combined the viscoelastic and phase transition theories to establish a new framework for the constitutive models of SMPs.

One such model, proposed by Li *et al.* (2017a), is based on multiplicative decompositions of the deformation gradient and incorporates the time factor. The molecular mechanism assumed for SMPs in this model is that the cross-linked network of SMPs undergoes reorientation and deformation under external loads. During the cooling process, a reversible phase (secondary cross-links) appears to lock the deformed shape, which then disappears during the heating recovery stage. To depict this mechanism, different constitutive structures are defined separately for temperatures above and below the glass transition temperature T_g, as illustrated in Figure 7.3.6.

In this model, the rubbery phase is considered a simple, isotropic, and incompressible hyperplastic material that takes into account stress relaxation and creep under sustained loading conditions. To represent the behavior of the rubbery phase ($T > T_g$), two incompressible hyperplastic elements and a viscous damper are introduced, as depicted in Figure 7.3.6(a). These elements collectively form the rubbery phase branch of the SMP model.

In the glassy phase, a new reversible phase consisting of secondary cross-links is initiated, which serves to lock the temporary shape of the material when the temperature is below T_g. As shown in Figure 7.3.6(b), the reversible phase branch is represented by springs in parallel with a viscous damper. Consequently, the SMP model in the glassy phase ($T < T_g$) is a combination of the rubbery phase branch and the reversible phase branch.

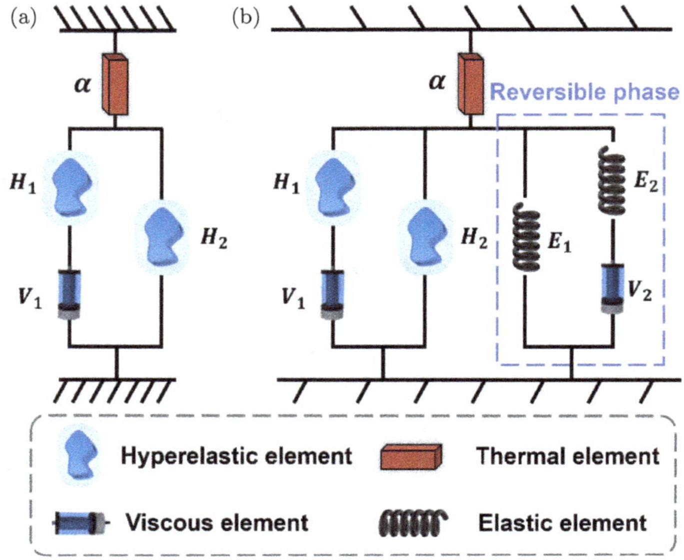

Figure 7.3.6 Schematic representation of the proposed constitutive model: (a) constitutive model for SMPs at $T > T_{\mathrm{g}}$ (rubbery state) and (b) constitutive model for SMPs at $T \leq T_{\mathrm{g}}$ (glassy state).

Accordingly, the Cauchy stress σ of each phase can be decomposed as a combination of different elements:

$$\begin{cases} \sigma = \sigma_{H1} + \sigma_{H2} \quad (\text{Rubbery phase}(T > T_{\mathrm{g}})) \\ \sigma = \sigma_{H1} + \sigma_{H2} + \sigma_{E1} + \sigma_{E2} \quad (\text{Glassy phase}(T \leq T_{\mathrm{g}})). \end{cases} \tag{7.3.25}$$

To represent the distinct structures of the model in each phase, the deformation state of each phase is treated separately. The classic Mooney–Rivlin model is generally employed to describe the free energy of the shape memory in the rubbery phase branch. On the other hand, the deformation gradient in the reversible phase branch is derived using the Hencky strain definition, as introduced by Hencky (1928).

This model was further calibrated using experimental data obtained from polyurethane SMP and Veriflex-E epoxy SMP. The shape memory behaviors under different pre-strain levels and multiple loading conditions were analyzed. The simulation results demonstrated that the model is capable of accurately predicting both small and large strain cases, and it exhibits wide applicability to various types of SMPs.

This relatively comprehensive constitutive model not only incorporates the concept of phase transition but also captures the viscoelastic characteristics of SMPs. It provides a holistic framework for understanding and describing the complex behaviors exhibited by SMPs.

The previous model was developed under the assumption that the secondary phase appears or disappears under certain stimuli. However, further research on polymer phase transitions has revealed that phase transitions can occur multiple times due to transformations between two or more phases. To address this, a novel model was developed by combining viscoelasticity and phase transition theories (Li and Liu, 2018).

In this model, the SMP is considered a mixture of a rubbery phase and a glassy phase. However, unlike the previous model, the rubbery phase is now treated as a viscoelastic material rather than an elastic material. It is represented by a standard Kelvin element and a spring element connected in series. For the glassy phase at low temperatures, where most molecular chains of SMPs are in a frozen state, the model simplifies to a simple spring element, neglecting viscosity.

The volume fraction of each phase in the model represents the number of domains in each phase and varies with changes in temperature. The detailed structure of the proposed model is presented in Figure 7.3.7.

Following a similar derivation process to the earlier model, the total stress and strain of this proposed model can be expressed as

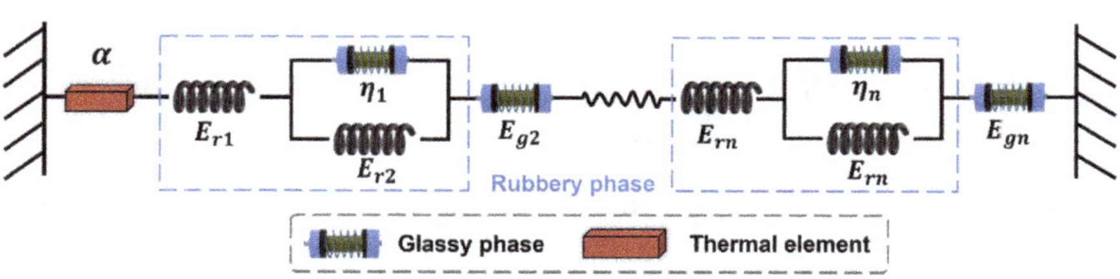

Figure 7.3.7 Schematic representation of the proposed constitutive model: SMPs are assumed to be composed of a thermal element and two types of phase elements. The ratio of these two kinds of phase elements varies with the instantaneous temperature.

follows:

$$\begin{cases} \varepsilon_{\text{total}} = \Sigma\Delta\gamma_{\text{r}}^{i}(\varepsilon_{\text{r1}} + \varepsilon_{\text{r2}}^{i}) + \Sigma\Delta\gamma_{\text{g}}^{j}(\varepsilon_{\text{g-mechanics}} + \varepsilon_{\text{frozen}}^{j}) + \varepsilon_{\text{T}} \\ \sigma_{\text{total}} = \sigma_{\text{r}}^{i} = \sigma_{\text{g}}^{j} \\ \sigma_{\text{r}}^{i} = E_{\text{r1}}\varepsilon_{\text{r1}}^{i} = E_{\text{r2}}\varepsilon_{\text{r2}}^{i} + \eta\dot{\varepsilon}_{\text{r2}}^{i}, \sigma_{\text{g}}^{j} = E_{\text{g}}\varepsilon_{\text{g-mechanics}}^{j} \end{cases}, \tag{7.3.26}$$

where $\Delta\gamma_{\text{r}}^{i}$ and $\Delta\gamma_{\text{g}}^{j}$ denote the volume fraction of the jth rubbery phase and glassy phase, respectively. ε_{r1}, $\dot{\varepsilon}_{\text{r2}}^{i}$, $\varepsilon_{\text{g-mechanics}}$, $\varepsilon_{\text{frozen}}^{j}$, and ε_{T} denote the strain of two springs in the ith rubbery state, the residual mechanical strain, the frozen strain in the jth glassy state, and the total thermal strain, respectively. E_{r1}, E_{r2}, and E_{g} are Young's moduli of the springs in the rubbery and glassy states, and η is the viscosity of the viscous damping element in the rubbery state. In the study, an evolution equation for each step of a SMP thermomechanical cycle was developed, and the model parameters were calibrated using data from a series of experiments, including an isothermal uniaxial tensile test and a stress relaxation test. This model could capture the critical features of SMPs' mechanical behavior as well as the rate dependency of polymers and provide a credible description of the experimental results of a polyurethane SMP under different pre-strains. In particular, the proposed model could fully embody the effects of four factors (stress relaxation, frozen strain, thermal strain, and Young's modulus) on the stress evolution of the cooling step during a SMP cycle. Even so, by considering the glassy state as a pure elastic polymer, the proposed model is only applicable for small deformations, which somewhat dampend its mainstream adoption.

7.3.4 *Constitutive Model of Water-Triggered Shape Memory Hydrogels*

Hydrogels with SMEs, known as SMHs, have garnered significant interest in recent years. These unique hydrogels are capable of retaining a temporary shape and subsequently recovering their initial shape when exposed to external environmental stimuli, including water, temperature, pH, and ion concentration.

One notable advantage of SMHs is their remarkable reversible strain capability, surpassing 2600%, which is considerably higher than the reversible strain exhibited by traditional SMPs. Additionally, SMHs offer several desirable features, such as biocompatibility, self-healing properties, lightweight nature, and responsiveness to multiple stimuli.

As a result of these distinctive characteristics, SMHs hold great promise for a wide range of applications. They can be utilized in fields such as drug delivery systems, actuation mechanisms, soft robotics, and energy storage. The exceptional properties and versatility of SMHs make them valuable materials with exciting prospects for advancement in various domains.

For SMHs that are activated by external stimuli, such as water, there is still a need for a suitable constitutive model. As a result, the development of a new constitutive model for SMHs activated by external stimuli becomes necessary. In this regard, the authors' group drew inspiration from the phase transition theory of SMPs and the Flory–Rehner free-energy theory of hydrogels to investigate the mechanical properties of water-triggered SMHs.

7.3.4.1 *Phase transition and internal state variables*

In the water-triggered shape memory process, the hydrogel's programmed shape at a high water content can be maintained when the hydrogel is dehydrated to a low water content under constraint. Subsequently, the initial shape can be recovered by hydrating the temporarily shaped hydrogel back to a high water content. Throughout this process, the polymer networks of the hydrogel exhibit different states depending on the water content.

At high water content, the polymer networks of the hydrogel exist in a sparse domain due to the presence of a large amount of free water distributed around them. However, as the hydrogel is dehydrated, the free water is lost, leaving behind bound water. This causes the polymer networks to transition into a dense domain. Thus, we assume that the hydrogel with high water content primarily exists in the sparse phase, while the hydrogel with low water content primarily exists in the dense phase. The terms "dense" and "sparse" are used to describe the states of the polymer networks at low and high water contents, respectively.

In this study, we consider the hydrogel as a mixture of two extreme phases, namely the "dense phase" and the "sparse phase," depending

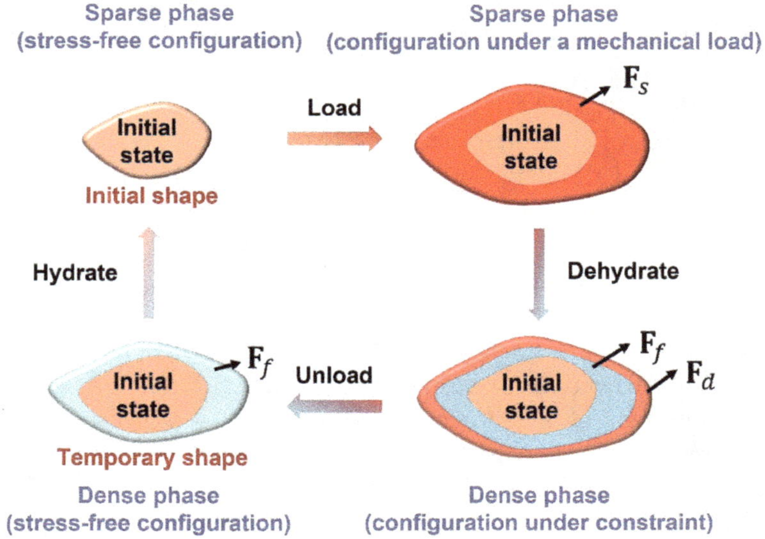

Figure 7.3.8 Schematic diagram of a typical water-triggered shape memory process. $\mathbf{F}_{\mathrm{s}}$ and $\mathbf{F}_{\mathrm{d}}$ denote the elastic deformation gradients of the sparse and dense phases, respectively; $\mathbf{F}_{\mathrm{f}}$ denotes the frozen deformation gradient.

on the water content. As the hydrogel undergoes dehydration, the sparse phase gradually transforms into the dense phase, and vice versa. We refer to this process as the phase transition in hydrogels.

To describe the storage and release of programmed deformation during the phase transition, an internal state variable called the frozen deformation gradient, $\mathbf{F}_{\mathrm{f}}$, is introduced in the dense phase. Figure 7.3.8 illustrates a typical water-triggered shape memory process. Initially, the hydrogel is in the sparse phase and subjected to a mechanical load $\mathbf{F}_{\mathrm{s}}$. As the water content decreases, the sparse phase undergoes a phase transition and transforms into the dense phase.

During the phase transition under constraint, a significant portion of the pre-deformation becomes locked in the dense phase, represented by the frozen deformation $\mathbf{F}_{\mathrm{f}}$. The remaining elastic deformation in the dense phase is denoted by $\mathbf{F}_{\mathrm{d}}$. When the hydrogel is unloaded at low water content, the elastic deformation $\mathbf{F}_{\mathrm{d}}$ in the dense phase is released, while the frozen deformation $\mathbf{F}_{\mathrm{f}}$ is retained. Subsequently, as the hydrogel is hydrated to a high water content, the frozen deformation $\mathbf{F}_f$ is released, resulting in the recovery of the temporary shape to its initial shape.

Based on the above analysis, the relationship between the deformation gradients in the two phases can be expressed as follows:

$$\mathbf{F} = \mathbf{F}_s = \mathbf{F}_d\mathbf{F}_f, \tag{7.3.27}$$

where $\mathbf{F}$ denotes the mapping of material coordinates from the reference state to the current state. To elucidate such SMEs in the phase transition process, we propose an evolution model for the frozen deformation gradient $\mathbf{F}_f$ in the shape memory process, i.e.,

$$\mathbf{F}_f = \begin{cases} I, & \text{initial value} \\ l\left(\frac{\mathbf{F}}{\lambda_s} - I\right) + I, & \dot{\mu} < 0 \\ \text{unchanged}, & \dot{\mu} \geq 0 \end{cases}, \tag{7.3.28}$$

where l is a parameter that denotes the degree of the deformation storage, λ_s is the free-swelling stretch relative to the dry polymer state at the corresponding chemical potential, $\dot{\mu}$ is the rate of change of the chemical potential, $\dot{\mu} < 0$ is the dehydrating process, and $\dot{\mu} > 0$ is the hydrating process. In the initial state, the frozen deformation gradient is assumed to be a unit tensor because there is no frozen deformation. In the constraint-dehydrate process, i.e., $\dot{\mu} < 0$, frozen deformation is supposed to be related to the deformation gradient in the current state in Equation (7.3.28). As a result, the programmed deformation can be stored in $\mathbf{F}_f$ after dehydration under constraints. In the hydration process, i.e., $\dot{\mu} > 0$, the frozen deformation in the dense phase is assumed to be constant. The frozen deformation in the dense phase is released as the dense phase transforms into the sparse phase. Consequently, when the hydrogel completely transforms from the dense phase to the sparse phase, the frozen deformation can be totally released after hydration.

To quantify the degree of the phase transition, the volume fractions of the dense and sparse phases in hydrogel are defined as ϕ_d and ϕ_s, respectively, and $\phi_d + \phi_s = 1$. As mentioned earlier, the hydrogel with high water content is primarily in the sparse phase. Hence, the volume fraction of the sparse phase in this state equals to one, i.e., $\phi_s = 1$, and the volume fraction of the dense phase in this state equals to zero, i.e., $\phi_d = 0$. Here, the volume fractions of the two phases are assumed to be related to the normalized chemical potential $\hat{\mu}$ and specify that the range of the chemical potential of the shape memory process occurs from $\hat{\mu}_\mathrm{l}$ to $\hat{\mu}_\mathrm{h}$. The normalized chemical potential $\hat{\mu}$ is equal to μ/kT. According to the assumption of phase transition, we can obtain the boundary value of ϕ_d, $\phi_\mathrm{d}(\hat{\mu}_\mathrm{l}) = 1$, and $\phi_\mathrm{d}(\hat{\mu}_\mathrm{h}) = 0$. Similar to the phase volume fraction in SMPs [38], we assume that the volume fraction of dense phase ϕ_d is

$$\phi_\mathrm{d}(\hat{\mu}) = 1 - \frac{1}{1 + \exp\left(-\frac{\hat{\mu}-\hat{\mu}_\mathrm{r}}{\mu_\mathrm{z}}\right)}, \tag{7.3.29}$$

where μ_Z is a parameter that characterizes the width of the phase transition zone and $\hat{\mu}_\mathrm{r}$ is the reference chemical potential at the phase transformation center (as shown in Figure 7.3.9). In Equation (7.3.29), the dense phase volume fraction ϕ_d is approximately equal to zero at a high chemical potential $\hat{\mu}_\mathrm{h}$, i.e., the gel is entirely in the sparse phase. In contrast, at a low chemical potential, $\hat{\mu}_\mathrm{l}$, ϕ_d is approximately equal to one, i.e., the gel is in the dense phase (Figure 7.3.9).

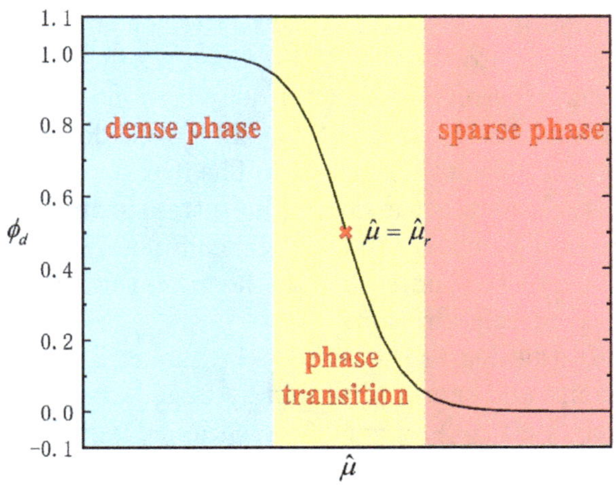

Figure 7.3.9 Relationship between the dense volume fraction ϕ_d and the normalized chemical potential $\hat{\mu}$; $\hat{\mu}_\mathrm{r}$ denotes the reference normalized chemical potential at the phase transformation center.

7.3.4.2 *Constitutive equation of shape memory hydrogels*

We use the total deformation gradient of the polymer network $\mathbf{F}$ and the chemical potential of the solvent μ in the current state as two independent variables for water-triggered SMHs. First, the free energy $W(\mathbf{F}, C)$, which is a function of the total deformation gradient $\mathbf{F}$ and the water concentration C, is developed. Subsequently, free energy $\widehat{W}(\mathbf{F}, \mu)$ which is related to the total deformation gradient $\mathbf{F}$ and the chemical potential μ, is further derived.

According to the constitutive framework for neutral gels (Hong *et al.* 2018), the free-energy function of the SMHs is assumed to be a sum of two parts:

$$W(\mathbf{F}, C) = W_{\text{stretch}} + W_{\text{mix}}, \tag{7.3.30}$$

where W_{stretch} is the energy due to the stretching of the polymer networks and W_{mix} is the energy due to the mixing of water and polymer networks.

To describe the evolution of the stretching free energy during the phase transition process, we divide the stretching free energy of the polymer networks into the sum of the free energies of the two phases, i.e.,

$$W_{\text{stretch}} = \phi_{\text{d}} W_{\text{d}} + \phi_{\text{s}} W_{\text{s}}, \tag{7.3.31}$$

where W_{d} and W_{s} denote the free energies of the dense and sparse phases, respectively. The objective of this model is to demonstrate the modeling of SMEs in hydrogels rather than to investigate alternative forms of hyperelastic materials. Here, the model adopts the well-known free-energy function to describe the stretching free energies, i.e.,

$$W_{\text{d}} = \frac{G_{\text{d}}}{2}(I_{1\text{d}} - 3 - 2\log J_{\text{d}}) \tag{7.3.32}$$

in the dense phase and

$$W_{\text{s}} = \frac{G_{\text{s}}}{2}(I_{1\text{s}} - 3 - 2\log J_{\text{s}}) \tag{7.3.33}$$

in the sparse phase, where G_{d} and G_{s} denote the shear moduli of the dense and sparse phases, respectively. $I_{1\text{d}} = \text{tr}(\mathbf{F}_{\text{d}}^{\text{T}}\mathbf{F}_{\text{d}})$,

$I_{1\mathrm{s}} = \mathrm{tr}(\mathbf{F}_\mathrm{s}^\mathrm{T}\mathbf{F}_\mathrm{s})$, $J_\mathrm{d} = \det(\mathbf{F}_\mathrm{d})$, and $J_\mathrm{s} = \det(\mathbf{F}_\mathrm{s})$. The shear modulus of the sparse phase is

$$G_\mathrm{s} = NkT. \tag{7.3.34}$$

For the mixing free energy of the hydrogel, a general form (Ding *et al.* 2016; Xu and Liu, 2019) is considered as follows:

$$W_\mathrm{mix} = -\frac{kT}{v}\left(vC\log\left(1+\frac{1}{vC}\right)+\frac{\chi}{1+vC}\right). \tag{7.3.35}$$

In this model, the chemical potential of the water μ is used to investigate the change in water content, which is the conjugate variable of the concentration of the water C. The chemical potential is equal to the derivative of the free energy with respect to C, i.e.,

$$\mu = \frac{\partial W}{\partial C}. \tag{7.3.36}$$

Utilizing the Legendre transformation and Equation (7.3.36), a new free-energy function $\widehat{W}$ related to the deformation and chemical potential is introduced:

$$\hat{W}(\mathbf{F},\mu) = W(\mathbf{F},C) - \mu C. \tag{7.3.37}$$

Considering that all molecules in the gel are incompressible, the volume of the gel is equal to the sum of the volumes of the dry network and solvent, i.e., $J = 1 + vC$, and $J = \det\mathbf{F}$. Subsequently, by substituting Equations (7.3.30)–(7.3.35) into Equation (7.3.37), the free-energy function with respect to the deformation gradient and chemical potential can be obtained:

$$\begin{aligned}\hat{W}(\mathbf{F},\mu) = {} & \frac{\phi_\mathrm{d}\mathrm{G}_\mathrm{d}}{2}(I_{1\mathrm{d}} - 3 - 2\log J_\mathrm{d}) \\ & + \frac{\phi_\mathrm{s}NkT}{2}(I_{1\mathrm{s}} - 3 - 2\log J_\mathrm{s}) \\ & - \frac{kT}{v}\left[(J-1)\log\left(\frac{J}{J-1}\right)+\frac{\chi}{J}\right] - \frac{\mu}{v}(J-1).\end{aligned} \tag{7.3.38}$$

The Cauchy stress $\boldsymbol{\sigma}$ is defined as

$$\boldsymbol{\sigma} = \frac{1}{J}\frac{\partial\widehat{W}}{\partial\mathbf{F}}\cdot\mathbf{F}^\mathrm{T}. \tag{7.3.39}$$

Substituting Equation (7.3.38) into Equation (7.3.39), the constitutive relationship related to the total deformation gradient $\mathbf{F}$ and the chemical potential of the solvent μ can be expressed as

$$\frac{\boldsymbol{\sigma} v}{kT}(\mathbf{F},\mu) = \frac{\phi_{\rm d} G_{\rm d} v}{JkT}(\mathbf{B}_{\rm d} - \mathbf{I}) + \frac{\phi_{\rm s} N v}{J}(\mathbf{B}_{\rm s} - \mathbf{I}) + \left[\log\left(1 - \frac{1}{J}\right) + \frac{1}{J} + \frac{\chi}{J^2} - \frac{\mu}{kT}\right]\mathbf{I}, \qquad (7.3.40)$$

where $\mathbf{B}_{\rm d}$ and $\mathbf{B}_{\rm s}$ are the left Cauchy–Green deformation tensors of $\mathbf{F}_{\rm d}$ and $\mathbf{F}_{\rm s}$, respectively, and $\mathbf{I}$ is the second-order unit tensor. To simplify the calculation process, we normalize the stress by kT/v and normalize the chemical potential by kT, i.e., $\hat{\mu} = \mu/kT$. At room temperature (25°), $kT/v = 4 \times 10^7$ Pa. To determine the frozen deformation gradient in Equation (7.3.37), the free-swelling stretch $\lambda_{\rm s}$ can be obtained from Equation (7.3.40) under a free-swelling process. During the free-swelling process of a gel, $\mathbf{F} = \lambda_{\rm s}\mathbf{I}$, and the corresponding stress is equal to zero. By setting the stress in Equation (7.3.40) to zero, the relationship between the swelling stretch $\lambda_{\rm s}$ and the corresponding chemical potential $\mu_{\rm s}$ can be obtained:

$$\phi_{\rm d} G_{\rm d}(\lambda_{\rm s}^2 - 1) + \phi_{\rm s} NkT(\lambda_{\rm s}^2 - 1) + \lambda_{\rm s}^3 \log\left(1 - \frac{1}{\lambda_{\rm s}^3}\right) + 1 + \frac{\chi}{\lambda_{\rm s}^3} - \frac{\mu_{\rm s}}{v}\lambda_{\rm s}^3 = 0. \qquad (7.3.41)$$

Using the Equation (7.3.41), we can derive the free-swelling stretch at any given chemical potential and determine the corresponding frozen deformation gradient. Together with Equations (7.3.27)–(7.3.29), the constitutive relationship in Equation (7.3.40) can be used to describe the shape memory behaviors of water-triggered SMHs.

7.4 Discussion on Different Constitutive Models of Soft Materials

In Section 7.2, the constitutive models of hydrogels were discussed in detail. These models are categorized based on various environmental stimuli, including neutral gel, salt concentration-sensitive gel, pH-sensitive gel, temperature-sensitive gel, photothermal-sensitive gel, and magnetic-sensitive gel. While the theoretical formulations of these models share common basic principles, they differ in terms of incorporating specific free-energy density components that are relevant to each stimulus type.

The neutral gel constitutive model serves as the fundamental model upon which other models are built. It combines the diffusion and large deformation theories. The main difference among the other models lies in the consideration of different free-energy density components. The constitutive model for salt concentration-sensitive gel incorporates an additional term that accounts for the mixing of the solvent and ions into the basic free-energy density. This term captures the stretching of the network and the mixing of polymer chains with the solvent. Building upon the salt concentration-sensitive gel model, the pH-sensitive hydrogel model introduces another free-energy density component that describes the dissociation of acidic groups. This addition enables the modeling of pH-dependent behavior.

The temperature-sensitive gel model shares the same free-energy density function as the neutral gel model; however, the interaction parameter χ is linked to temperature variations. This allows for the representation of temperature-induced effects. The photothermal-sensitive gel model is developed by including a component related to photochemical reactions. This addition accounts for the influence of light on the gel's behavior. Lastly, the magnetic-sensitive gel model incorporates a term related to magnetization, enabling the modeling of magnetic-responsive behavior. In summary, these various constitutive models for hydrogels are distinguished by the inclusion of specific free-energy density components that correspond to the unique characteristics and stimuli associated with each type of gel.

In Section 7.3, detailed discussions on the constitutive models of SMPs were presented. While there are various types of SMPs triggered by different stimuli, we primarily focused on reviewing the theories related to thermally induced SMPs, as the intrinsic mechanisms of thermally induced SMPs share similarities with other types.

The constitutive models for SMPs can generally be categorized into rheological models and phenomenological phase transition models. The rheological models of SMPs are based on the viscoelasticity theories of polymers and can be represented using the spring-dashpot framework. However, these basic viscoelastic models cannot fully capture the thermomechanical behaviors of SMPs. To address this, researchers have made improvements by introducing nonlinear terms and considering the effects of rate and temperature dependences. Rheological models, although requiring complex model parameters that need to be fitted through experimental curves, can provide accurate predictions of the thermomechanical performance, including rate and temperature dependencies, of SMPs.

The classical phenomenological model, based on the phase transition concept, was proposed after careful examination of extensive experimental data and deep insights into the molecular mechanisms of the SME. Liu *et al.* (2006) considered epoxy-based SMPs as a mixture of frozen and active phases, where the volume fractions of these two phases can transform with changes in temperature. This approach offers a clear physical interpretation; however, it is applicable only to certain types of SMPs. Consequently, researchers have further developed this approach to incorporate the large deformation behaviors of SMPs and consider rate dependency in their specific models.

Moreover, several new constitutive models have been introduced, aiming to combine the advantages of the rheological and phenomenological models. These models have a framework similar to that of viscoelastic models of SMPs, and researchers only need to define multiple phases within the system.

Additionally, as hydrogels exhibit SMEs and have garnered increasing interest in recent years, a new constitutive model for SMHs is discussed in Section 7.3. Overall, Section 7.3 delves into the constitutive models of both SMPs and SMHs, covering rheological models, phenomenological phase transition models, and the integration of their respective advantages.

To facilitate the practical application of hydrogels and SMPs in engineering, modeling and simulation methodologies play a crucial role in understanding the deformation behaviors of these materials. In the case of neutral gels, salt concentration-sensitive gels, pH-sensitive hydrogels, and temperature-sensitive gels, robust FEMs and meshless methods have been proposed. These methods have proven effective in accurately predicting the deformation behavior and understanding the underlying deformation mechanisms of hydrogel structures.

However, when it comes to photothermal-sensitive gels and magnetic sensitive gels, there is still significant work to be done in implementing the constitutive models into FEM. Efficient numerical schemes need to be developed to investigate the deformation of complex structures made of photothermal- and magnetic-sensitive gels. Currently, there are limited implementations of constitutive models for SMPs in FEM. Examples include the simplified three-element model and the phase-evolution-based thermomechanical constitutive model. Therefore, integrating these SMP constitutive models into finite element solver packages, such as ABAQUS, by coding them as user material subroutines, such as UMAT and UEL, still requires coding efforts and development.

In summary, while there are established FEMs and meshless methods for modeling the deformation of certain hydrogel and SMP types, further work is needed to implement constitutive models for photothermal- and magnetic-sensitive gels in FEMs. Additionally, incorporating SMP constitutive models into finite element solver packages requires coding efforts to create user material subroutines.

7.5 Summary

This chapter aims to enhance conceptual understanding and explore recent advancements in constitutive models for hydrogels and SMPs. Various types of hydrogels have been examined, with a focus on monophase theories that incorporate different components of free-energy density for a unified approach. Additionally, three main types of SMPs have been introduced, which emphasize their rheology, phase transition, or viscoelasticity. By gaining a better understanding of the mechanics of hydrogels and SMPs, it becomes possible to develop novel applications that surpass the performance of conventional engineering materials. The authors hope that this chapter will serve as a fundamental guide for researchers involved in the mechanics of soft materials, aiding them in further investigations into hydrogels and SMPs, as well as in their efforts toward the research and development of soft machines.

General References

Afroze, F., Nies, E., Berghmans, H. (2000). Phase transitions in the system poly (*N*-isopropylacrylamide)/water and swelling behaviour of the corresponding networks. *J. Mol. Struct.* 554(1), 55–68.

Beebe, D.J., Moore, J.S., Bauer, J.M., Yu, Q., Liu, R.H., Devadoss, C., Jo, B.-H. (2000). Functional hydrogel structures for autonomous flow control inside microfluidic channels. *Nature* 404, 588–590.

Behl, M., Razzaq, M.Y., Lendlein, A. (2010). Multifunctional shape-memory polymers. *Adv. Mater.* 22(31), 3388–3410.

Chester, S.A., Anand, L. (2010). A coupled theory of fluid permeation and large deformations for elastomeric materials. *J. Mech. Phys. Solids* 58(11), 1879–1906.

Chester, S.A., Di Leo, C.V., Anand, L. (2015). A finite element implementation of a coupled diffusion-deformation theory for elastomeric gels. *Int. J. Solids Struct.* 52, 1–18.

Diani, J., Liu, Y.P., Gall, K. (2006). Finite strain 3D thermoviscoelastic constitutive model for shape memory polymers. *Polym. Eng. Sci.* 46(4), 486–492.

Ding, Z., Liu, Z., Hu, J., Swaddiwudhipong, S., Yang, Z. (2013). Inhomogeneous large deformation study of temperature-sensitive hydrogel. *Int. J. Solids Struct.* 50(16–17), 2610–2619.

Ding, Z., Toh, W., Hu, J., Liu, Z., Ng, T.Y. (2016). A simplified coupled thermo-mechanical model for the transient analysis of temperature-sensitive hydrogels. *Mech. Mater.* 97, 212–227.

Flory, P.J. (1942). Thermodynamics of high polymer solutions. *J. Chem. Phys.* 10(1), 51–61.

Flory, P.J., Rehner, J. (1943). Statistical mechanics of cross-linked polymer networks I. Rubberlike elasticity. *J. Chem. Phy.* 11(11), 512–512.

He, Y., Guo, S., Liu, Z., Liew, K.M. (2015). Pattern transformation of thermo-responsive shape memory polymer periodic cellular structures. *Int. J. Solids Struct.* 71, 194–205.

He, Y., Li, Y., Liu, Z., Liew, K.M. (2017a). Buckling analysis and buckling control of thin films on shape memory polymer substrate. *Eur. J. Mech. A/Solids* 66, 356–369.

He, Y., Zhou, Y., Liu, Z., Liew, K.M. (2017b). Pattern transformation of single-material and composite periodic cellular structures. *Mater. Des.* 132, 375–384.

He, Y., Zhou, Y., Liu, Z., Liew, K.M. (2018). Buckling and pattern transformation of modified periodic lattice structures. *Extreme Mech. Lett.* 22, 112–121.

Hencky, H. (1928). Über die Form des Elastizitätsgesetzes bei ideal elastischen Stoffen. *Z. Techn. Phys.* 9, 215–220.

Hong, W., Liu, Z., Suo, Z. (2009). Inhomogeneous swelling of a gel in equilibrium with a solvent and mechanical load. *Int. J. Solids Struct.* 46(17), 3282–3289.

Hong, W., Zhao, X., Zhou, J., Suo, Z. (2008). A theory of coupled diffusion and large deformation in polymeric gels. *J. Mech. Phys. Solids* 56(5), 1779–1793.

Hu, J., Toh, W., Liu, Z. (2018). Study on deformation behavior of magneto-thermal sensitive hydrogels. In *Proceedings of 2018 National Conference on Solid Mechanics*, Harbin, China.

Hu, J., He, Y., Lei, J., Liu, Z., Swaddiwudhipong, S. (2014). Mechanical behavior of composite gel periodic structures with the pattern transformation. *Struct. Eng. Mech.* 50(5), 605–616.

Hu, J., Zhou, Y., Liu, Z., Ng, T.Y. (2017). Pattern switching in soft cellular structures and hydrogel-elastomer composite materials under compression. *Polymers* 9(6), 229.

Hu, J.L., Chen, S.J. (2010). A review of actively moving polymers in textile applications. *J. Mater. Chem.* 20(17), 3346–3355.

Huang, R., Zheng, S.J., Liu, Z.S., Ng, T.Y. (2020). Recent advances of the constitutive models of smart materials — Hydrogels and shape memory polymers. *Int. J. Appl. Mech.* 12, 2050014.

Huggins, M.L. (1941). Solutions of long chain compounds. *J. Chem. Phys.* 9(5), 440–440.

Huggins, M.L. (1964). A revised theory of high polymer solutions. *J. Am. Chem. Soc.* 86(17), 3535–3540.

Keplinger, C., Sun, J.Y., Foo, C.C., Rothemund, P., Whitesides, G.M., Suo, Z.G. (2013). Stretchable, transparent, ionic conductors. *Science* 341, 984–987.

Lei, J., Zhou, Z., Liu, Z. (2019). Side chains and the insufficient lubrication of water in polyacrylamide hydrogel — A new insight. *Polymers* 11, 1845.

Lei, J., Xu, S., Li, Z., Liu, Z. (2020). Study on large deformation behavior of polyacrylamide hydrogel using dissipative particle dynamics. *Front. Chem.* 8, 115.

Leng, J.S., Lu, H.B., Liu, Y.J., Huang, W.M., Du, S.Y. (2009). Shape-memory polymers — A class of novel smart materials. *MRS Bull.* 34(11), 848–855.

Li, Y., Liu, R., Liu, Z. (2018). The dynamic behaviors of a shape memory polymer membrane. *Acta Mechanica Solida Sinica* 31(5), 635–651.

Li, Y.X., Liu, Z.S. (2018). A novel constitutive model of shape memory polymers combining phase transition and viscoelasticity. *Polymer* 143, 298–308.

Li, Y.X., Guo, S.S., He, Y.H., Liu, Z.S. (2015). A simplified constitutive model for predicting shape memory polymers deformation behavior. *Int. J. Comput. Mater. Sci. Eng.* 4(1), 1550001.

Li, Y.X., He, Y.H., Liu, Z.S. (2017a). A viscoelastic constitutive model for shape memory polymers based on multiplicative decompositions of the deformation gradient. *Int. J. Plast.* 91, 300–317.

Li, Y.X., Hu, J.Y., Liu, Z.S. (2017b). A constitutive model of shape memory polymers based on glass transition and the concept of frozen strain release rate. *Int. J. Solids Struct.* 124, 252–263.

Li, Z., Liu, Z. (2019). Energy transfer speed of polymer network and its scaling-law of elastic modulus — New insights. *J. Appl. Phys.* 126(21), 215101.

Liu, F., Cheng, Y. (2018). The improved element-free Galerkin method based on the nonsingular weight functions for inhomogeneous swelling of polymer gels. *Int. J. Appl. Mech.* 10(4), 1850047.

Liu, R., Li, Y., Liu, Z. (2019). Experimental study of thermo-mechanical behavior of a thermosetting shape-memory polymer. *Mech. Time-Depend. Mater.* 23(3), 249–266.

Liu, Y., Du, H., Liu, L., Leng, J. (2014). Shape memory polymers and their composites in aerospace applications: A review. *Smart Mater. Struct.* 23(2), 023001.

Liu, Y.P., Gall, K., Dunn, M.L., Greenberg, A.R., Diani, J. (2006). Thermomechanics of shape memory polymers: Uniaxial experiments and constitutive modeling. *Int. J. Plasticity* 22(2), 279–313.

Liu, Z., Swaddiwudhipong, S., Hong, W. (2013). Pattern formation in plants via instability theory of hydrogels. *Soft Matter.* 9(2), 577–587.

Liu, Z., Hong, W., Suo, Z., Swaddiwudhipong, S., Zhang, Y. (2010). Modeling and simulation of buckling of polymeric membrane thin film gel. *Comput. Mater. Sci.* 49(1), S60–S64.

Liu, Z.S., Toh, W., Ng, T.Y. (2015). Advances in mechanics of soft materials: A review of large deformation behavior of hydrogels. *Int. J. Appl. Mech.* 7(5), 1530001.

Lu, H.B., Wang, X.D., Xiang, Z.Y., Fu, Y.Q. (2019). A cooperative domain model for multiple phase transitions and complex conformational relaxations in polymers with shape memory effect. *J. Phys. D: Appl. Phys.* 52(24).

Lu, H.B., Wang, X.D., Yao, Y.T., Fu, Y.Q. (2018). A 'frozen volume' transition model and working mechanism for the shape memory effect in amorphous polymers. *Smart Mater. Struct.* 27(6), 065023.

Mao, Y., Lin, S., Zhao, X., Anand, L. (2017). A large deformation viscoelastic model for double-network hydrogels. *J. Mech. Phys. Solids* 100, 103–130.

Marcombe, R., Cai, S., Hong, W., Zhao, X., Lapusta, Y., Suo, Z. (2010). A theory of constrained swelling of a pH-sensitive hydrogel. *Soft Matter.* 6(4), 784–793.

Morshedian, J., Khonakdar, H.A., Rasouli, S. (2005). Modeling of shape memory induction and recovery in heat-shrinkable polymers. *Macromol. Theory Simul.* 14(7), 428–434.

Nguyen, T.D., Qi, H.J., Castro, F., Long, K.N. (2008). A thermoviscoelastic model for amorphous shape memory polymers: Incorporating structural and stress relaxation. *J. Mech. Phys. Solids* 56(9), 2792–2814.

Pan, Z., Huang, R., Liu, Z. (2019). Prediction of the thermomechanical behavior of particle reinforced shape memory polymers. *Polym. Compos.* 40(1), 353–363.

Pan, Z., Zhou, Y., Zhang, N., Liu, Z. (2018). A modified phase-based constitutive model for shape memory polymers. *Polym. Int.* 67(12), 1677–1683.

Pan, Z.Z., Liu, Z.S. (2018). A novel fractional viscoelastic constitutive model for shape memory polymers. *J. Polym. Sci. Part B: Polym. Phys.* 56(16), 1125–1134.

Qi, H.J., Nguyen, T.D., Castroa, F., Yakacki, C.M., ShandaSa, R. (2008). Finite deformation thermo-mechanical behavior of thermally induced shape memory polymers. *J. Mech. Phys. Solids* 56(5), 1730–1751.

Reese, S., Böl, M., Christ, D. (2010). Finite element-based multi-phase modelling of shape memory polymer stents. *Comput. Methods Appl. Mech. Eng.* 199(21), 1276–1286.

Tobushi, H., Hara, H., Yamada, E., Hayashi, S. (1996a). Thermomechanical properties in a thin film of shape memory polymer of polyurethane series. *Smart Mater. Struct.* 5(4), 483–491.

Tobushi, H., Hayashi, S., Ikai, A., Hara, H. (1996b). Thermomechanical properties of shape memory polymers of polyurethane series and their applications. *J. De Physique Iv* 6(C1), 377–384.

Tobushi, H., Hashimoto, T., Hayashi, S., Yamada, E. (1997). Thermomechanical constitutive modeling in shape memory polymer of polyurethane series. *J. Intell. Mater. Syst. Struct.* 8(8), 711–718.

Tobushi, H., Okumura, K., Hayashi, S., Ito, N. (2001). Thermomechanical constitutive model of shape memory polymer. *Mech. Mater.* 33(10), 545–554.

Toh, W., Ding, Z., Ng, T.Y., Liu, Z. (2015). Wrinkling of a polymeric gel during transient swelling. *J. Appl. Mech.-Trans. ASME* 82(6), 061004.

Toh, W., Ding, Z., Ng, T.Y., Liu, Z. (2016). Light intensity controlled wrinkling patterns in photo-thermal sensitive hydrogels. *Coupled Syst. Mech.* 5(4), 315–327.

Toh, W., Liu, Z., Ng, T.Y., Hong, W. (2013). Inhomogeneous large deformation kinetics of polymeric gels. *Int. J. Appl. Mech.* 5(1), 1350001.

Toh, W., Ng, T.Y., Hu, J., Liu, Z. (2014a). Mechanics of inhomogeneous large deformation of photo-thermal sensitive hydrogels. *Int. J. Solids Struct.* 51(25–26), 4440–4451.

Toh, W., Ng, T.Y., Liu, Z., Hu, J. (2014b). Deformation kinetics of pH-sensitive hydrogels. *Polym. Int.* 63(9), 1578–1583.

Wall, F.T. (1943). Statistical Thermodynamics of Rubber. *III. J. Chem. Phys.* 11, 527–530.

Xiao, R., Guo, J., Nguyen, T.D. (2015). Modeling the multiple shape memory effect and temperature memory effect in amorphous polymers. *RSC Adv.* 5(1), 416–423.

Xu, S., Liu, Z. (2019). A nonequilibrium thermodynamics approach to the transient properties of hydrogels. *J. Mech. Phys. Solids*, 127, 94–110.

Yuk, H., Zhang, T., Parada, G.A., Liu, X., Zhao, X. (2016). Skin-inspired hydrogel-elastomer hybrids with robust interfaces and functional microstructures. *Nat. Commun.* 7, 12028.

Zhao, R., Kim, Y., Chester, S.A., Sharma, P., Zhao, X. (2019). Mechanics of hard-magnetic soft materials. *J. Mech. Phys. Solids* 124, 244–263.

Zheng, S., Liu, Z. (2019). Constitutive model of salt concentration-sensitive hydrogel. *Mech. Mater.* 136, 103092.

Zhou, Y., Hu, J., Liu, Z. (2019). Deformation behavior of fiber-reinforced hydrogel structures. *Int. J. Struct. Stab. Dyn.* 19(3), 1950032.

Chapter 8

Applications of Continuum Mechanics

Table of Contents

8.1 Introduction

This chapter explores various applications of continuum mechanics, including solid mechanics, fluid mechanics, and the mechanics of soft materials. In solid mechanics, the focus is on the study of deformation and stress in solid bodies subjected to prescribed forces and kinematic constraints. In many cases, small stresses and strains are assumed, allowing the use of linear strain–displacement relationships and Hooke's law. The governing equations, derived using the Lagrangian description, are then utilized to solve for stresses and displacements.

In linearized elasticity, geometric changes are considered negligible, and the squares of displacement gradients are ignored, i.e., $|\nabla u|^2 \approx 0$, implying that the distinction between deformed and undeformed geometries, the second Piola–Kirchhoff stress tensor $\mathbf{S}$, and the Cauchy stress tensor $\boldsymbol{\sigma}$ are not necessary. Furthermore, the current coordinates $\mathbf{x}$ are used instead of the material coordinates $\mathbf{X}$ (and, correspondingly, $\boldsymbol{\sigma}$).

For fluid mechanics, a spatial (or Eulerian) description is employed to formulate the governing equations. In this chapter, we focus on an isotropic, Newtonian fluid, and relevant equations are summarized accordingly.

In this chapter, we also explore examples of large deformations in the mechanics of soft materials. We specifically focus on the response of smart materials, such as hydrogels and shape memory polymers (SMPs), to various stimuli. We begin by discussing the homogeneous deformation of hydrogels, specifically focusing on neutral gels. The behavior of hydrogels under large deformations is examined, considering their unique properties and responses.

Next, we shift our attention to salt concentration-sensitive hydrogels and investigate their behavior under large deformations. The influence of varying salt concentrations on the deformation response of these hydrogels is studied and analyzed. Additionally, we delve into the deformation behavior of SMPs. To study the shape memory process of SMPs, we employ a simple constitutive model. This model allows us to analyze and understand the intricate behavior of SMPs during large deformation scenarios.

By examining these examples, we aim to gain insights into the mechanics of soft materials subjected to large deformations and their unique characteristics.

8.2 Solid Mechanics Problems

8.2.1 *Governing Equations*

The governing equations of a three-dimensional (3D) elastic body involve several relationships and equations. First, there are six strain–displacement relations that relate the six components of the strain tensor $\boldsymbol{\varepsilon}$ to the three components of the displacement vector $\mathbf{u}$. Second, there are three equations of motion that relate the six components of the stress tensor $\boldsymbol{\sigma}$ to the external forces and the material properties. Lastly, there are six stress–strain equations that describe the constitutive behavior of the material and relate the six stress components to the six strain components. Altogether, there are 15 coupled equations involving 15 scalar field variables.

These equations can be solved using various methods, such as theoretical analysis or numerical techniques. In the case of linearized elasticity, where small deformations are assumed, we employ the notation $\mathbf{x} = \mathbf{X}, \boldsymbol{\varepsilon} = \mathbf{E}, \boldsymbol{\sigma} = \mathbf{S}$ to simplify the equations. The governing equations can be expressed in vector form or in Cartesian component form, depending on the preferred mathematical representation.

8.2.1.1 *Strain–displacement equations*

The linearized strain–displacement relations are summarized as follows. Here, the subscripts 1, 2, and 3 denote the x, y, and z of the rectangular Cartesian coordinates:

$$\boldsymbol{\varepsilon} = \frac{1}{2}[\nabla\mathbf{u} + (\nabla\mathbf{u})^T], \tag{8.2.1}$$

$$\varepsilon_{11} = \frac{\partial u_1}{\partial x_1}, \quad \varepsilon_{22} = \frac{\partial u_2}{\partial x_2}, \quad \varepsilon_{33} = \frac{\partial u_3}{\partial x_3}$$

$$\varepsilon_{23} = \frac{1}{2}\left(\frac{\partial u_2}{\partial x_3} + \frac{\partial u_3}{\partial x_2}\right), \quad \varepsilon_{13} = \frac{1}{2}\left(\frac{\partial u_1}{\partial x_3} + \frac{\partial u_3}{\partial x_1}\right),$$

$$\varepsilon_{12} = \frac{1}{2}\left(\frac{\partial u_1}{\partial x_2} + \frac{\partial u_2}{\partial x_1}\right). \tag{8.2.2}$$

8.2.1.2 *Equations of motion*

Next, we summarize the linearized equations of motion under the assumption that the stress tensor is symmetric and $\boldsymbol{\sigma} = \boldsymbol{\sigma}^T$. The equilibrium equations of a deformation body (Figure 8.2.1) are obtained as shown in the following, or the equilibrium equations are further simplified by setting the acceleration terms to zero. Here, $\mathbf{f}$ is the body force vector measured per unit mass:

$$\nabla \cdot \boldsymbol{\sigma} + \rho_0 \mathbf{f} = \rho_0 \frac{\partial^2 \mathbf{u}}{\partial t^2}, \tag{8.2.3}$$

$$\begin{aligned}
\frac{\partial \sigma_{11}}{\partial x_1} + \frac{\partial \sigma_{12}}{\partial x_2} + \frac{\partial \sigma_{13}}{\partial x_3} + \rho_0 f_1 &= \rho_0 \frac{\partial^2 u_1}{\partial t^2},\\
\frac{\partial \sigma_{21}}{\partial x_1} + \frac{\partial \sigma_{22}}{\partial x_2} + \frac{\partial \sigma_{23}}{\partial x_3} + \rho_0 f_2 &= \rho_0 \frac{\partial^2 u_2}{\partial t^2},\\
\frac{\partial \sigma_{31}}{\partial x_1} + \frac{\partial \sigma_{32}}{\partial x_2} + \frac{\partial \sigma_{33}}{\partial x_3} + \rho_0 f_3 &= \rho_0 \frac{\partial^2 u_3}{\partial t^2}.
\end{aligned} \tag{8.2.4}$$

8.2.1.3 *Constitutive equations*

The stress–strain equations of a linear, isotropic, elastic body are presented here:

$$\boldsymbol{\sigma} = 2\mu\boldsymbol{\varepsilon} + \lambda[\mathrm{tr}(\boldsymbol{\varepsilon})]\mathbf{I}, \tag{8.2.5}$$

$$\begin{Bmatrix} \sigma_{11} \\ \sigma_{22} \\ \sigma_{33} \\ \sigma_{23} \\ \sigma_{13} \\ \sigma_{12} \end{Bmatrix} = \frac{E}{(1+\nu)(1-2\nu)} \begin{bmatrix} 1-\nu & \nu & \nu & 0 & 0 & 0 \\ \nu & 1-\nu & \nu & 0 & 0 & 0 \\ \nu & \nu & 1-\nu & 0 & 0 & 0 \\ 0 & 0 & 0 & \frac{1-2\nu}{2} & 0 & 0 \\ 0 & 0 & 0 & 0 & \frac{1-2\nu}{2} & 0 \\ 0 & 0 & 0 & 0 & 0 & \frac{1-2\nu}{2} \end{bmatrix} \begin{Bmatrix} \varepsilon_{11} \\ \varepsilon_{22} \\ \varepsilon_{33} \\ 2\varepsilon_{23} \\ 2\varepsilon_{13} \\ 2\varepsilon_{12} \end{Bmatrix}. \tag{8.2.6}$$

Equations (8.2.1)–(8.2.6) hold true for all problems involving linearized elasticity. The differences between various problems lie in the (a) geometry of the domain, (b) boundary conditions, and (c) values of the material parameters. These factors influence the specific solutions and behaviors of the system, while the underlying governing equations remain the same. By appropriately specifying the geometry, boundary conditions, and material parameters, we can apply these equations to analyze a wide range of linearized elasticity problems.

8.2.1.4 *Boundary conditions*

The boundary condition can be expressed as

$$\mathbf{u} = \hat{\mathbf{u}} \text{ on } \Gamma_u, \quad \hat{n} \cdot \boldsymbol{\sigma} = \hat{\mathbf{t}} \text{ on } \Gamma_{\boldsymbol{\sigma}}, \tag{8.2.7}$$

$$u_i = \hat{u}_i \text{ on } \Gamma_u, \quad \sigma_{ij} n_j = \hat{t}_i \text{ on } \Gamma_{\boldsymbol{\sigma}}, \tag{8.2.8}$$

where Γ_u and $\Gamma_{\boldsymbol{\sigma}}$ are disjoint portions (except for a point) of the boundary whose union is equal to the total boundary Γ, and the quantities with a hat are the specified values. Note that only one element of the pair $(\hat{u}_i, \hat{t}_i)$, for any $i = 1, 2, 3$, may be specified at a point on the boundary.

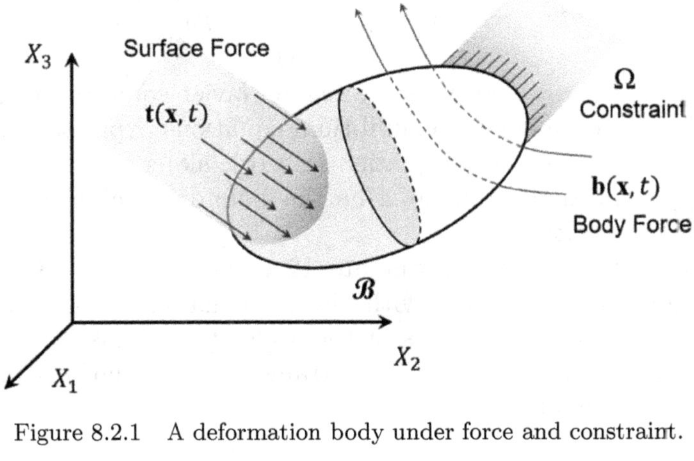

Figure 8.2.1 A deformation body under force and constraint.

In addition to the 15 equations listed in Equations (8.2.1), (8.2.3), and (8.2.5), there are six compatibility conditions among six components of strain:

$$\nabla \times (\nabla \times \boldsymbol{\varepsilon})^T = 0, \quad e_{ikr}e_{jls}\varepsilon_{ij,kl} = 0. \tag{8.2.9}$$

Recall that the compatibility equations are necessary and sufficient conditions on the strain field to ensure the existence of a corresponding displacement field. When a displacement field is given, there is a unique strain field associated with it, as described by Equation (8.2.1), and compatibility conditions are not required in this case. The compatibility conditions come into play when the strain or stress field is given and the displacement field needs to be determined.

In most formulations of boundary-value problems in elasticity, the 15 equations with 15 unknowns are not used directly. Instead, they are often reduced to either three equations in terms of the displacement field or six equations in terms of the stress field.

By substituting the strain–displacement equations into the stress–strain relations and then into the equations of equilibrium, the 15 equations can be combined into three equations.

Thus, we have

$$\mu\nabla^2\mathbf{u} + (\mu+\lambda)\nabla(\nabla\cdot\mathbf{u}) + \rho_0\mathbf{f} = \rho_0\frac{\partial^2\mathbf{u}}{\partial t^2}$$

$$\mu u_{i,jj} + (\mu+\lambda)u_{j,ji} + \rho_0 f_i = \rho_0\frac{\partial^2 u_i}{\partial t^2}. \tag{8.2.10}$$

These equations are known as the Lamé–Navier equations of elasticity, and they represent the equilibrium equations expressed in terms of the displacement field. Equation (8.2.10), along with appropriate boundary conditions, can describe the boundary-value problem of linearized elasticity.

Alternatively, we can formulate 12 equations from (8.2.3) and (8.2.5), and combine them with the six equations from (8.2.9) to obtain six equations in terms of the stress field. This can be done by substituting the constitutive (strain–stress) equations into the compatibility equations.

By following these steps, we can arrive at the final set of equations:

$$\nabla^2\boldsymbol{\sigma} + \tfrac{1}{1+\nu}\nabla[\nabla \mathrm{tr}(\boldsymbol{\sigma})] = -\frac{\nu\rho_0}{1-\nu}(\nabla\cdot\mathbf{f})\mathbf{I} - \rho_0[\nabla\mathbf{f} + (\nabla\mathbf{f})^T]$$

$$\sigma_{ij,kk} + \tfrac{1}{1+\nu}\sigma_{kk,ij} = -\frac{\nu\rho_0}{1-\nu}f_{k,k}\delta_{ij} - \rho_0(f_{j,i} + f_{i,j}). \quad (8.2.11)$$

The six equations in the above set of equations are called Michell's equations, which provide the necessary and sufficient conditions for an equilibrated stress field to be compatible with the displacement field in the body. The traction boundary conditions are valid for this formulation. When the body force is uniform, we have $\nabla\cdot\mathbf{f} = 0$, $\nabla\mathbf{f} = \mathbf{0}$, and Michell's equations reduce to Beltrami's equations:

$$\nabla^2\boldsymbol{\sigma} + \frac{1}{1+\nu}\nabla[\nabla \mathrm{tr}(\boldsymbol{\sigma})] = \mathbf{0}, \quad \sigma_{ij,kk} + \frac{1}{1+\nu}\sigma_{kk,ij} = 0. \quad (8.2.12)$$

8.2.2 *Solution of Two-Dimensional Problems*

In the field of elasticity, there is a class of problems whose solutions, which include displacements and stresses, do not vary along one of the coordinates due to specific geometric configurations, material properties, boundary conditions, and external loads. These problems are known as plane elasticity problems.

Plane elasticity problems can be further categorized into two types: plane strain problems and plane stress problems. In both cases, the governing equations are described by a set of two coupled partial differential equations, which are expressed in terms of two dependent variables representing the two components of the displacement vector.

The key difference between plane strain problems and plane stress problems lies in the coefficients of the differential equations. Although the governing equations for these two classes of problems are similar, the coefficients differ based on the specific problem type.

8.2.2.1 *Plane strain problems*

Let us now consider a structural element that exhibits prismatic features, where one dimension, known as the prismatic axis, is significantly larger than the other dimensions. In addition, the applied

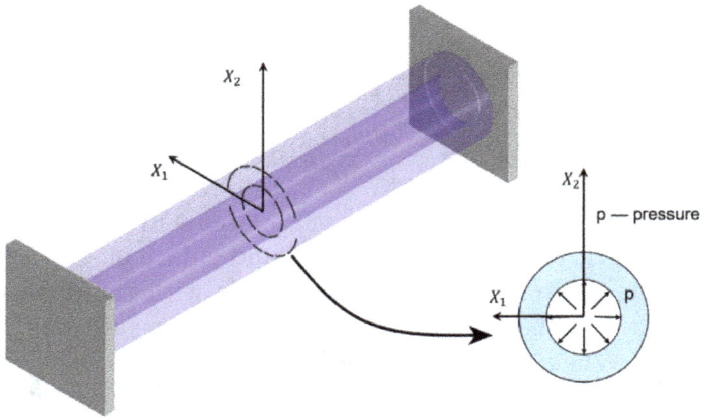

(a)

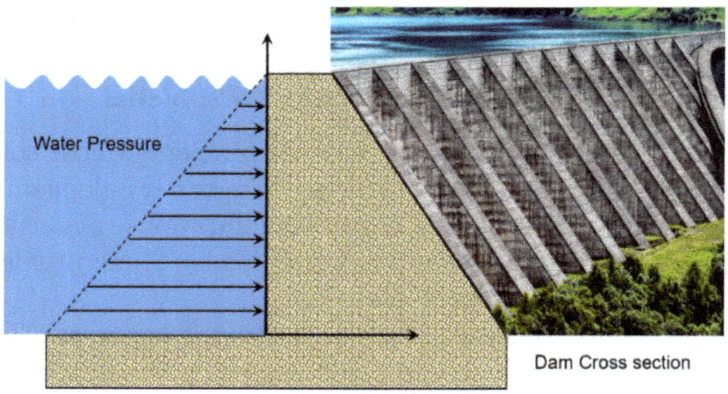

(b)

Figure 8.2.2 Plane strain problems: (a) a cylinder under pressure and (b) a dam.

loads act perpendicular to the prismatic axis, as depicted in Figure 8.2.2(a).

Under these specific conditions, the strain components $\varepsilon_{13}, \varepsilon_{23}, \varepsilon_{33}$ become zero. This state is referred to as the plane strain. Examples of plane strain problems include retaining walls, dams (as illustrated in Figure 8.2.2(b)), tunnels, and similar structures. It is important to note that in order to consider a state of plane strain, the variables involved, such as the applied load, cross-sectional shape, and material properties, must remain constant along the prismatic axis.

Plane strain problems are characterized by the displacement field

$$\mathbf{u} = u_1\mathbf{e}_1 + u_2\mathbf{e}_2, \quad [u_1 = u_1(x_1, x_2), u_2 = u_2(x_1, x_2), u_3 = 0], \tag{8.2.13}$$

where u_1, u_2, u_3 denote the components of the displacement vector $\mathbf{u}$ in the 3D Cartesian coordinate system.

The displacement field can result in the following strain field:

$$\varepsilon_{11} = \frac{\partial u_1}{\partial x_1}, \quad 2\varepsilon_{12} = \frac{\partial u_1}{\partial x_2} + \frac{\partial u_2}{\partial x_1}, \quad \varepsilon_{22} = \frac{\partial u_2}{\partial x_2},$$
$$\varepsilon_{13} = \varepsilon_{23} = \varepsilon_{33} = 0 \tag{8.2.14}$$

The stress components are calculated using the stress–strain relations

$$\sigma_{11} = (2\mu + \lambda)\varepsilon_{11} + \lambda\varepsilon_{22}, \quad \sigma_{22} = (2\mu + \lambda)\varepsilon_{22} + \lambda\varepsilon_{11}, \quad \sigma_{12} = 2\mu\varepsilon_{12},$$
$$\sigma_{33} = \lambda(\varepsilon_{11} + \varepsilon_{22}) = \nu(\sigma_{11} + \sigma_{22}), \quad \sigma_{13} = \sigma_{23} = 0 \tag{8.2.15}$$

or

$$\begin{Bmatrix} \sigma_{11} \\ \sigma_{22} \\ \sigma_{12} \end{Bmatrix} = \frac{E}{(1+\nu)(1-2\nu)} \begin{bmatrix} 1-\nu & \nu & 0 \\ \nu & 1-\nu & 0 \\ 0 & 0 & \dfrac{1-2\nu}{2} \end{bmatrix} \begin{Bmatrix} \varepsilon_{11} \\ \varepsilon_{22} \\ 2\varepsilon_{12} \end{Bmatrix}. \tag{8.2.16}$$

The equations of equilibrium become

$$\frac{\partial \sigma_{11}}{\partial x_1} + \frac{\partial \sigma_{12}}{\partial x_2} + \rho_0 f_1 = 0,$$
$$\frac{\partial \sigma_{21}}{\partial x_1} + \frac{\partial \sigma_{22}}{\partial x_2} + \rho_0 f_2 = 0. \tag{8.2.17}$$

Using boundary conditions, the problem can be solved.

8.2.2.2 *Plane stress problems*

A state of plane stress refers to a condition in which the stresses associated with one of the coordinates, either the third coordinate (z) or coordinate 3, are zero. In this state, the remaining stresses are

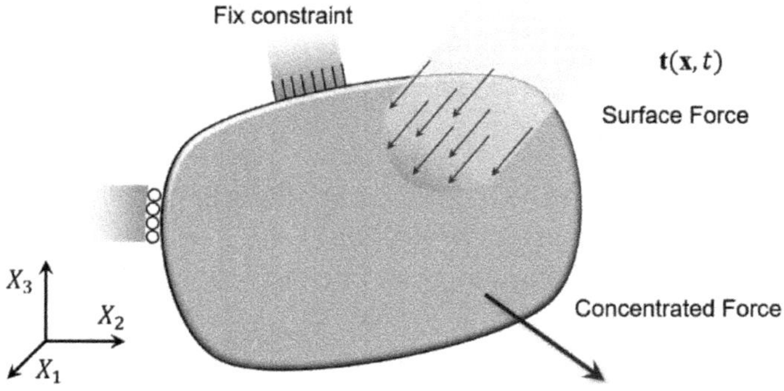

Figure 8.2.3 A thin plate in a state of plane stress problems.

functions of the other two coordinates, namely coordinates 1 and 2 (x and y, respectively):

$$\sigma_{13} = \sigma_{23} = \sigma_{33} = 0,$$
$$\sigma_{11} = \sigma_{11}(x_1, x_2), \quad \sigma_{12} = \sigma_{12}(x_1, x_2), \quad \sigma_{22} = \sigma_{22}(x_1, x_2). \tag{8.2.18}$$

An example of a plane stress problem is provided by a thin plate subjected to loads in the x, y plane that are independent of z, as shown in Figure 8.2.3.

The stress–strain relations of a plane stress state for an isotropic material can be obtained:

$$\begin{Bmatrix} \sigma_{11} \\ \sigma_{22} \\ \sigma_{12} \end{Bmatrix} = \frac{E}{1-\nu^2} \begin{bmatrix} 1 & \nu & 0 \\ \nu & 1 & 0 \\ 0 & 0 & \dfrac{1-\nu}{2} \end{bmatrix} \begin{Bmatrix} \varepsilon_{11} \\ \varepsilon_{22} \\ 2\varepsilon_{12} \end{Bmatrix}. \tag{8.2.19}$$

The equations of equilibrium and boundary conditions for a plane stress problem are the same as those listed for a plane strain problem. It is important to note that the governing equations for plane stress and plane strain differ only in terms of the constitutive equations used for each case.

Therefore, we can unify the formulation for both plane strain and plane stress problems. This can be achieved by introducing a parameter s:

$$s = \begin{cases} \dfrac{1}{1-\nu}, & \text{for plane strain;} \\ 1+\nu, & \text{for plane stress.} \end{cases} \tag{8.2.20}$$

Then, the constitutive equations of plane stress as well as plane strain can be expressed as

$$\begin{aligned} \sigma_{\alpha\beta} &= 2\mu \left[\varepsilon_{\alpha\beta} + \left(\frac{s-1}{2-s} \right) \varepsilon_{\gamma\gamma} \delta_{\alpha\beta} \right], \\ \varepsilon_{\alpha\beta} &= \frac{1}{2\mu} \left[\sigma_{\alpha\beta} - \left(\frac{s-1}{s} \right) \sigma_{\gamma\gamma} \delta_{\alpha\beta} \right], \end{aligned} \tag{8.2.21}$$

where α, β, and γ take values of 1 and 2 (or x and y). The compatibility equations for plane stress and plane strain problems takes the form

$$\varepsilon_{\alpha\alpha,\beta\beta} - \varepsilon_{\alpha\beta,\alpha\beta} = 0, \quad (\alpha, \beta = 1, 2), \tag{8.2.22}$$

or, in terms of stress components,

$$\nabla^2 \sigma_{\alpha\alpha} = -s f_{\alpha,\alpha}. \tag{8.2.23}$$

Comparing the constitutive equations of plane strain and plane stress, it is clear that the plane strain equations can be transformed into corresponding plane stress equations, and vice versa, through a simple change in material parameters as follows.

From plane stress to plane strain:
By applying these transformations, the constitutive equations for plane stress can be converted into the corresponding equations for plane strain:

$$E \to \frac{E}{1-\nu^2} \quad \text{and} \quad \nu \to \frac{\nu}{1-\nu}. \tag{8.2.24}$$

From plane strain to plane stress:

$$E \to \frac{(1+2\nu)E}{(1+\nu)^2} \quad \text{and} \quad \nu \to \frac{\nu}{1+\nu}. \tag{8.2.25}$$

8.2.2.3 *Airy stress function*

The Airy stress function is a potential function introduced to identically satisfy the equations of equilibrium, Equation (8.2.17). First, we assume that the body force vector $\mathbf{f}$ is derivable from a scalar potential V_f such that

$$\rho\mathbf{f} = -\rho\nabla V_f \quad \text{or} \quad \rho f_1 = -\frac{\partial V_f}{\partial x_1}, \quad \rho f_2 = -\frac{\partial V_f}{\partial x_2}. \tag{8.2.26}$$

When body forces are derivable from a potential V_f, they are said to be conservative. Next, we introduce the Airy stress function $\Phi(x_1, x_2)$ such that

$$\sigma_{11} = \frac{\partial^2\Phi}{\partial x_2^2} + V_f, \quad \sigma_{22} = \frac{\partial^2\Phi}{\partial x_1^2} + V_f, \quad \sigma_{12} = -\frac{\partial^2\Phi}{\partial x_1 \partial x_2} \tag{8.2.27}$$

Thus, this definition of $\Phi(x_1, x_2)$ automatically satisfies the equations of equilibrium (8.2.17).

The stresses derived from Equation (8.2.27) are subjected to compatibility conditions. Substituting for $\sigma_{\alpha\beta}$ in terms of $\Phi(x_1, x_2)$ from Equation (8.2.27) into the compatibility conditions, we can obtain

$$\nabla^4\Phi + (2 - s)\nabla^2 V_f = 0, \tag{8.2.28}$$

where $\nabla^4 = \nabla^2\nabla^2$ is the biharmonic operator, which, in two dimensions, has the form

$$\nabla^4 = \frac{\partial^4}{\partial x_1^4} + 2\frac{\partial^4}{\partial x_1^2 \partial x_2^2} + \frac{\partial^4}{\partial x_2^4}. \tag{8.2.29}$$

If the body forces are zero, we have $V_f = 0$ and Equation (8.2.28) reduces to the biharmonic equation

$$\nabla^4\Phi = 0. \tag{8.2.30}$$

Therefore, the solution to a plane elastic problem using the Airy stress function involves finding a solution to Equation (8.2.30) and satisfying the boundary conditions of the problem. The most challenging aspect is obtaining a solution to the fourth-order Equation (8.2.30) within a specified domain. The form of the Airy stress function is often determined using either the inverse method or the semi-inverse method.

Next, we examine several examples that demonstrate the application of the Airy stress function approach.

Example 8.2.1

Suppose that the Airy stress function is a second-order polynomial (the lowest order that gives a nonzero stress field) of the form

$$\Phi(x_1, x_2) = c_1 x_1 x_2 + c_2 x_1^2 + c_3 x_2^2. \tag{8.2.31}$$

Assuming that the body force field is zero, determine if the constants c_1, c_2, and c_3 correspond to a possible state of stress for some boundary-value problems (the inverse method).

Solution:

Clearly, the biharmonic equation is trivially satisfied by Φ in Equation (8.2.31). The corresponding stress field is

$$\sigma_{11} = \frac{\partial^2 \Phi}{\partial x_2^2} = 2c_3, \quad \sigma_{22} = \frac{\partial^2 \Phi}{\partial x_1^2} = 2c_2, \quad \sigma_{12} = -\frac{\partial^2 \Phi}{\partial x_1 \partial x_2} = -c_1. \tag{8.2.32}$$

Thus, the constants represent a uniform stress state throughout the body and are independent of the geometry. Thus, there are an infinite number of problems for which the stress field is a solution. In particular, the rectangular domain with the boundary stresses is shown in Figure 8.2.4.

Note that there are very few cases that can be solved analytically, even for plane problems. Therefore, in practice, numerical methods, such as FEM and mesh-free methods, are used to solve solid mechanics.

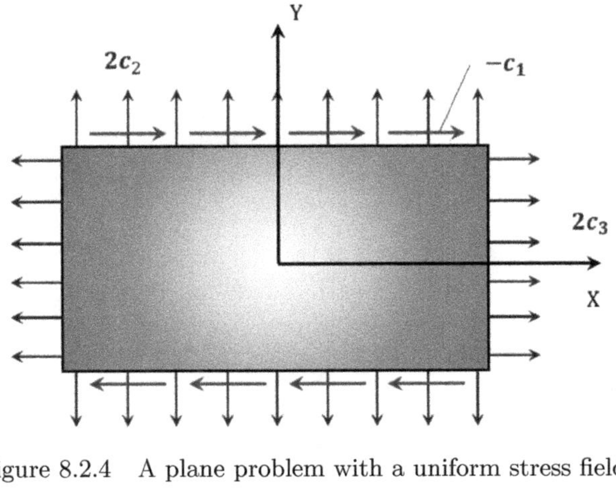

Figure 8.2.4 A plane problem with a uniform stress field.

8.3 Fluid Mechanics Problems

8.3.1 *Governing Equations*

In the majority of cases, matter exists in two states: solid and fluid. The difference between the two is that a solid can resist shear force in static deformation, whereas a fluid cannot. Fluid mechanics finds application in various fields such as meteorology, oceanography, aerodynamics, hydrodynamics, and engineering.

In essence, we can state that solids can resist shear stress, while liquids exhibit either very low resistance to it (in the case of viscous fluids, such as oil) or no resistance at all (in the case of non-viscous fluids, such as water). When a shear force is applied to a fluid, it causes continuous deformation.

Typically, fluids can exist in a state of rest or motion. A fluid at rest can only experience hydrostatic pressure and no shear stress. Therefore, the stress vector at a point in a fluid at rest can be expressed as follows:

$$\mathbf{t} = \mathbf{n} \cdot \boldsymbol{\sigma} = -p\mathbf{n} \quad \text{or} \quad \boldsymbol{\sigma} = -p\mathbf{I}, \tag{8.3.1}$$

where $\mathbf{n}$ is the unit vector normal to the surface and p is called the hydrostatic pressure. It is clear that hydrostatic pressure is equal to the negative of the mean stress from Equation (8.3.1):

$$p = -\frac{1}{3}\sigma_{ii} = -\tilde{\sigma}. \tag{8.3.2}$$

In general, for a compressible fluid, p is related to temperature θ and density ρ by an equation of the form

$$\Upsilon(p, \rho, \theta) = 0. \tag{8.3.3}$$

This equation is called the equation of state. Recall from Section 6.9 in Chapter 6 that the hydrostatic pressure p is not equal, in general, to the thermodynamic pressure p appearing in the constitutive equation of a fluid in motion:

$$\boldsymbol{\sigma} = -p(\theta)\mathbf{I} + \mathfrak{S}(\mathbf{D}) = -p + \boldsymbol{\tau}, \tag{8.3.4}$$

where $\boldsymbol{\tau}$ is the viscous stress tensor, which is a function of the motion, namely, the rate-of-deformation tensor $\mathbf{D}$, and $\boldsymbol{\tau}$ vanishes when a fluid is at rest.

8.3.2 *Summary of Equations for Fluids*

The basic equations of viscous fluids are listed here. From the previous chapters, we can obtain the following equations:

Continuity equation:

$$\frac{\partial \rho}{\partial t} + \operatorname{div}(\rho v) = 0; \quad \frac{\partial \rho}{\partial t} + \frac{\partial v_i}{\partial x_i}\rho = 0. \tag{8.3.5}$$

Equations of motion:

$$\nabla \cdot \boldsymbol{\sigma} + \rho \mathbf{f} = \rho \left(\frac{\partial \boldsymbol{v}}{\partial t} + \mathbf{v} \cdot \nabla \mathbf{v} \right); \quad \frac{\partial \sigma_{ji}}{\partial x_j} + \rho f_i = \rho \frac{\mathrm{D} v_i}{\mathrm{D} t}. \tag{8.3.6}$$

Energy balance equation:

$$\rho \frac{\mathrm{De}}{\mathrm{D}t} = \boldsymbol{\sigma} : \mathbf{D} - \nabla \cdot \mathbf{q} + \rho r_{\mathrm{h}}; \quad \rho \frac{\mathrm{De}}{\mathrm{D}t} = \sigma_{ij} D_{ij} - \frac{\partial q_i}{\partial x_i} + \rho r_{\mathrm{h}}. \tag{8.3.7}$$

Constitutive equation:

$$\boldsymbol{\sigma} = -p\mathbf{I} + 2\mu \mathbf{D} + \lambda(\operatorname{tr}(\mathbf{D}))\mathbf{I}, \quad \sigma_{ij} = -p\delta_{ij} + 2\mu D_{ij} + \lambda D_{kk}\delta_{ij}. \tag{8.3.8}$$

Heat conduction equation:

$$\mathbf{q} = -k\nabla\theta; \quad q_i = -k\frac{\partial \theta}{\partial x_i}. \tag{8.3.9}$$

Kinetic equation of state:

$$p = p(\rho, \theta). \tag{8.3.10}$$

Caloric equation of state:

$$e = e(\rho, \theta). \tag{8.3.11}$$

Rate of deformation–velocity equations:

$$\mathbf{D} = \frac{1}{2}[\nabla \mathbf{v} + (\nabla \mathbf{v})^T]; \quad D_{ij} = \frac{1}{2}\left[\frac{\partial v_i}{\partial x_j} + \frac{\partial v_j}{\partial x_i}\right]. \tag{8.3.12}$$

Therefore, there are 22 equations and 22 variables. We can solve them.

Here, we summarize the governing equations of fluid flows for the isothermal case. The above equations can be combined to yield the following equations:

$$\frac{\partial \rho}{\partial t} + \nabla \cdot (\rho v) = 0; \quad \frac{\partial \rho}{\partial t} + \frac{\partial (\rho v_i)}{\partial x_i} = 0, \tag{8.3.13}$$

$$\mu \nabla^2 \mathbf{v} + (\mu + \lambda)\nabla(\nabla \cdot \mathbf{v}) - \nabla p + \rho \mathbf{f} = \rho\left(\frac{\partial \boldsymbol{v}}{\partial t} + \mathbf{v} \cdot \nabla \mathbf{v}\right);$$

$$\mu v_{i,jj} + (\mu + \lambda) v_{j,ji} - \frac{\partial p}{\partial x_i} + \rho f_i = \rho\left(\frac{\partial v_i}{\partial t} + v_j \frac{\partial v_i}{\partial x_j}\right). \tag{8.3.14}$$

The above two equations are known as the Navier–Stokes equations. There are four equations and five variables. When combined with the state equation, we can solve them.

For incompressible fluids, ρ is a known function of position; thus, we have four equations with four unknown variables:

$$\nabla \cdot (v) = 0, \quad \frac{\partial (v_i)}{\partial x_i} = 0, \tag{8.3.15}$$

$$\mu \nabla^2 \mathbf{v} - \nabla p + \rho \mathbf{f} = \rho\left(\frac{\partial \boldsymbol{v}}{\partial t} + \mathbf{v} \cdot \nabla \mathbf{v}\right),$$

$$\mu v_{i,jj} - \frac{\partial p}{\partial x_i} + \rho f_i = \rho\left(\frac{\partial v_i}{\partial t} + v_j \frac{\partial v_i}{\partial x_j}\right). \tag{8.3.16}$$

The expanded forms of these four equations in rectangular Cartesian coordinate systems are presented:

$$\frac{\partial v_1}{\partial x_1} + \frac{\partial v_2}{\partial x_2} + \frac{\partial v_3}{\partial x_3} = 0, \tag{8.3.17}$$

$$\mu\left(\frac{\partial^2 v_1}{\partial x_1^2} + \frac{\partial^2 v_1}{\partial x_2^2} + \frac{\partial^2 v_1}{\partial x_3^2}\right) - \frac{\partial p}{\partial x_1} + \rho f_1$$

$$= \rho\left(\frac{\partial v_1}{\partial t} + v_1 \frac{\partial v_1}{\partial x_1} + v_2 \frac{\partial v_1}{\partial x_2} + v_3 \frac{\partial v_1}{\partial x_3}\right), \tag{8.3.18}$$

$$\mu\left(\frac{\partial^2 v_2}{\partial x_1^2}+\frac{\partial^2 v_2}{\partial x_2^2}+\frac{\partial^2 v_2}{\partial x_3^2}\right)-\frac{\partial p}{\partial x_2}+\rho f_2$$
$$=\rho\left(\frac{\partial v_2}{\partial t}+v_1\frac{\partial v_2}{\partial x_1}+v_2\frac{\partial v_2}{\partial x_2}+v_3\frac{\partial v_2}{\partial x_3}\right), \tag{8.3.19}$$

$$\mu\left(\frac{\partial^2 v_3}{\partial x_1^2}+\frac{\partial^2 v_3}{\partial x_2^2}+\frac{\partial^2 v_3}{\partial x_3^2}\right)-\frac{\partial p}{\partial x_3}+\rho f_3$$
$$=\rho\left(\frac{\partial v_3}{\partial t}+v_1\frac{\partial v_3}{\partial x_1}+v_2\frac{\partial v_3}{\partial x_2}+v_3\frac{\partial v_3}{\partial x_3}\right). \tag{8.3.20}$$

In general, finding exact solutions to the Navier–Stokes equations for all conditions is an impossible task. The principal reason is the strong nonlinearity of the equations, and consequently, the exact solutions only exist under some special conditions.

8.3.3 *Inviscid Fluid Statics*

For incompressible inviscid fluids (i.e., fluids with zero viscosity), the constitutive equation for stress is

$$\boldsymbol{\sigma}=-p\mathbf{I},\quad \sigma_{ij}=-p\delta_{ij}, \tag{8.3.21}$$

where p is the hydrostatic pressure, and the equations of motion reduce to

$$-\nabla p+\rho\mathbf{f}=\rho\left(\frac{\mathrm{D}\mathbf{v}}{\mathrm{D}t}\right). \tag{8.3.22}$$

8.3.4 *Parallel Flow (Navier–Stokes Equations)*

A flow is called parallel if only one velocity component is nonzero (i.e., all fluid particles moving in the same direction). Suppose that the x_1-axis is taken along the flow direction, and let $v_2 = v_3 = 0$ as well as the body forces f_1, f_2, and f_3 be negligible. Then, it follows that

$$\frac{\partial v_1}{\partial x_1}=0\to v_1=v_1(x_2,x_3,t),\qquad \text{and}\qquad v_2=v_3=0. \tag{8.3.23}$$

Consequently, the three equations of motion in (8.2.4) simplify to the following linear differential equations:

$$-\frac{\partial p}{\partial x_1}+\mu\left(\frac{\partial^2 v_1}{\partial x_2^2}+\frac{\partial^2 v_1}{\partial x_3^2}\right)=\rho\frac{\partial v_1}{\partial t},\quad \frac{\partial p}{\partial x_2}=\frac{\partial p}{\partial x_3}=0. \tag{8.3.24}$$

The last equation in the above implies that p is only a function of x_1. Thus, given the pressure gradient $\frac{\mathrm{d}p}{\mathrm{d}x_1}$, the first equation can be used to determine v_1.

8.4 Large Deformation of Hydrogels

In this section, we utilize the constitutive equations of hydrogels to examine their significant deformations. Owing to the inherent complexity of hydrogels, only a limited number of problems can be solved using analytical solutions. Consequently, numerical methods, such as the finite element method (FEM), are employed to solve various examples.

8.4.1 *The Homogeneous Deformation of Hydrogels*

Here, we present a range of analytical and numerical examples to illustrate the utilization of hydrogel structures in homogeneous deformation. The phenomenon of homogeneous swelling had previously been analytically analyzed by Treloar (1950). Due to their homogeneity, these examples can be examined using both analytical and finite element methods.

8.4.1.1 *Free swelling*

We consider a cubic gel block immersed in a solvent, leading to its free swelling until reaching chemical potential equilibrium. As discussed earlier in Chapter 7, the free-energy function proposed by Flory and Rehner (1943) is utilized for this purpose:

$$\begin{aligned} W &= \frac{1}{2}NkT[F_{iK}F_{iK} - 3 - 2\log(\det \mathbf{f})] \\ &\quad - \frac{kT}{v}\left[vC\log\left(1 + \frac{1}{vC}\right) + \frac{\chi}{1+vC}\right], \end{aligned} \tag{8.4.1}$$

where N is the number of polymeric chains per reference volume and χ is a dimensionless measure of the enthalpy of mixing. When $\chi > 0$, the solvent molecules have a greater affinity for themselves than for the long-chained polymers.

Introducing another free-energy function $\widehat{W}$ by using a Legendre transformation and incompressible conditions, the desired new free-energy function can be obtained:

$$\widehat{W}(\mathbf{F},\mu) = \frac{1}{2}NkT(I-3-2\log J) - \frac{kT}{v}\left[(J-1)\log\frac{J}{J-1}+\frac{\chi}{J}\right] - \frac{\mu}{v}(J-1), \tag{8.4.2}$$

where $I = F_{iK}F_{iK}$ and $J = \det \mathbf{F}$ are invariants of the deformation gradient. As mentioned in the previous chapter, when the deformation gradient of the network, $\mathbf{F}$, and the concentration of solvent, C, are used as the independent variables for the free-energy function, the Lagrange multiplier Π is needed to enforce the condition of molecular incompressibility.

In this case, however, we employ the deformation gradient of the network, $\mathbf{F}$, and the solvent's chemical potential, μ, as the independent variables. As a result, the condition of molecular incompressibility is enforced without the need for a Lagrange multiplier. Instead, incompressible conditions are incorporated into the Flory–Rehner free-energy function (8.4.1) to eliminate the variable C. This fully specifies a boundary-value problem where the variable C does not appear during the process of solving it but can be calculated once $\mathbf{F}$ is determined.

Thus, we can obtain the constitutive equation as follows:

$$\frac{s_{iK}}{kT/v} = Nv(F_{iK}-H_{iK}) + \left[J\log\left(1-\frac{1}{J}\right)+1+\frac{\chi}{J}-\frac{\mu}{kT}J\right]H_{iK}. \tag{8.4.3}$$

This equation of state establishes a relationship between stress and the deformation gradient when a gel is maintained at a constant chemical potential through a reservoir of solvent molecules. When the stress field within the gel is both inhomogeneous and anisotropic, the deformation gradient field exhibits the same characteristics. As a result, the volumetric strain J (and, consequently, the volume fraction of the solvent in the gel) will generally display inhomogeneity and anisotropy.

We have normalized the chemical potential by kT and the stress by kT/v. A representative value of the volume per molecule is

$v = 10^{-28}\,\mathrm{m}^3$. At room temperature, $kT = 4 \times 10^{-21}\,\mathrm{J}$ and $kT/v = 4 \times 10^7\,\mathrm{Pa}$. The Flory–Rehner free-energy function introduces two dimensionless material parameters: Nv and χ. In the absence of solvent molecules, the dry network has a shear modulus NkT under small-strain conditions, with representative values being $NkT = 10^4 - 10^7\,\mathrm{N/m^2}$, which gives the range $Nv = 10^{-4} - 10^{-1}$. The parameter χ is a dimensionless measure of the enthalpy of mixing, with representative values being $\chi = 0 - 1.2$. For applications that require gels with large swelling ratios, materials with low χ values are used. In the following numerical examples, we take the values $Nv = 10^{-3}$ and $\chi = 0.1$.

The free-energy function (8.4.1) becomes singular when the network is devoid of solvent, i.e., $vC = 0$. This singularity arises due to the entropy of mixing but is inconsequential in practice, as gels typically contain a substantial number of solvent molecules. However, in the above context, we have selected the dry network as the reference state. If a numerical calculation involves this state, the singularity can pose issues. To circumvent this singularity, we can opt for a reference state with $vC > 0$.

In the FEM simulation, we select a reference state where the network, in the absence of any mechanical load, reaches equilibrium with a solvent of chemical potential μ_0. Compared to the dry network, the network in this state undergoes isotropic swelling with equal stretches in all directions: $\lambda_1 = \lambda_2 = \lambda_3$. We denote this stretch during free-swelling as λ_0, which is related to the chemical potential μ_0 by setting the stress in Equation (8.4.3) to zero. This can be expressed as follows:

$$Nv\left(\frac{1}{\lambda_0} - \frac{1}{\lambda_0^3}\right) + \log\left(1 - \frac{1}{\lambda_0^3}\right) + \frac{1}{\lambda_0^3} + \frac{\chi}{\lambda_0^6} = \frac{\mu_0}{kT}. \tag{8.4.4}$$

Based on Equation (8.4.4), we analytically determine the stretch of a free-swelling gel as a function of the solvent's chemical potential. Figure 8.4.1 illustrates the relationship between the free-swelling stretch and the chemical potential of the solvent molecules. In order to validate the implementation of the FEM, we also employ it to simulate the system concurrently. In the FEM simulation, we represent the gel block using one or several eight-node brick elements. The block is constrained to prevent rigid-body motion while allowing

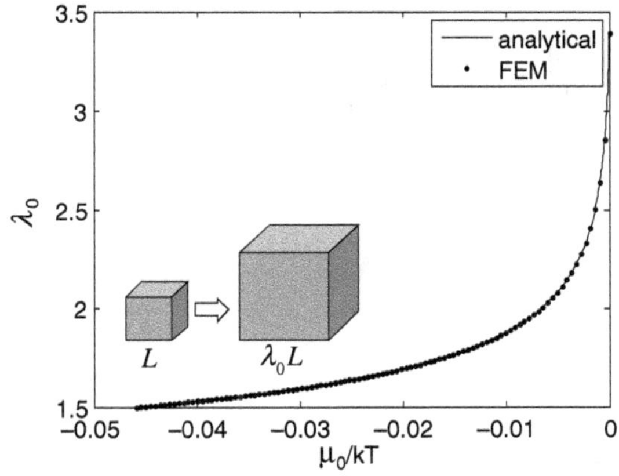

Figure 8.4.1 The stretch of a free-swelling gel is plotted as a function of the chemical potential of the solvent.

free swelling. The chemical potential of the solvent molecules gradually varies. Figure 8.4.1 compares the stretches obtained through the FEM with those obtained analytically (Hong *et al.*, 2009; Liu *et al.*, 2022).

8.4.1.2 *A rod of a gel equilibrated with a solvent and subjected to a uniaxial force*

A gel rod is immersed in a solvent with a chemical potential μ and subjected to a uniaxial stress s_1 along the longitudinal direction. The deformation state can be described by the longitudinal stretch λ_1 and two equal transverse stretches $\lambda_2 = \lambda_3$. The stresses in the transverse directions are negligible, allowing us to simplify Equation (8.4.3) as follows:

$$Nv\left(\lambda_2 - \frac{1}{\lambda_2}\right) + \left[\lambda_1\lambda_2^2 \log\left(1 - \frac{1}{\lambda_1\lambda_2^2}\right) + 1 + \frac{\chi}{\lambda_1\lambda_2^2} - \frac{\mu}{kT}\lambda_1\lambda_2^2\right]\frac{1}{\lambda_2} = 0. \tag{8.4.5}$$

This equation determines the transverse stretch λ_2 for a given longitudinal stretch λ_1. Equation (8.4.5) also relates the longitudinal

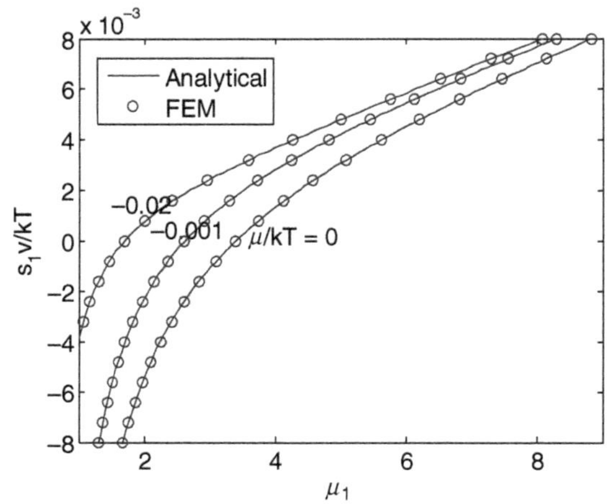

Figure 8.4.2 A rod of a gel is subjected to uniaxial stress and is in contact with a solvent of a given chemical potential. The applied stress is plotted as a function of the stretch, while the solvent is held at several levels of the chemical potential.

stress to the stretches:

$$\frac{vs_1}{kT} = Nv\left(\lambda_1 - \frac{1}{\lambda_1}\right) + \left[\lambda_1\lambda_2^2 \log\left(1 - \frac{1}{\lambda_1\lambda_2^2}\right) + 1 + \frac{\chi}{\lambda_1\lambda_2^2} - \frac{\mu}{kT}\lambda_1\lambda_2^2\right]\frac{1}{\lambda_1}. \tag{8.4.6}$$

We utilize four eight-node brick elements to model the gel block. Figure 8.4.2 compares the results obtained from the FEM with those derived from Equations (8.4.5) and (8.4.6). As anticipated, as the chemical potential of the solvent increases, the gel undergoes greater swelling and exhibits increased compliance.

8.4.2 *Large Deformation for Salt Concentration-Sensitive Hydrogel*

When exposed to a solvent, hydrogels can undergo significant swelling, increasing their size manifold. Among various hydrogel types, salt concentration-sensitive hydrogels find wide-ranging applications, including sensors, actuators, artificial muscles, and drug delivery systems. Building upon the constitutive equations discussed in the previous chapter, we illustrate the practicality of this theory by presenting two typical cases: free swelling and constrained swelling.

In the case of salt concentration-sensitive hydrogels, the Donnan equation allows us to reduce the free-energy function W to only two independent variables, namely $W(J, c_0)$. Additionally, by imposing the constraint of molecular incompressibility, the theory determines the true stress as follows:

$$\sigma_{ij} = \frac{F_{jK}}{J}\frac{\partial W}{\partial F_{iK}} - \frac{\mu}{v}\delta_{ij}, \tag{8.4.7}$$

where μ is the chemical potential in the salt solution and can be specified as

$$\mu = -2kTvc_0. \tag{8.4.8}$$

Using Equation (8.4.7) and the function $W(J, c_0)$ specified in the previous chapter, we derive the stress expression as follows:

$$\begin{aligned} \frac{\sigma_{ij}}{kT/v} &= \frac{Nv}{J}\left(F_{iK}F_{jK} - \delta_{ij}\right) + \log\frac{J-1}{J} + \frac{1}{J} + \frac{\chi}{J^2} + 2\nu c_0 \\ &\quad + \nu\left[c^+\left(\log\frac{c^+}{c_0} - 1\right) + c^-\left(\log\frac{c^-}{c_0} - 1\right)\right. \\ &\quad \left. + J\left(\frac{\partial c^+}{\partial J}\log\frac{c^+}{c_0} + \frac{\partial c^-}{\partial J}\log\frac{c^-}{c_0}\right)\right]. \end{aligned} \tag{8.4.9}$$

It is important to note that the derivation from the free-energy function to Equation (8.4.9) follows a rigorous mathematical differentiation process. This mathematical rigor allows for easy implementation of the FEM in practice. Additionally, it is worth mentioning that in the past decade, many relevant studies have assumed that the concentration of ions is independent of J. However, by utilizing the Donnan equilibrium and large deformation theory, we challenge this assumption and enable a proper FEM implementation.

In this context, we employ the formulated theory of salt concentration-sensitive hydrogels, as discussed in Chapter 7. This theory serves as the basis for theoretical predictions, and FEM results can also be generated based on this theory.

We now apply the present theory to two typical cases: a free-swelling case (Figure 8.4.3(a)) and a constrained-swelling case

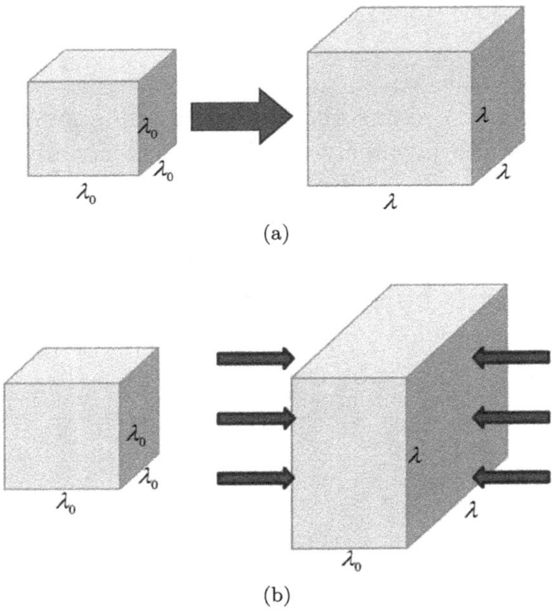

Figure 8.4.3 Schematic diagrams of (a) free swelling from the dry state; (b) an initially isotropic gel cube subjected to constraints on one pair of parallel sides and swelling in the lateral direction.

(Figure 8.4.3(b)). The theory allows us to investigate the relationships among stretch, ion concentration, and stress.

8.4.2.1 *Free swelling*

Consider the case of the free-swelling condition and define λ as the swelling stretch, so

$$J = \lambda^3. \tag{8.4.10}$$

The static equilibrium means that the stress vanishes, so Equation (8.4.9) becomes

$$\begin{aligned} &N\nu\left(\lambda - \frac{1}{\lambda}\right) + \lambda^2 \log\frac{\lambda^3 - 1}{\lambda^3} + \frac{1}{\lambda} + \frac{\chi}{\lambda^4} \\ &+ \lambda^2\nu\left[c^+\left(\log\frac{c^+}{c_0} - 1\right) + c^-\left(\log\frac{c^-}{c_0} - 1\right)\right. \\ &\left. + \lambda^3\left(\frac{\partial c^+}{\partial J}\log\frac{c^+}{c_0} + \frac{\partial c^-}{\partial J}\log\frac{c^-}{c_0}\right)\right] + 2\lambda^2\nu c_0 = 0, \end{aligned} \tag{8.4.11}$$

where

$$\frac{\partial c^+}{\partial J} = -\frac{C_0}{2\lambda^6} - \frac{1}{2}\frac{C_0^2}{\lambda^9}\frac{1}{\sqrt{\dfrac{C_0^2}{\lambda^6} + 4c_0^2}}, \tag{8.4.12}$$

$$\frac{\partial c^-}{\partial J} = \frac{C_0}{2\lambda^6} - \frac{1}{2}\frac{C_0^2}{\lambda^9}\frac{1}{\sqrt{\dfrac{C_0^2}{\lambda^6} + 4c_0^2}}. \tag{8.4.13}$$

By solving Equations (8.4.11)–(8.4.13), we can determine the equilibrium state of the salt concentration-sensitive gel when immersed in a salt solution. The results are influenced by the following dimensionless parameters: the crosslinking density Nv, mixing enthalpy parameter χ, and the nominal concentration of fixed charges vC_0. Figure 8.4.4 illustrates the theoretical outcomes for free swelling with $Nv = 10^{-3}$ and $\chi = 0.1$.

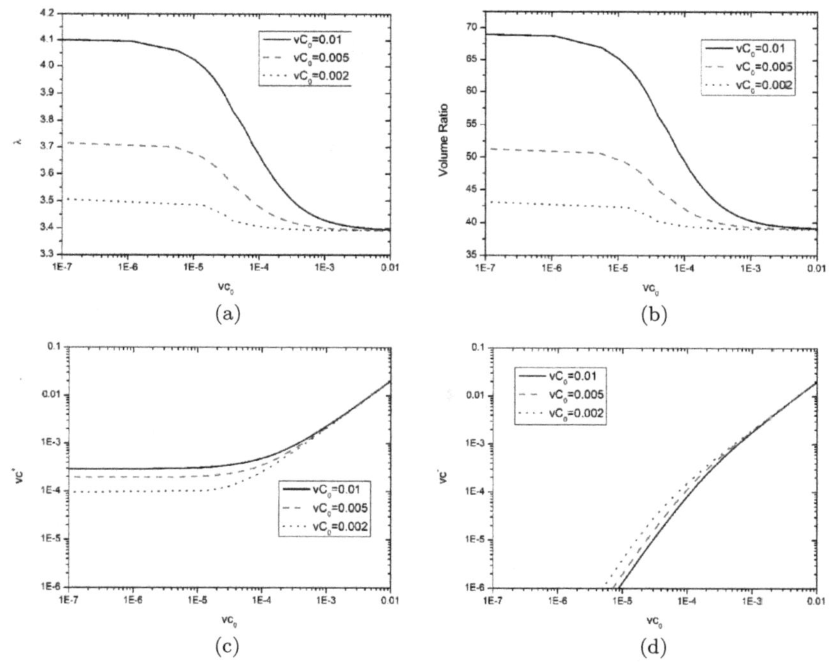

Figure 8.4.4 During the free-swelling process, the (a) stretch, (b) volume ratio, (c) true concentration of counter ion, and (d) true concentration of co-ion as functions of salt concentration in the solution with different nominal concentrations of fixed charges.

From Figures 8.4.4(a) and 8.4.4(b), it is evident that an increase in the salt concentration within the external solution leads to a continuous decrease in stretch and subsequent volume reduction. The ion concentrations within the gel also exhibit variations corresponding to the salt concentration in the surrounding solution (Figures 8.4.4(c) and 8.4.4(d)). It is important to note that we only consider ion concentrations ranging from 10^{-6} to 10^{-1}, and values outside this range are not taken into consideration.

8.4.2.2 *Constrained swelling*

In this section, we illustrate the swelling behavior of the gel under constraint, as depicted in Figure 8.4.3(b). When the gel is constrained between opposing faces, it is allowed to swell freely in the lateral directions. In the lateral directions, the gel remains stress-free, while stresses are induced in the longitudinal direction. The swelling stretch is determined by the following expression:

$$\begin{aligned} &N\nu\frac{(\lambda^2-1)}{\lambda_0\lambda^2} + \log\frac{\lambda_0\lambda^2-1}{\lambda_0\lambda^2} + \frac{1}{\lambda_0\lambda^2} + \frac{\chi}{(\lambda_0\lambda^2)^2} \\ &+\nu\left[c^+\left(\log\frac{c^+}{c_0}-1\right) + c^-\left(\log\frac{c^-}{c_0}-1\right)\right. \\ &\left. +\lambda_0\lambda^2\left(\frac{\partial c^+}{\partial J}\log\frac{c^+}{c_0} + \frac{\partial c^-}{\partial J}\log\frac{c^-}{c_0}\right)\right] + 2\nu c_0 = 0. \end{aligned} \tag{8.4.14}$$

In this constrained case, Equations (8.4.12) and (8.4.13) become

$$\frac{\partial c^+}{\partial J} = -\frac{C_0}{2(\lambda_0\lambda^2)^2} - \frac{1}{2}\frac{C_0^2}{(\lambda_0\lambda^2)^3}\frac{1}{\sqrt{\dfrac{C_0^2}{(\lambda_0\lambda^2)^2}+4c_0^2}}, \tag{8.4.15}$$

$$\frac{\partial c^-}{\partial J} = \frac{C_0}{2(\lambda_0\lambda^2)^2} - \frac{1}{2}\frac{C_0^2}{(\lambda_0\lambda^2)^3}\frac{1}{\sqrt{\dfrac{C_0^2}{(\lambda_0\lambda^2)^2}+4c_0^2}}. \tag{8.4.16}$$

The stress caused by the constraint in the gel along the thickness direction can be given by

$$\frac{\sigma}{kT/v} = \frac{Nv}{\lambda_0\lambda^2}(\lambda_0^2-\lambda^2). \tag{8.4.17}$$

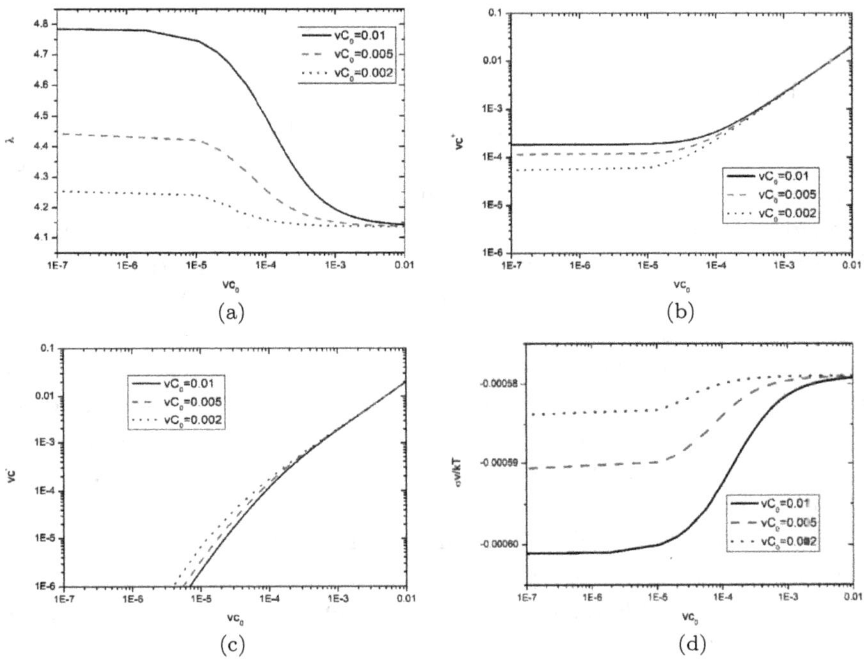

Figure 8.4.5 During constrained swelling, the (a) stretch, (b) true concentration of the counter ion, (c) true concentration of the co-ion, and (d) the nominal stress as a function of salt concentration in the solution with different nominal concentrations of fixed charges.

By solving Equations (8.4.14)–(8.4.17), we can determine the equilibrium state of the salt concentration-sensitive gel when it is under constraint and immersed in a salt solution. The obtained results are presented in Figure 8.4.5 for $\lambda_0 = 1.5$. Figure 8.4.5 exhibits similar trends to those observed in the free-swelling case. Additionally, the variation in stress with salt concentration can be observed in Figure 8.4.5(d).

8.5 Deformation Behavior of Shape Memory Polymers

As discussed in the previous chapter, although the constitutive models mentioned above can accurately describe the behavior of many SMPs, they tend to be complex and involve numerous model parameters. In certain cases, a simpler and more effective model is sufficient for qualitatively investigating the deformation behavior of SMPs.

The generalized Kelvin model, widely used in the theory of viscoelasticity, is a representative model capable of explaining polymer stress relaxation.

In this chapter, we propose and study a simplified three-element model to simulate the stress–strain–temperature characteristics of polyurethane-based SMPs under different loading conditions. To generalize this simplified model, we extend it to a three-dimensional isotropic case. Furthermore, we implement this model into the ABAQUS software using a user-defined subroutine, UMAT, to study the overall deformation behavior of SMPs. Additionally, the model takes into account the thermal expansion effect. Due to the high modulus of SMPs in the glassy state, stress is significantly influenced by the thermal expansion of the polymer, leading to creep and stress relaxation. This phenomenon is considered in the simplified model (Li *et al.*, 2015).

To validate the applicability of the simplified model, we compare the simulated results using the constitutive relations of the present model with available experimental data, demonstrating a good agreement between them.

8.5.1 *Simple Constitutive Model of SMPs*

A simplified three-element viscoelastic model, as shown in Figure 8.5.1, combines an elastic spring and a Kelvin element in series. This model consists of two elastic spring elements and one viscous element, requiring three parameters: two elastic modulus parameters and one viscous parameter. In the following, we provide a brief introduction to the constitutive equations governing this model.

The constitutive relation for the spring element is typically described by Hooke's law:

$$\sigma_{E_1} = E_1(T) \cdot \varepsilon_{E_1}, \tag{8.5.1}$$

$$\sigma_{E_2} = E_2(T) \cdot \varepsilon_{E_2}, \tag{8.5.2}$$

where $E_1(T)$ and $E_2(T)$ are elastic moduli, depending on the Kelvin temperature T, σ_{E_1} and σ_{E_2} are the stresses, and ε_{E_1} and ε_{E_2} are the strains in the elastic spring elements. On the other hand, the dashpot element in the Kelvin element possesses the property of stress dependent on viscous flow. The viscous flow is assumed to be Newtonian, and the relationship between stress and viscosity can be expressed as

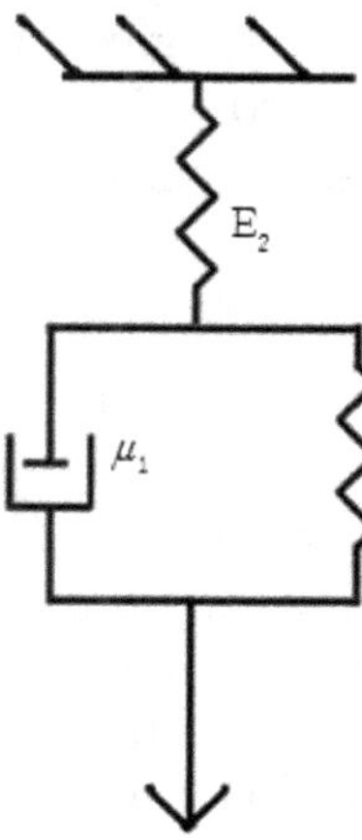

Figure 8.5.1 Schematic diagram of simplified three-element model for SMPs.

$$\sigma_{\mu 1} = \mu_1(T) \cdot \frac{d\varepsilon_{\mu 1}}{dt}. \tag{8.5.3}$$

where $\mu_1(T)$ is apparent viscosity, as shown in Figure 8.5.1, depending on the temperature T, and σ_{μ_1} and ε_{μ_1} are the stress and strain in the dashpot element.

The effect of thermal expansion, which is assumed to be independent of the mechanical behavior, is expressed as thermal strain ε_T:

$$\varepsilon_T = \alpha(T - T_0), \tag{8.5.4}$$

where α is thermal expansion coefficient and T_0 is the reference temperature.

In this model, an elastic spring element is connected in series with a Kelvin element. The Kelvin element consists of another spring element and a dashpot element arranged in parallel. By applying the rules for series and parallel systems, we can derive the following equations for the entire model:

$$\sigma = \sigma_{E_2} = \sigma_{E_1} + \sigma_{\mu 1}, \tag{8.5.5}$$

$$\varepsilon = \varepsilon_M + \varepsilon_T = \varepsilon_{E_2} + \varepsilon_{E_1} + \varepsilon_T, \tag{8.5.6}$$

where σ and ε are the total stress and strain, respectively, ε_M is the mechanical strain, and ε_T is thermal strain obtained from Equation (8.5.4). The strain in the dashpot element is $\varepsilon_{\mu_1} = \varepsilon_{E_1}$.

By substituting the corresponding constitutive equations for each element from Equations (8.5.1) to (8.5.4) into Equations (8.5.5) and (8.5.6), we can derive the one-dimensional constitutive equation for the model as follows:

$$\sigma + \frac{\mu_1(T)}{(E_1(T)+E_2(T))}\frac{\mathrm{d}\sigma}{\mathrm{d}t} = \frac{\mu_1(T)}{(1+E_1(T)/E_2(T))}\left(\frac{\mathrm{d}\varepsilon}{\mathrm{d}t} - \alpha\frac{\mathrm{d}T}{\mathrm{d}t}\right) + \frac{1}{(1/E_1(T)+1/E_2(T))}(\varepsilon - \alpha(T-T_0)). \tag{8.5.7}$$

Based on this constitutive equation, we have developed the UMAT subroutine for ABAQUS and generalized the constitutive equations to analyze 3D isotropic solids (Li *et al.*, 2015):

$$\begin{cases} \sigma_{xx} - \nu(\sigma_{yy}+\sigma_{zz}) + \dfrac{\mu_1(T)}{(E_1(T)+E_2(T))}\dfrac{\mathrm{d}\sigma_{xx}}{\mathrm{d}t} \\ \quad = \dfrac{\mu_1(T)}{(1+E_1(T)/E_2(T))}\left(\dfrac{\mathrm{d}\varepsilon_{xx}}{\mathrm{d}t} - \alpha\dfrac{\mathrm{d}T}{\mathrm{d}t}\right) \\ \qquad + \dfrac{1}{(1/E_1(T)+1/E_2(T))}(\varepsilon_{xx} - \alpha(T-T_0)) \\ \sigma_{yy} - \nu(\sigma_{zz}+\sigma_{xx}) + \dfrac{\mu_1(T)}{(E_1(T)+E_2(T))}\dfrac{\mathrm{d}\sigma_{yy}}{\mathrm{d}t} \\ \quad = \dfrac{\mu_1(T)}{(1+E_1(T)/E_2(T))}\left(\dfrac{\mathrm{d}\varepsilon_{yy}}{\mathrm{d}t} - \alpha\dfrac{\mathrm{d}T}{\mathrm{d}t}\right) \\ \qquad + \dfrac{1}{(1/E_1(T)+1/E_2(T))}(\varepsilon_{yy} - \alpha(T-T_0)) \\ \sigma_{zz} - \nu(\sigma_{xx}+\sigma_{yy}) + \dfrac{\mu_1(T)}{(E_1(T)+E_2(T))}\dfrac{\mathrm{d}\sigma_{zz}}{\mathrm{d}t} \\ \quad = \dfrac{\mu_1(T)}{(1+E_1(T)/E_2(T))}\left(\dfrac{\mathrm{d}\varepsilon_{zz}}{\mathrm{d}t} - \alpha\dfrac{\mathrm{d}T}{\mathrm{d}t}\right), \\ \qquad + \dfrac{1}{(1/E_1(T)+1/E_2(T))}(\varepsilon_{zz} - \alpha(T-T_0)) \\ \sigma_{xy} + \dfrac{\mu_1(T)}{(E_1(T)+E_2(T))}\dfrac{\mathrm{d}\sigma_{xy}}{\mathrm{d}t} = \mu(T)\gamma_{xy} + \tilde{\mu}(T)\dfrac{\mathrm{d}\gamma_{xy}}{\mathrm{d}t} \\ \sigma_{yz} + \dfrac{\mu_1(T)}{(E_1(T)+E_2(T))}\dfrac{\mathrm{d}\sigma_{yz}}{\mathrm{d}t} = \mu(T)\gamma_{yz} + \tilde{\mu}(T)\dfrac{\mathrm{d}\gamma_{yz}}{\mathrm{d}t} \\ \sigma_{zx} + \dfrac{\mu_1(T)}{(E_1(T)+E_2(T))}\dfrac{\mathrm{d}\sigma_{zx}}{\mathrm{d}t} = \mu(T)\gamma_{zx} + \tilde{\mu}(T)\dfrac{\mathrm{d}\gamma_{zx}}{\mathrm{d}t} \end{cases} \tag{8.5.8}$$

where ν is the Poisson ratio, and $\mu(T)$ and $\tilde{\mu}(T)$ are the temperature-dependent material parameters ($\mu(T)$ is the shear modulus), which can be obtained from $E_1(T)$, $E_2(T)$, $\mu_1(T)$, and the Poisson ratic ν:

$$\mu(T) = \frac{1}{2(1+\nu)} \frac{E_1(T)E_2(T)}{(E_1(T)+E_2(T))}, \tag{8.5.9}$$

$$\tilde{\mu}(T) = \frac{1}{2(1+\nu)} \frac{\mu_1(T)}{(1+E_1(T)/E_2(T))}. \tag{8.5.10}$$

Thus, introducing volumetric strain $\varepsilon_V = \varepsilon_{xx} + \varepsilon_{yy} + \varepsilon_{zz}$, Equation (8.5.8) can be further generalized as

$$\begin{cases} \sigma_{xx} + \tilde{\nu}(T)\dfrac{\mathrm{d}\sigma_{xx}}{\mathrm{d}t} = \lambda(T)(\varepsilon_V - 3\alpha(T-T_0)) \\ \quad + 2\mu(T)(\varepsilon_{xx} - \alpha(T-T_0)) + \tilde{\lambda}(T)\left(\dfrac{\mathrm{d}\varepsilon_V}{\mathrm{d}t} - 3\alpha\dfrac{\mathrm{d}T}{\mathrm{d}t}\right) \\ \quad + 2\tilde{\mu}(T)\left(\dfrac{\mathrm{d}\varepsilon_{xx}}{\mathrm{d}t} - \alpha\dfrac{\mathrm{d}T}{\mathrm{d}t}\right) \\ \sigma_{yy} + \tilde{\nu}(T)\dfrac{\mathrm{d}\sigma_{yy}}{\mathrm{d}t} = \lambda(T)(\varepsilon_V - 3\alpha(T-T_0)) \\ \quad + 2\mu(T)(\varepsilon_{yy} - \alpha(T-T_0)) + \tilde{\lambda}(T)\left(\dfrac{\mathrm{d}\varepsilon_V}{\mathrm{d}t} - 3\alpha\dfrac{\mathrm{d}T}{\mathrm{d}t}\right) \\ \quad + 2\tilde{\mu}(T)\left(\dfrac{\mathrm{d}\varepsilon_{yy}}{\mathrm{d}t} - \alpha\dfrac{\mathrm{d}T}{\mathrm{d}t}\right) \\ \sigma_{zz} + \tilde{\nu}(T)\dfrac{\mathrm{d}\sigma_{zz}}{\mathrm{d}t} = \lambda(T)(\varepsilon_V - 3\alpha(T-T_0)) \\ \quad + 2\mu(T)(\varepsilon_{zz} - \alpha(T-T_0)) + \tilde{\lambda}(T)\left(\dfrac{\mathrm{d}\varepsilon_V}{\mathrm{d}t} - 3\alpha\dfrac{\mathrm{d}T}{\mathrm{d}t}\right) \\ \quad + 2\tilde{\mu}(T)\left(\dfrac{\mathrm{d}\varepsilon_{zz}}{\mathrm{d}t} - \alpha\dfrac{\mathrm{d}T}{\mathrm{d}t}\right) \\ \sigma_{xy} + \tilde{\nu}(T)\dfrac{\mathrm{d}\sigma_{xy}}{\mathrm{d}t} = \mu(T)\gamma_{xy} + \tilde{\mu}(T)\dfrac{\mathrm{d}\gamma_{xy}}{\mathrm{d}t} \\ \sigma_{yz} + \tilde{\nu}(T)\dfrac{\mathrm{d}\sigma_{yz}}{\mathrm{d}t} = \mu(T)\gamma_{yz} + \tilde{\mu}(T)\dfrac{\mathrm{d}\gamma_{yz}}{\mathrm{d}t} \\ \sigma_{zx} + \tilde{\nu}(T)\dfrac{\mathrm{d}\sigma_{zx}}{\mathrm{d}t} = \mu(T)\gamma_{zx} + \tilde{\mu}(T)\dfrac{\mathrm{d}\gamma_{zx}}{\mathrm{d}t} \end{cases}, \tag{8.5.11}$$

where $\tilde{\nu}(T)$, $\lambda(T)$, $\tilde{\lambda}(T)$ are the temperature-dependent material parameters, which are related to $E_1(T)$, $E_2(T)$, $\mu_1(T)$, respectively, through the following relations:

$$\tilde{\nu}(T) = \frac{\mu_1(T)}{E_1(T) + E_2(T)}, \tag{8.5.12}$$

$$\lambda(T) = \frac{\nu}{(1+\nu)(1-2\nu)} \frac{E_1(T)E_2(T)}{(E_1(T) + E_2(T))}, \tag{8.5.13}$$

$$\tilde{\lambda}(T) = \frac{\nu}{(1+\nu)(1-2\nu)} \frac{\mu_1(T)}{(1 + E_1(T)/E_2(T))}. \tag{8.5.14}$$

To determine the solution to the constitutive equations using the FEM, we have adopted the central difference method. Additionally, the three-dimensional constitutive equations have been implemented into the ABAQUS UMAT subroutine to simulate the shape memory behaviors of polyurethane-based SMPs. It is important to note that this model employs a first-order strain approximation in the strain tensor, thus limiting its applicability to small-strain behavior.

To validate the accuracy of these constitutive equations, we have used thermo-mechanical testing data obtained from thin films of polyurethane from the polyester polyol series, as conducted by Tobushi *et al.* (1997), as reference data. From these testing results, we extract the glass transition temperature T_g, the coefficient of thermal expansion α in units of K^{-1}, and the elastic modulus $E(T_g)$ at T_g, as well as the retardation time $\tau(T_g)$ and viscosity $\mu(T_g)$ at T_g. In order to compare the simulated results with the experimental data, the experimental parameters are appropriately transformed to those relevant to the three-element model, specifically E, τ, and μ.

During the initial process of the stress relaxation test, the stress rate is infinitely high, and the dashpot element in Figure 8.5.1 behaves as a rigid component, providing an effectively instantaneous response. As a result, the dashpot and the spring E_1, which are in parallel with the dashpot, do not undergo deformation. Only the spring E_2 in the model is capable of deformation. Therefore, at $T = T_g$, we have the following relationship:

$$E_2(T_g) = E(T_g). \tag{8.5.15}$$

With the stress relaxation test proceeds, viscoelastic materials are relaxed gradually, and stress in viscoelastic solids decays to an equilibrium stress. The dashpot is fully stretched and doesn't support the load. The two springs are placed in series. Thus, at $T = T_g$, we have

$$\frac{E_1(T_g)E_2(T_g)}{(E_1(T_g) + E_2(T_g))} = E_\infty(T_g) = \frac{\mu(T_g)}{\tau(T_g)}. \tag{8.5.16}$$

In this model, only the dashpot element shows viscous property, so we assume that

$$\mu_1(T_g) = \mu(T_g). \tag{8.5.17}$$

Tobushi *et al.* (1997) proposed an exponential relation between material parameters and temperature in the glass transition region, $T_g - T_w \leq T \leq T_g + T_w$:

$$E = E_g \exp\left[a_E\left(\frac{T_g}{T} - 1\right)\right], \tag{8.5.18}$$

$$\tau = \tau_g \exp\left[a_\tau\left(\frac{T_g}{T} - 1\right)\right], \tag{8.5.19}$$

$$\mu = \mu_g \exp\left[a_\mu\left(\frac{T_g}{T} - 1\right)\right], \tag{8.5.20}$$

where E_g, τ_g, and μ_g denote values of E, τ, and μ at $T = T_g$. a_E, a_τ, and a_μ are constant parameters. The values of E, τ, μ above and below the glass transition region are represented by the constant values, respectively (Tobushi *et al.*, 1997).

8.5.2 *The Shape Memory Process of SMPs*

In this section, we present the simulation results of the shape memory behavior of a thin film of polyurethane using the three-element model. The material parameters, boundary conditions, and loading procedures in these simulations are kept consistent with those employed in Tobushi's experiments (1997, 2001). The experimental results indicate that the strain and stress behavior vary significantly within the temperature range of $T_g - 20\,\text{K} \leq T \leq T_g + 20\,\text{K}$, while

Table 8.5.1 Values of material parameters for the three-element model simulations adapted from experimental results reported by Tobushi *et al.* (1997).

Material parameters	Values
E_g/Mpa	146
a_E	38.1
τ_g/s	521
a_τ	35.4
μ_g/GPa·s	14
a_μ	44.2
T_h/K	348
T_l/K	308
T_g/K	328
α/K^{-1}	11.6e–5
ν	0.48

showing moderate variation outside this temperature range. To simplify the analysis, we define a lower temperature, $T_l = T_g - 20\,\text{K}$, and a higher temperature, $T_h = T_g + 20\,\text{K}$. The simulations are performed within the temperature range between T_l and T_h. All the parameters used in the three-element model are listed in Table 8.5.1. These parameters are incorporated into the simplified three-element model and implemented in the form of user subroutine code within the ABAQUS software.

The mechanical behavior of polyurethane under two different conditions, namely free strain and fixed strain constraints, is investigated separately. First, the shape memory behavior of polyurethane under a free-strain condition with various pre-strains is simulated and analyzed. The stress–strain–temperature relationship for polyurethane with a pre-strain of 2.4% in the free-strain recovery cycle is shown in Figure 8.5.2. The entire process can be divided into four steps.

In the first step, labeled as loading (①), the polyurethane undergoes pre-deformation from its initial shape (point A with zero stress and zero strain) to a deformed shape (point B with pre-strain) by applying a mechanical load at temperature T_h. The corresponding strain and stress at point B are referred to as the pre-strain and pre-stress states, respectively.

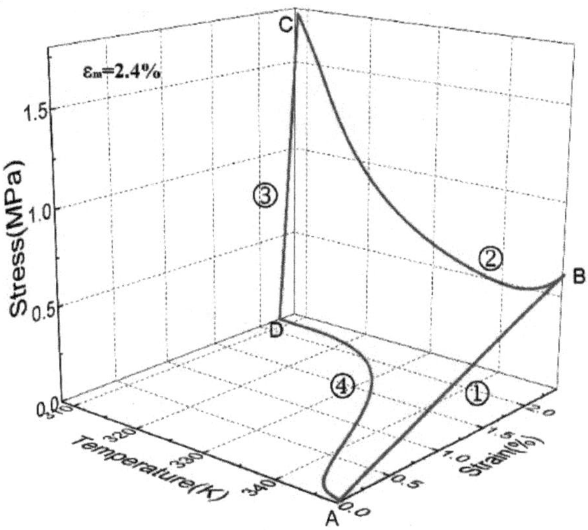

Figure 8.5.2 Stress–strain–temperature diagram in the numerical simulations using the three-element model under free-strain recovery with a pre-strain of 2.4%.

The second step, known as the cooling process ((2)), involves maintaining the pre-deformed shape until the temperature reaches the lower temperature T_l (point C). In this cooling process, the stress needs to be increased to counteract the thermal contraction effect and preserve the pre-deformed shape.

Subsequently, the third step, referred to as the unloading process ((3)), occurs as the externally applied load is removed at the lower temperature T_l, causing the material to return from point C to point D.

In the final step ((4)), the shape memory effect is activated by raising the temperature again, resulting in the recovery of the initial shape at point A.

To validate the accuracy of the three-element model in the free-strain recovery cycle, the simulated results of stress–strain, stress–temperature, and strain–temperature at each step are compared with experimental data. Specifically, the results for different pre-strains, namely $\varepsilon_m = 2.4\%$ and $\varepsilon_m = 10\%$, are considered. The simulated results are also compared with those obtained from Tobushi's model. The comparisons are presented in Figures 8.5.3–8.5.5.

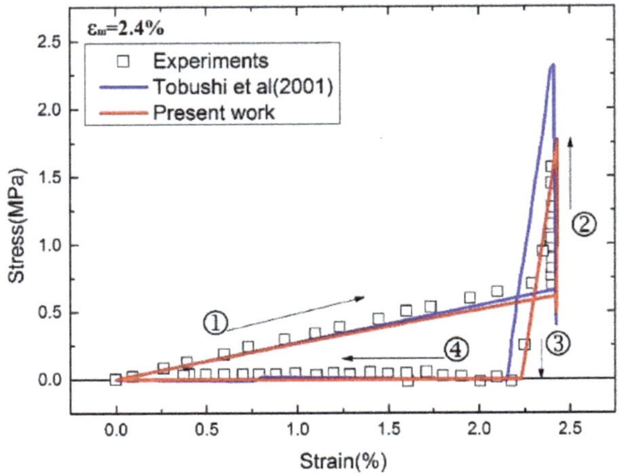

(a)

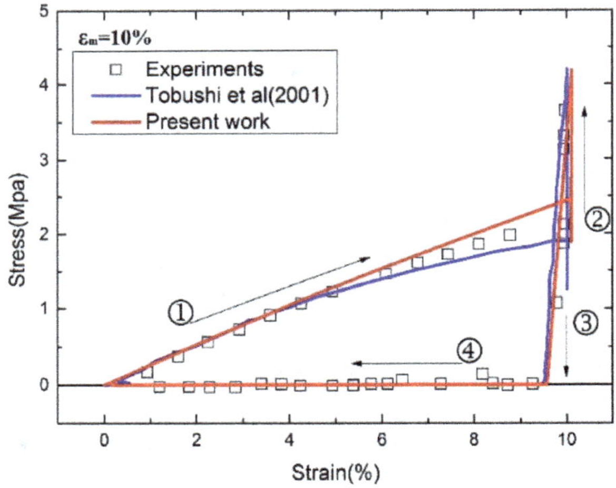

(b)

Figure 8.5.3 Comparisons of stress–strain curves during free-strain recovery among the three-element model, Tobushi's model, and experiments under different pre-strain conditions: (a) $\varepsilon_{\mathrm{m}} = 2.4\%$; (b) $\varepsilon_{\mathrm{m}} = 10\%$. Experiments are reported by Tobushi *et al.* (2001). Better agreement can be observed between the three-element model and experiments.

From these figures, it can be observed that there is a strong agreement between the simulated results and the experimental data. In fact, the agreement between the simulated results and the experimental data is even better than the agreement between Tobushi's

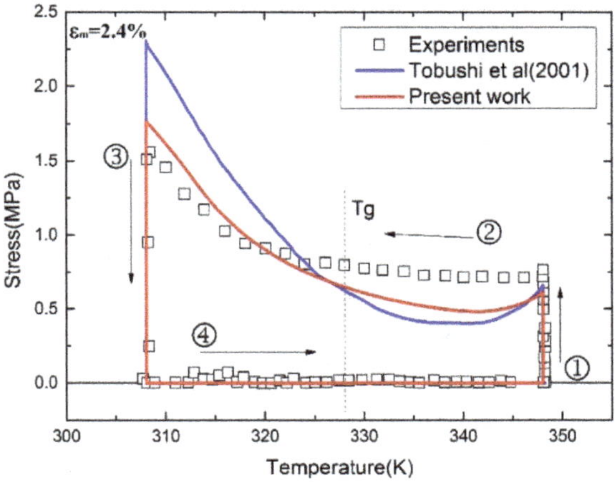

(a)

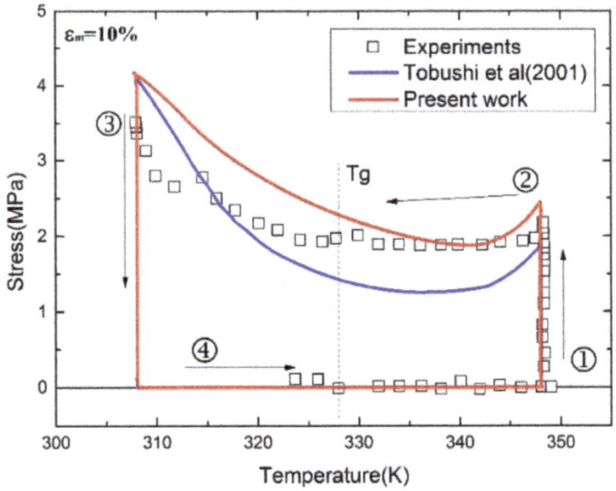

(b)

Figure 8.5.4 Comparisons of stress–temperature curves during free-strain recovery among the three-element model, Tobushi's model, and experiments under different pre-strain conditions: (a) $\varepsilon_m = 2.4\%$; (b) $\varepsilon_m = 10\%$. Experiments are reported by Tobushi *et al.* (2001). Better agreement can be observed between the three-element model and experiments.

model and the experimental results. This indicates that the three-element model is capable of accurately predicting the behavior of the free-strain recovery cycle. Thus, the predicted results obtained from the three-element model are validated for the free strain recovery cycle process of SMPs.

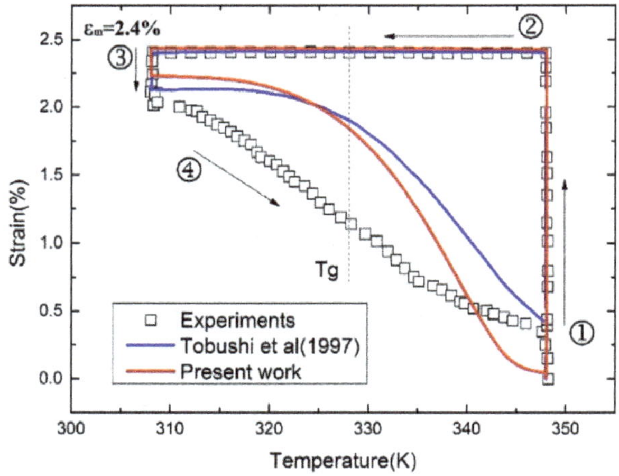

(a)

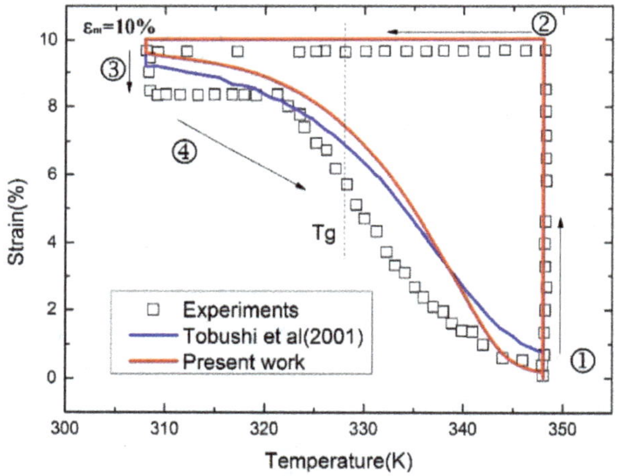

(b)

Figure 8.5.5 Comparisons of strain–temperature curves during free strain recovery among the three-element model, Tobushi's model, and experiments under different pre-strain conditions: (a) $\varepsilon_{\mathrm{m}} = 2.4\%$; (b) $\varepsilon_{\mathrm{m}} = 10\%$. Experiments are reported by Tobushi *et al.* (2001). A better agreement can be observed between the three-element model and experiments.

Besides the typical shape memory cycle (①→ ②→ ③→ ④), there are also some constrained recovery processes, such as process ⑤, as shown in Figure 8.5.6. Process ⑤ is a stress recovery process under a constant fixed strain constraint. This is followed by

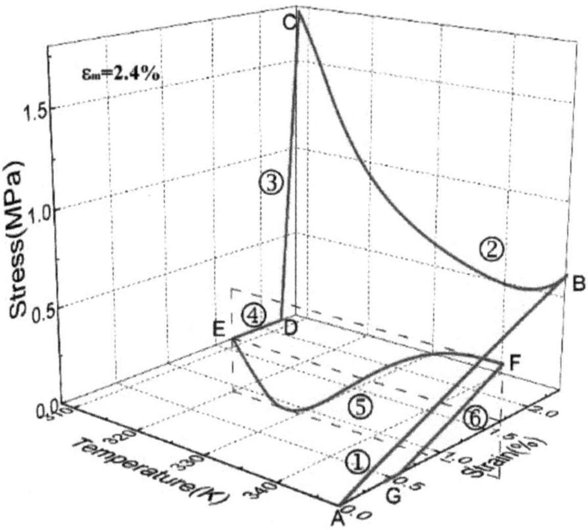

Figure 8.5.6 Stress–strain–temperature diagram obtained from the numerical simulations using the three-element model under a fixed strain constraint with a pre-strain of 2.4%.

unloading step ⑥, during which the strain returns to G. At point G, the corresponding strain is called "residual strain." Typically, the residual strain is negligible, and the final state returns to the starting point A. The constrained-strain recovery cycle process of SMPs is shown in Figure 8.5.6.

To further validate the applicability of the three-element model in the constrained fixed-strain recovery cycle, the simulated results of stress–strain and stress–temperature at each step are compared with the experimental data. The comparisons are made for different pre-strains, namely $\varepsilon_{\mathrm{m}} = 2.4\%$. Unfortunately, there are no available experimental data for the pre-strain $\varepsilon_{\mathrm{m}} = 10\%$, so the corresponding simulated results are not included in this comparison. The results under $\varepsilon_{\mathrm{m}} = 2.4\%$ are shown in Figures 8.5.7 and 8.5.8.

From these figures, it can be observed that the simulated results demonstrate a better match with the experimental data compared to the results obtained from Tobushi's model. This indicates that the three-element model is effective in predicting the deformation and stress in the constrained fixed-strain recovery cycle. Therefore, the three-element model proves to be a reliable approach for studying the behavior of SMPs in the constrained fixed-strain recovery cycle.

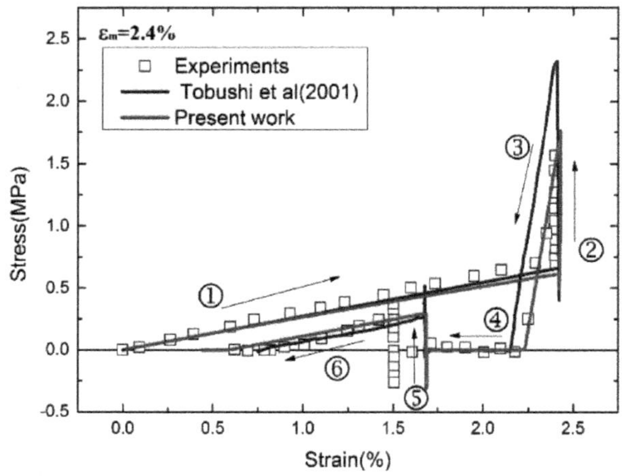

Figure 8.5.7 Comparisons of stress–strain curves in the constrained fixed strain recovery among the three-element model, Tobushi's model, and experiments under pre-strain conditions: $\varepsilon_{\mathrm{m}} = 2.4\%$; experiments are reported by Tobushi *et al.* (2001). Better agreement can be observed between the three-element model and experiments.

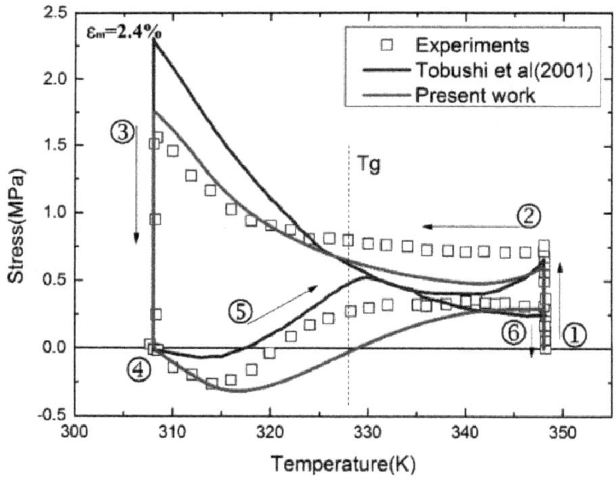

Figure 8.5.8 Comparisons of stress–temperature curves in the constrained fixed strain recovery among the three-element model, Tobushi's model, and experiments under pre-strain conditions: $\varepsilon_{\mathrm{m}} = 2.4\%$; experiments are reported by Tobushi *et al.* (2001). Better agreement can be observed between the three-element model and experiments.

8.6 Summary

This chapter primarily focused on the applications of continuum mechanics, specifically in the fields of solid mechanics and fluid mechanics. In particular, we delved into the analysis of 2D plane problems, namely the plane strain problem and the plane stress problem. In the case of hydrogels and SMPs, we explored their deformation behavior through both analytical solutions and FEM techniques. For a more comprehensive understanding of these topics, interested readers and students can refer to Liu's book, published in 2023.

When dealing with more intricate problems, numerical methods, such as the FEM and mesh-free method, prove to be valuable tools for obtaining solutions. It is important to recognize that continuum mechanics serves as the fundamental framework upon which FEM has been built in many special topics. By employing FEM, we can tackle complex problems and gain insights into various mechanical phenomena encountered in the realm of solid mechanics.

General References

Flory, P.J., Rehner, J. (1943). Statistical mechanics of cross? linked polymer networks II. *Swelling. J. Chem. Phys.* 11(11), 521–526.

Hong, W., Liu, Z., Suo, Z. (2009). Inhomogeneous swelling of a gel in equilibrium with a solvent and mechanical load. *Int. J. Solids Struct.* 46(17), 3282–3289.

Li, Y.X., Guo, S.S., He, Y.H., Liu, Z.S. (2015). A simplified constitutive model for predicting shape memory polymers deformation behavior. *Int. J. Comput. Mater. Sci. Eng.* 4(1), 1550001.

Liu, Z.S., Toh, W., Ng, T.Y. (2015). Advances in mechanics of soft materials: A review of large deformation behavior of hydrogels. *Int. J. Appl. Mech.* 7(5), 1530001.

Liu Z.S. *et al.* (2022). *Mechanics of Soft Materials: Large Deformation Behavior of Hydrogels* (Xi'an Jiaotong University Press, Xi'an China).

Tobushi, H., Hashimoto, T., Hayashi, S., Yamada, E. (1997). Thermomechanical constitutive modeling in shape memory polymer of polyurethane series. *J. Intell. Mater. Syst. Struct.* 8(8), 711–718.

Tobushi, H., Okumura, K., Hayashi, S., Ito, N. (2001). Thermomechanical constitutive model of shape memory polymer. *Mech. Mater.* 33(10), 545–554.

Index

www.ingramcontent.com/pod-product-compliance
Lightning Source LLC
Chambersburg PA
CBHW050257270825
31738CB00004B/133
9789811283789